CARE IN PRACTICE

FOR CfE HIGHER

Janet Miller

HODDER GIBSON
AN HACHETTE UK COMPANY

The Publishers would like to thank the following for permission to reproduce copyright material:

Photo credits p.4 (all) from the former Heatherbank Museum of Social Work (supplied by Janet Miller); p.7 from the former Heatherbank Museum of Social Work (supplied by Janet Miller); p.12 (top three) © Kennedy Care Group, (bottom two) © Duke of Edinburgh's Award; p.59 Andrew Parry and Robin Maclean; p.130 © Pavla Zakova - Fotolia.com; p.141 © godfer - Fotolia.com; p.150 © Duke of Edinburgh's Award; p.167 © doble.d - Fotolia.com; p.199 © Rex; p.205 (left) © Harry MacFadyan, (right) © epa european pressphoto agency b.v. / Alamy; p.220 © Janet Miller; p.284 (all) © Duke of Edinburgh's Award; p.285 (both) © Harry MacFadyan; p.286 © Alzheimer Scotland; p.298 © Scottish Social Services Council.

Every effort has been made to trace all copyright holders, but if any have been inadvertently overlooked the Publishers will be pleased to make the necessary arrangements at the first opportunity.

This book is dedicated to the memory of my mother, Olive Simpson, who died in 1966 when she was far too young, and of my father, Arthur Simpson, who died swimming his daily lengths at the age of 87. Both of them experienced positive care at various times in their lives, for which I am very grateful.

Orders: please contact Bookpoint Ltd, 130 Park Drive, Milton Park, Abingdon, Oxon OX14 4SE. Telephone: (44) 01235 827720. Fax: (44) 01235 400454. Lines are open 9.00–5.00, Monday to Saturday, with a 24-hour message answering service. Visit our website at www.hoddereducation.co.uk. Hodder Gibson can be contacted direct on: Tel: 0141 848 1609; Fax: 0141 889 6315; email: hoddergibson@hodder.co.uk

First published in 2015 by
Hodder Gibson, an imprint of Hodder Education,
An Hachette UK Company
2a Christie Street
Paisley PA1 1NB

Second edition first published 2007
This edition first published 2015

Impression number 5 4 3 2 1
Year 2019 2018 2017 2016 2015

Cover photo ©STILLFX/iStock/Thinkstock
Illustrations by DC Graphic Design Limited and Aptara, Inc.
Typeset in ITC Century Std Light 10.5/13.5pt by Aptara, Inc.
Printed in Italy

A catalogue record for this title is available from the British Library.

ISBN 978 1 4718 5191 9

Contents

Contents *continued*

Contents *continued*

Figures and tables

Foreword

Why work in **care**? Because some of the most disadvantaged and vulnerable people in our society need you. It's not easy. It's demanding, complex work and needs skilled, confident workers – but there is nothing more rewarding. Lifelong learning and the ability to reflect on what you've learned is essential in enabling you to do your job well and continually to improve your practice. This book is full of sound, helpful and practical advice, with some examples based on real experience. There is no substitute for listening to and learning from people's real-life stories.

We are in challenging, exciting times. Services are changing and public expectations are changing. In Scotland, we recognise that we must focus on outcomes; people working in social services are helping others on a daily basis to live full and happy lives. They need to be able to work with colleagues from other services, such as the NHS, education, housing and the police. And most importantly, to work with service users and carers in a collaborative, respectful way. We are increasingly focused on early intervention and prevention, rather than on crisis care.

Demand for services is increasing because people are living longer and because poverty and inequality in our communities are growing. Although there are fewer young people in society, a higher proportion of them have very complex needs. For this reason, employers are looking for workers who are resilient, adaptable and flexible, and who are committed to their own development. Above all, they are looking for people with sound values, which underpin everything they do.

People who use social services expect them to be personalised and to focus on meeting their needs. They want workers to listen to them, respect them and recognise their expertise. Self-directed support means they will increasingly plan and even buy their own services, and this can feel challenging to professionals. But they are the experts on their own lives and your job is to help them to unlock their potential. Care practice has always been grounded in strong values, respecting the individual, guarding privacy and confidentiality, and promoting independence. We know that caring, skilled workers can make a huge difference to people's lives, and that workers get real job satisfaction from helping people to make a contribution to society and fulfil their aspirations.

We live in an increasingly digital world, which presents fantastic opportunities for learners, for workers and for people who use services. You can access information, use e-learning tools, communicate with people across the world in an instant and manage your life in a completely different way to ten years ago. You can constantly refresh your knowledge of theory, evidence and practice. This does, of course, bring its own challenges, and online safety should be an integral part of everyone's learning. But the benefits it brings are far greater, and the worlds of work, education and life in general have been revolutionised.

Caring is very much a practical activity, and no amount of reading or attending courses will replace doing and learning on the job. Learning, reading and achieving qualifications help you do the job better, however, and make you feel confident. This in turn makes the people you care for feel confident because they know you are committed to learning and improving your skills, and all of this will contribute to better quality services.

Anna Fowlie

Chief Executive, Scottish Social Services Council (SSSC)

Acknowledgements

For the third edition

Revising *Care in Practice for CfE Higher* for this third edition has been an adventure. In the eight years that have passed since the second edition there has been a lot of progress in thinking and practice. Many people have helped me in bringing this edition up to date.

I owe my greatest debt to Susan Gibb, my co-editor of the previous edition, whose work is still greatly reflected in this edition. I also continue to benefit from the thinking of Ellen Lancaster and George Baker, contributing writers of the second edition.

The following people and organisations have especially helped with this third edition: Francis Scott, Debbie McIntosh and Eddie McCaffrey of Aspire Scotland Ltd., who invited me to their headquarters in Kilbirnie, gave a wonderful PowerPoint presentation on their work and thinking in relation to children and young people, and contributed directly to Chapters 1 and 6; Roy McGivney and Moira McMillan, whom I met at the 'Living Well with Dementia' event in 2014, and who subsequently met with me in Dundee to share their experience, thinking and wisdom; Yvonne Stewart of Dementia Scotland Consultancy and Training; the staff at Alzheimer Scotland for photographs; Jamie Mitchell of the Duke of Edinburgh's Award Scheme for her account of the scheme in Chapter 6 and for photographs; Mike Martin, of Mike Martin Associates and the Open University, for his contribution on advocacy in Chapter 6; Neil Macleod of SSSC for workforce information; Jacqui Allison (subject leader), Christine Greer, Stacy Dornan and all of the NC Health and Social Care students at Perth UHI, for contributing their thinking in relation to the value base and care practice; Frances Barbour for her work on reflective thinking and referencing; Joanne Gaughan of TRFS (The Richmond Fellowship Scotland) for her account and lovely case studies in Chapters 2 and 6; Harry MacFadyen for his musical contribution; Adrian Snowball for sharing his experiences of care in Chapter 7; Anna Fowlie, Alison Harold and Sandra Wilson of SSSC; Janice McDade of Focus Training and Learning; George and Pat Alexander; Marion Austin; my LinkedIn network; Sue Marshall-Jennings, Danni, Kylie and Linzi of Kennedy Care Group; Bob Dickie and my family, for providing valuable thinking and encouragement; John Mitchell and Ella Stephenson at Hodder Gibson and copyeditor Jo Lincoln for such a thorough and friendly approach; SQA for constructive comments, especially in relation to personalisation; and the many other people not mentioned, for providing help and support as I was developing this edition of *Care in Practice*.

For the second edition

In addition to all of the people who helped with the first edition, we would like to thank the following people for their contributions to the second edition: Laura Weir of the Voluntary Sector Social Services Workforce Unit (Scotland) for providing invaluable administrative assistance, charts and diagrams; our employing agencies (VSSSWU, CCPS and Cardonald College), and our colleagues, families and friends, for their support of our endeavours; Kibble Education and Care Centre (Paisley) and the Retail Trust (Glasgow) for providing examples of good practice; Marion Miller for providing further writings; Carole Wilkinson, Chief Executive of the Scottish Social Services Council (SSSC), for kindly providing the foreword to the second edition. We are grateful to Doris Graham for permission to adapt her material from the first edition of this book; John Mitchell and Katherine Bennett of Hodder Gibson and our editor Mairi Sutherland, for their generous help and encouragement throughout the editing process. Andrew Parry and Robin Maclean have once again contributed their talent to the cartoons.

For the first edition

Many people helped us to put the first edition of this book together. The following list hardly does justice to all of the people who gave us assistance. If we haven't mentioned you by name we apologise and say thank you anyway. Thanks to: service users and staff of Sense Scotland, Crookfur Cottage Homes and East Dunbartonshire Social Work Department; to Lorna Trainer, Section Leader, and our colleagues at Cardonald College, who had to keep the team going while we were busy writing; to Rachel Ball and Laura Smith at Outlook, Kirkintilloch, and to SHS, Edinburgh for information on person-centred planning; to Rev. Alastair Ramage of the Heatherbank Museum of Social Work, Glasgow Caledonian University; to the Social Care Association in Scotland and in Surbiton; to Mary Cartledge and Sharon McBean of the Graphics Department; to art student Michael Gaughan; to library staff and HNC Social Care students at Cardonald College; to Margaret and Roseanne Miller for diagrams and Marion Miller for her writings; to Mike, Siobhan and Martin Hollis; to Alexis Horsfield and John Hamilton of Greater Glasgow Health Board and to Steven Ryecroft of Eastbank Health Promotion Centre; to Dr Andy Furlong of the Department of Sociology, University of Glasgow; to Elisabeth Tribe at Hodder and Stoughton; to Tom Stannage of the Higher Still Development Unit; to Robin Maclean and Andrew Parry for cartoons; to the Scottish Office Department of Health; and to Blackwell's Publishers, Health Education Library Scotland, SHEPS, Care Sector Consortium, HarperCollins, Waheeda Parveen, Bob Holman, and to our families, friends and colleagues.

Introduction

There is a better place and we have a key part to play in achieving it.

(Beresford, 2010)

Care practice is not an ordinary job; it is a professional activity that requires you to use a **value** base and knowledge, skills and understanding to make the best possible provision with and for people who use services. It is hard work but, as with any career: the more you give, the more you get back; the more effort you put in, the more rewarding the work is; the more you learn, the greater the fulfilment. The best care workers are those who genuinely care about the people they are working with and who never lose the capacity to ask questions of themselves and of the work they do.

Although this book won't make you an expert in care practice it does offer signposts, suggestions and opportunities to begin the process of becoming as good as you can be. The chapters have been written for those who are starting out on a career or course in care, or for those who wish to further their knowledge and skills in this and related areas. The subjects and format of the book do, however, specifically cover the syllabus of the Scottish CfE Higher in Care, and also contain material for National 4 and 5 Care. The book is also useful for those undertaking Scottish Vocational Qualifications **SVQ**2 and SVQ3 in Social Services (Children and Young People) and Social Services and Healthcare, the HNC Social Care, HNC Health Care and other care qualifications.

Many people have contributed directly to the content of this book and I have discussed care practice with many others, some who use services, some who provide them, some who have participated in or shared the care of family members or friends, some who are students or professionals or facilitators or course leaders. Sometimes they told me about what they considered to be good practice, sometimes about poor practice. The dividing line nearly always concerned the way in which care was provided, the values and principles applied and whether people felt that they were listened to. The other skills of the worker were a bonus, but where people felt dissatisfied it was usually because they hadn't been treated with respect and they felt that they hadn't been heard. Sometimes their treatment was discriminatory, neglectful or even downright abusive.

I hope that this book will go some way towards helping you to be as good a practitioner as you can be. The content of Chapter 2 is crucial to this. There are also other messages set out in Chapter 7, emphasising the need for you to be reflective, creative and never to stop learning. The book, while separated into distinct chapters, aims to provide a holistic foundation for building a body of values, knowledge, skills and understanding that will prove valuable in your practice.

There are some wonderful resources that you can use to enhance your learning, including speaking to service users and carers, and accessing online resources, books, videos and conferences. Some of these resources are listed at the end of chapters. Particularly helpful are the websites of SSKS (Social Services Knowledge Scotland), SCIE (Social Care

Institute for Excellence), SSSC (Scottish Social Services Council), the Care Inspectorate and the Scottish Government. There are many others, often hosted by independent **third sector** and **private sector** organisations, which can also be helpful to you. Do use them.

This book is a revision of the second edition of *Care in Practice*. There have been quite a few changes made to the syllabus and assessment requirements, as well as in the world of care practice, since the last edition. These have been taken into account in this new edition. There is much new material, but where the material presented in the previous edition still applies and cannot be better stated, it is included here. This includes material prepared by other authors, who are listed in the Acknowledgements.

There has been an attempt to reach agreement about terminology, emphasising that the language used by care workers is extremely important in order to avoid being confusing, discriminatory or patronising. In general, the term 'service user' is used to refer to people who use care services and 'carer' for those who provide informal care on a regular basis, often family members and friends. These terms, adopted by SSSC (Scottish Social Services Council) in the Code of Practice for Social Service Workers (see Appendix 2), are those that are most in evidence in much of the current care and social work literature. They are not universally used but they are terms that attempt to avoid stigma, implications of possession or dependence, and patronising overtones. The term 'service user' places a firm emphasis on the people being worked with as users of a service, and this comes with the expectation that this service will meet needs in ways that respect the worth and dignity of individuals. The term 'client' is also in current usage and possesses similar advantages to those of 'service user'. 'Client' is currently used in counselling and some social work literature, and on some occasions in this book. The term 'care worker' is used to refer to anyone working in the care field. It is an all-embracing term, though it is recognised that in practice such workers have many different titles, including 'social service worker' used by SSSC, and 'personal assistant' (PA) within the **self-directed support** agenda.

Care practice is essentially a practical subject and no amount of reading and study can replace the value of actually doing the job. It is the combination of learning and practice, the application of values, knowledge, skills and understanding to practice situations, and the attributes of the care worker, which determine the quality of the service provided. Although a practice placement is not a requirement of the CfE Higher Care course, it is recommended that participants try to gain as much experience as possible – through voluntary work, a placement, visits to care agencies or employment – in order to complement the more academic content of the syllabus.

The aims of this book, and those of the national specifications for CfE Higher, coincide to emphasise the provision of the following opportunities, included in SQA's skills framework: to develop your literacy, writing skills, health and well-being, **relationships**, employability, enterprise, citizenship, thinking skills, and the ability to apply, analyse and evaluate. These skills are achieved through learning about the values, skills, knowledge and understanding of the course, which fall into the following areas:

- Applying detailed knowledge and understanding of needs and care services.
- Applying detailed knowledge and understanding of human development and behaviour and psychological theories.
- Using sociological theories to demonstrate knowledge and understanding of the ways in which social influences can impact on individuals.

- Investigating detailed features of positive care practice.
- Investigating, analysing, evaluating and presenting information.

The book is divided into seven chapters. This division is somewhat arbitrary since the chapters are all related to one another and in the end come back to providing the values, knowledge, skills and understanding that are needed to work with service users and carers. The relationships among disciplines are frequently emphasised and it is hoped that the reader will be able to appreciate these relationships in order to gain an integrated and 'holistic' understanding of care practice. This stresses not only that the disciplines in general are related to one another, but specifically that the whole person in a social situation should be seen as possessing interrelated needs. This theme of interconnectedness and integration is returned to in the final chapter, which attempts to pull together the various threads of the book into a coherent whole.

A summary of each of the chapters follows. A table of the relationship between the chapters of the book and the CfE Higher units is provided on page xvi.

Chapter 1: Care: context and services is essentially an introductory chapter. It sets the scene for care practice, examining what is meant by care and the contexts in which it takes place. It looks at care work in the past and care work today, including an examination of **institutionalisation** and how to avoid it and **personalisation** and how to promote it. It also investigates informal and **formal care**, and the main providers of care and care services. There is an examination of **legislation** and policy for care practice, as well as the attributes that make a good care worker. Examples are provided where relevant, as they are elsewhere in the book. This chapter provides an introduction and some syllabus content for all units of the CfE Higher Care and is a relevant introduction to National 4 and 5 Care, as well as to other care qualifications.

Chapter 2: Values and principles begins with an examination of the values and **principles** that underpin all care practice, including the principles of the National Care Standards (Scotland) and the Code of Practice for Social Service Workers. **Discrimination** and **anti-discriminatory practice** are looked at in some detail. The chapter proceeds to discuss effective **communication** and relationships, with the 'oomph factor' seen as 'that bit extra', adding enthusiasm and enjoyment to the mix of skills that a care worker needs. The works of Carl Rogers and Gerard Egan are considered in relation to using communication skills to work with service users.

Chapter 3: An Introduction to human development and behaviour examines the concepts of development and **behaviour** and the **nature/nurture debate**. It goes on to look in detail at some basic developmental concepts that underpin and influence development and behaviour: **attachment** and separation; transition and loss; **resilience**; socialisation. Strands of development are explained: social, physical, emotional, cognitive, cultural and spiritual (SPECCS). Human development is then examined from infancy to old age using a lifespan perspective. This section is full of generalisations and it is emphasised that the changes outlined will differ from person to person and **culture** to culture. A multicultural approach is promoted. Examples and active learning encourage you to consider how the knowledge and understanding gained is important to care practice.

Chapter 4: Psychological approaches and theories considers what is meant by **psychology** and goes on to look at how this can help you to understand human development and behaviour. Psychological approaches and theories are used to facilitate an understanding of development and behaviour. Three psychological approaches (psychodynamic, cognitive/behavioural and humanistic) are explained and there is an evaluation of two psychological theories within each approach. You have the opportunity to consider how an understanding of psychology can help you as a care worker to understand behaviour and development.

Chapter 5: Social influences and sociology includes a consideration of what is meant by sociology and social influences. Sociological concepts and five sociological theories are considered: functionalist, conflict, symbolic interactionist, social constructionist and feminist. The chapter proceeds to examine the social influences of and on the family, inequality and poverty, and discrimination in terms of sociological theory. You have the opportunity to apply your knowledge to the care context.

Chapter 6: Positive care practice aims to enable you to understand the processes of positive care practice and to use person-centred and outcomes approaches. Needs, wants, wishes and dreams are examined in relation to the **assessment** process. Approaches to assessment, such as the National Practice Model included in **GIRFEC** (Getting it Right for Every Child), and Single Shared Assessment, are explored. A model of care is presented based on assessment, care planning, **implementation** and evaluation. Two models of care planning are looked at: the exchange model and person-centred planning. Implementation of **care plans** is examined in terms of positive care practice and care environments, looking at helping and therapeutic, organisational, physical and **community** environments. There are sections on self-directed support and personalisation, **advocacy** and **safeguarding**, and suggestions for implementation, for example using a strengths-based approach and promoting creative activities. The value of evaluation is emphasised through a process of **monitoring** and reviewing progress in the achievement of **outcomes**.

Chapter 7: Integration and course assessment aims to enable you to integrate your thinking about the various topics covered in the book, through the use of frequently asked questions (FAQs) and case study materials. You have another opportunity to look at needs and at the links between psychology and sociology. There are sections on thinking reflectively and on preparing for and planning your project. You have the opportunity to identify the main messages of the book and to apply your thinking to the account of the MacDonald and Ahmed families, updated from the first and second editions, and to Adrian's story of his experience of illness and recovery and the care he received along the way. At the end of the chapter there are some suggestions for less academic – though still relevant – reading as a break from the demands of taking a course.

Table 0.1 Links between the chapter topics and CfE Higher Care units

Chapter of book	Unit		
	Care: Values and principles	**Care: Human development**	**Care: Social influences**
Chapter 1: Care: context and services	Very relevant	Relevant	Relevant
Chapter 2: Values and principles	Extremely relevant	Relevant	Relevant
Chapter 3: An introduction to human development and behaviour	Relevant	Extremely relevant	Relevant
Chapter 4: Psychological approaches and theories	Relevant	Extremely relevant	Relevant
Chapter 5: Social influences and sociology	Relevant	Relevant	Extremely relevant
Chapter 6: Positive care practice	Extremely relevant	Relevant	Relevant
Chapter 7: Integration and course assessment	Very relevant	Very relevant	Very relevant

CHAPTER 1
Care: context and services

Almost all of us use a care service at some point in our lives. Everyone in Scotland should receive safe, high quality care that reflects their needs and protects their rights.

(Scottish Government National Care Standards Review, 2014)

Introduction

Care, and the context in which it takes place, is always evolving. Sometimes change is of genuine benefit to people who use services; sometimes there seems to be a step back before there is enough momentum and political will to move forwards again. This chapter introduces you to the care context and care services with the aim of enabling you to consider and reflect upon what is happening in relation to care in the twenty-first century. It sets the scene for a number of the themes and issues that will be developed in the following chapters and provides essential underpinning knowledge to enable you to understand the context of the other chapters of the book. It also provides you with opportunities to develop self-awareness and to consider the attributes that make a good care worker.

The material in this chapter is relevant to all of the units of the Care Higher. It also covers material that will be useful to learners studying Care at National 4 and 5 levels, Scottish Vocational Qualifications SVQ2 and SVQ3 in Social Services (Children and Young People) and Social Services and Healthcare, and for HNC Social Care and HNC Health Care.

By the end of this chapter you should be able to consider:

- ★ what is meant by care and care practice
- ★ care work in the past and today
- ★ what is meant by institutionalisation and why understanding it is so important
- ★ what is meant by personalisation and its place in current policy and practice
- ★ the implications of demographic change
- ★ the main providers of care and care services
- ★ legislation and policy for care practice
- ★ the attributes that make a good care worker.

Care and care practice

Activity ***What does 'care' mean?***

Care workers work with Barbara, aged 36, who has multiple sclerosis and lives at home, with John, aged 25, who has learning difficulties and attends a resource centre, with Anna, aged 11, who is looked after and accommodated in a children's unit, with Grace, aged 92, who lives in very sheltered accommodation, and with Hugo, aged 15, who attends a care and education centre for young people with autism.

What does 'care' mean in relation to each of these people?

The word 'care' is not as straightforward as it may at first seem. The Oxford English Dictionary defines care as 'the provision of what is necessary for health, welfare, maintenance and **protection** of someone or something' (Stevenson and Waite, 2011). When it comes to the 'care' in care practice, however, the term takes on an altogether more dynamic meaning, which encompasses enabling people to meet their needs through the application of a positive value base, knowledge, skills and understanding. The worth and dignity of every individual and the promotion of social justice and social welfare are emphasised. The individual is central to the meaning of care in this context, as they are in the practice of care. 'Care' in the twenty-first century has moved away from *looking after* people, to *working with* people whenever this is possible to meet their needs, wishes and aspirations through person-centred, personalised services.

People come to care work for all sorts of reasons and from many different walks of life. Before they became care workers, for instance, George worked as an administrator in a local authority housing department, Jenny worked in a large department store, Phil volunteered as a student with a soup kitchen, and Sue was an informal carer for her granddad. You may be reading this book because you are undertaking a care qualification before or after leaving school or as part of your learning while you are in further or higher education and/or employment. You may have been an informal carer yourself, providing care for a relative or friend, or you may be a parent, foster carer or **service user**. Whatever your background or age, you bring a wealth of life experience that will be useful to you in your work.

Care practice covers a wide variety of activities, carried out with a range of different individuals and groups in a wide spectrum of settings and locations. It often involves working across traditional boundaries such as those between health, social services, housing and education. The Care Inspectorate's list of the services it inspects gives you an idea of the range of care services in Scotland today. These are illustrated in Table 1.1.

Table 1.1 The range of care services inspected by the Care Inspectorate in 2014

Services for adults	Services for children and young people	Services for everybody
• Care homes for older people • **Support** services • Care homes for people with drug and alcohol misuse problems • Care homes for people with learning disability • Care homes for people with mental health problems • Adult placement services • Care homes for people with physical and sensory impairment • Housing support services • Services for people in criminal justice-supported accommodation • Short breaks and **respite care**	• Adoption agencies • Care homes for children and young people • Childcare agencies • Early education and childcare up to the age of 16 • Foster care and family placement services • School care accommodation services	• Care at home • Hospice care • Independent hospitals • Independent specialist clinics • Nurse agencies • Independent medical consultant and GP services • Dental services

Care past and present

Care has a long history, which continues to influence care provision in the twenty-first century, even if only by a determination to do things differently. To cover the whole of this history would fill many books. The following account and examples give you a very brief idea of social conditions and care in Scotland in the past and how this differs from the provision of care services today.

Care in the past

Care in the past was often provision for the most basic needs of food, clothing and shelter for people who were very sick, dying, homeless or travelling, for children without parents or who had been abandoned, for elderly people and people with disabilities. Sometimes this care was provided with compassion and concern, sometimes with a ruthlessness that seems to contradict the meaning of care. The photographs on page 4 show a mixture of care provision in the early to mid-twentieth century.

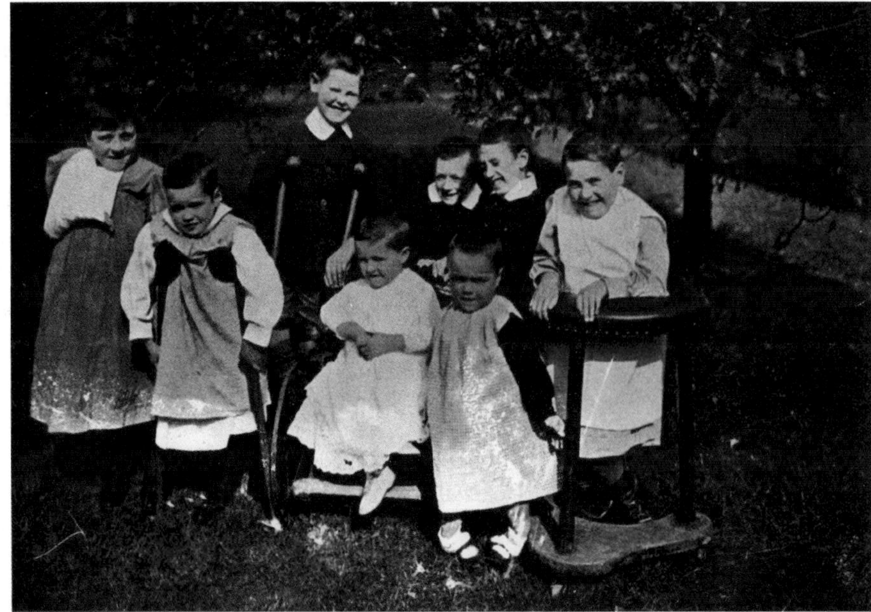

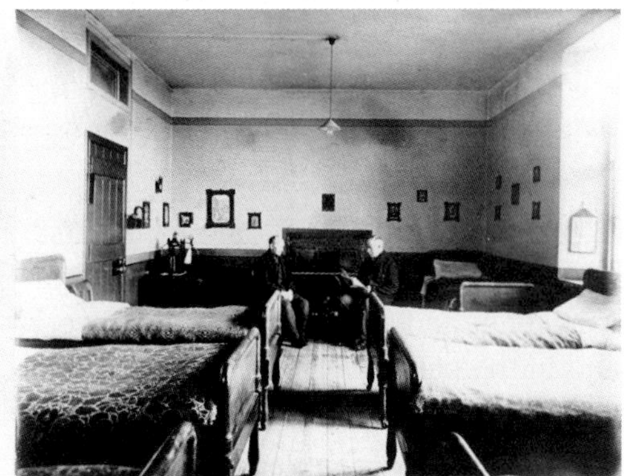

Figure 1.1 Care in the past

'Care' is usually of its time and is influenced by the dominant ideologies, economic conditions and cultural **norms** of a particular **society** at a particular point in its history. The Industrial Revolution of the eighteenth and nineteenth centuries, when huge numbers of people moved from rural environments to the cities to work in the newly built mills and factories, was a time of change in the provision of care. Before this, care, if it was provided at all, was provided by families, friends, religious bodies, philanthropic, caring individuals and societies, and for the most destitute, by 'Kirk sessions' under the Poor Laws of the sixteenth, seventeenth and early eighteenth centuries. Kirk sessions were the lowest court and also administered poor relief. They were made up of ministers, elders and deacons of the Church.

With the Industrial Revolution and the dire conditions that existed in many towns and cities, a new Poor Law for Scotland was passed in 1845, which transferred responsibility for the provision of medical and poor relief to approximately 800 Parish Boards. Parishes were authorised to raise a compulsory rate if there were otherwise insufficient funds, and to provide assistance to those who were both destitute and disabled. Poorhouses were established to accommodate the most destitute people. Assistance tended to be unequally distributed, with a distinction often made between the 'deserving' and the 'undeserving' poor. Those considered to be 'undeserving' – sometimes people with mental health problems or problems with alcohol, or just abandoned people or those unable to find work – were left without assistance except by a few enlightened individuals. Here are a few quotations to give an idea of conditions that existed in the cities of Scotland in the nineteenth century:

> *New homes very soon became slums. The single pump that supplied water to a street would also pour out cholera bacteria. Dirty water, raw sewage and the lack of washing facilities all promoted the spread of typhus. Lack of heating, damp, cold and overcrowded conditions for families in their 'single ends' were the ideal means of passing on tuberculosis. The unemployed, the old, the chronically ill, the dying, the deserted wives, the very young, all formed a mass of helpless people caught in the sump of social life. … The public health specialist Edwin Chadwick regarded Glasgow as the most insanitary city in Great Britain. … Certain districts of Glasgow and Edinburgh remained sinks of deprivation …*
>
> (Ross, 2013)

> *Dundee's medieval housing consisted of pends, closes, and backlands: all very dark, dank and forbidding … At the best of times these backlands were tight and cramped, and their proximity to each other offered a paucity of sunlight or fresh air; in the inevitable overcrowding that came with the huge increase in population these must have seemed utterly hellish. Ubiquitous squalor, a total lack of privacy, very unhealthy air, and all types of anti-social behaviour would be evident. But worst of all, with the utter lack of sewage, dreadfully inadequate toilet provision and unavailability of running water, Dundee in 1863, and for a long time afterwards, was in a state of sanitary chaos.*
>
> (Small, 2013)

The conditions in poorhouses were not much better than in the backlands and there was a great deal of **stigma** associated with entering them. The philosophy was that if they were too comfortable they would be overrun with people and that therefore they must meet only minimally the needs of the neediest individuals. Alongside provision by Parish Boards, however, there was also a Victorian ethos of charitable work and efforts to improve society. Some of this charitable work gave rise to measures that were of enormous assistance to some sections of society. For example, Mary Lily Walker in Dundee expanded the work of the Dundee Social Union (DSU), focusing on maternal and child welfare and on training social workers (Small, 2013). She established the first Nursing Mothers Restaurant in an attempt to increase women's opportunities to care for and breastfeed their babies, with an aim to reduce infant mortality. Robert Owen established New Lanark Mill in the early nineteenth century, providing decent homes, fair wages, free healthcare and education to his workers and their families. You can visit New Lanark today (**www.newlanark.org**): the village has been preserved as a heritage site. It shows what mill owners could do if they had an interest in the welfare of their workers.

Fortunately, as the nineteenth century came to a close, improvements in sanitation and water supply meant that the very worst typhus and cholera epidemics were consigned to history and there was general improvement in the health of the Scottish urban population. The provision of care, however, was still minimal, and was often provided by voluntary, charitable associations, or by Parish Boards, where there was a continuing stigma associated with the need for help. Care was also often provided in large **institutions**, which had consequences for the people living in them, as will become evident in the following section on institutionalisation.

Activity *The history of care provision*

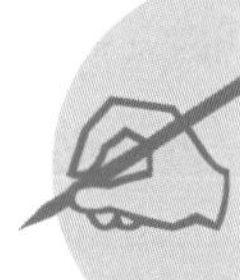

Undertake a short research project on the history of care provision in the area in which you live, are studying or working, or in which you have an interest. Describe the care provided.

Institutionalisation

One of the features of much care work in the past was the development of features of institutionalisation in the people receiving care. This occurred because of the ways in which care was delivered – often in large institutions, sometimes in remote places away from the rest of the population. These institutions may have been hospitals for people with physical or learning disabilities or mental ill health, or homes for older adults or the poorhouses for the destitute.

Institutionalisation describes a process by which the needs of the people whom the institution exists to serve become secondary to the needs of the institution itself. Individuals start to lose their identity as everything becomes secondary to the smooth and efficient running of the institution. Order and routine become the dominant factors. Both the people the institution is providing a service for and the staff become

Figure 1.2 A Scottish institution; this building is typical of many long-stay hospitals built in the nineteenth century

depersonalised. There is further consideration of the **labelling** that takes place in such institutions in Chapter 5, in the consideration of the sociological theory of **symbolic interactionism**. Erving Goffman's (1968) book *Asylums* has been particularly influential in promoting analysis of this process.

According to Goffman, the following are characteristics of institutionalisation:

- large numbers of people being cared for by small numbers of staff
- little contact with the outside world
- few meaningful activities, lots of empty time, enforced idleness
- large social distance between staff and service users, with staff in uniforms to emphasise differences
- staff behaving in an authoritarian manner
- working to a medical model, with its emphasis on treatment and attention to physical needs
- little chance of leaving the establishment, either temporarily or permanently
- lack of respect for the dignity of individuals, demonstrated through insults or lack of regard for privacy

- an almost total preoccupation among staff with the practical, task-oriented aspects of the job (mealtimes, bath times, etc.), with little thought or effort applied to imaginative ways of improving quality of life for the service users
- staff pre-occupied with their own affairs and communicating with one another as if service users weren't there.

People who spend a significant amount of time in such institutions will usually become institutionalised and display the following features:

- They become indifferent to their surroundings, to other people, the world, the future; to anything, in fact.
- They lose any motivation to do new things or sometimes to do anything at all.
- They lose the ability to make **choices**, decisions or plans of any sort. They expect others to do this for them.
- They become obedient to what people tell them to do.
- Standards of personal hygiene and cleanliness may go down, as service users have little sense of pride in themselves.
- Expectations are that little will change and that today, tomorrow and the next day will all be the same.
- Every now and then there is an outburst of temper or aggression, which is quickly dealt with.
- There can be a complete lack of enthusiasm.

The end result of this process is that the individual comes to depend on the institution for everything and finds it difficult to cope independently away from it. Many people who have moved out of institutions after many years find it difficult to adapt to life in the community. This is often a direct result of the effects of institutionalisation. They have not had interactions with a wide range of people or situations, so they lack confidence when faced with new activities of daily living, such as handling money, using public transport or making decisions about what food to buy.

Although this section is about care work in the past, it is unfortunately the case that many of the establishments that offer care to service users still continue to have elements of institutions and institutionalisation. One of the major tasks for care workers is to recognise the effects of institutionalisation and to take measures to reduce or minimise these effects on individuals.

Activity *Institutionalisation*

Read Julie's story on page 9 and identify at least five features of institutionalisation.

Julie's story

It was a summer day in the mid-1970s and Julie's first shift on the ward for 'mental defectives' in the local hospital, where she had been offered a summer job as a nursing assistant during her break from university. The ward she had been assigned to was called a villa but she could see little resemblance between the dilapidated red-brick building she now stood in and her uncle's holiday home in Spain. Sixty people appeared to spend every minute of their lives confined to this ward, where they were looked after by three or four nurses. The worst thing was the smell – a heady mixture of sweat, urine, stale food and disinfectant.

Julie felt ill at ease and self-conscious in her new nurse's uniform. She wasn't a nurse so why was she dressed like one? She also felt uncomfortable at being locked in this place, even though she had a bunch of keys securely attached to her belt. She was, if truth be told, even a little scared of the patients, some of whom looked quite frightening and were behaving in strange ways, pacing up and down or sitting rocking on the floor.

So far today she had helped to bath twenty of the patients in the ward, ticking off their names in a big bath book as they were processed two at a time in the white walled bathroom, with its two baths sitting in the middle of the floor. Each patient was bathed and received a change of underwear twice weekly. Julie had been amused to see the communal underwear at first, all marked with the hospital name and ward number, until she thought what it must be like not even to own your own pants.

Now it was dinner time and she had been asked to help with the two dozen patients in wheelchairs who were unable to feed themselves. 'You can do the feeders,' she had been told by the kindly old charge nurse. As she looked at the rows of patients lined up against the walls and away from the others sitting at tables, a big trolley with steaming hot steel cans of food was wheeled in by Bessie, the other nursing assistant on the shift.

'What do I do here?' she asked Bessie.

'Just fill the bowls and feed them,' replied Bessie. 'And watch out for chokers.'

She watched as Bessie spooned food from the steel containers into the large plastic bowls. Three half-slices of buttered bread were dropped in each first, followed by a ladleful of soup, brown mince, mashed potato and then a couple of splashes of milky tea from a huge battered teapot. The resulting mixture was mixed to a runny consistency.

'That's how you do the soft diets, love,' said Bessie. 'Sometimes if you're in a hurry you can put the custard in as well. All goes down the same way, you know. Now, you do that side and I'll do this.'

This story refers to practice that actually occurred in a Scottish hospital. The practice came to an end when a young student nurse who had been placed in the ward on temporary secondment was so appalled that she threatened to go straight to the press. This situation was not unusual. Another worker recalls:

> *I would agree with this. This is so similar to my early experiences as a student nurse in 1983–86 in the west of Scotland and as a junior staff nurse working in a hospital in England 1986–88.*

Care in the twentieth century

Many of the changes in care practice in the twentieth century, especially later in the century, were about counteracting institutionalisation and increasingly valuing the worth and dignity of all individuals. It is not the size of the institution that is most critical, nor do people necessarily become institutionalised just because they live in or attend an institution that provides care. People can still be institutionalised living in their own home if the care provided is institutionalising. It all depends upon how the service is delivered.

Activity *Counteracting institutionalisation*

Suggest ways in which you think things could be improved to counteract institutionalisation in Julie's story above.

Some of the things you may have thought of include:

- providing choices to service users
- not sticking to strict routines, but being flexible according to need
- staff wearing casual clothes, not uniforms
- plenty of stimulating activities on offer for those who wish to participate
- showing respect for the worth and needs of all individuals
- the privacy of single rooms
- privacy when bathing, dressing, etc.
- staff trained in the values and skills of care work
- making the building as 'homely' as possible
- wherever possible, using/adapting services that are available to everyone rather than offering specialised services
- wherever possible, supporting people in their own homes rather than in institutional settings.

The last quarter of the twentieth century began to see the review and closure of large institutions and an emphasis on the care of people in their own homes or in homely settings in the community. The National Health Service and Community Care Act 1990 was very significant in promoting this approach, completely revising the funding and philosophy of care provision. Some people believe that the closure of the large old institutions meant the end of institutionalisation, but unfortunately this is not necessarily the case. There is a current trend once again to build large homes for older adults, and great care needs to be taken not to replicate the mistakes, depersonalisation and disempowerment of the past. Institutionalisation can occur even in small units or people's own homes if workers do not practise a positive value base that promotes the worth, dignity and **inclusion** of everyone.

Care in the twenty-first century

This chapter is written at a time when care services in Scotland are going through a period of substantial change, meaning there are many new challenges for those working in this area. The changes have mostly arisen as a result of new policy and legislation and substantial reviews of how services are delivered. These changes, in turn, are at least in part a response to:

- **Demographic changes**. Demography refers to the structure of the population (see the section below).
- **Changes in the nature of family and family life**, with a variety of family structures and ways in which families communicate, provide or don't provide support, and cope or are unable to cope with difficulties. Chapter 5 provides further insight into the family.
- **Changes in political and personal ideologies and values**, with increasing emphasis on outcomes and the involvement of individuals in decision making about their own care.

Changes have sometimes, though not often enough, been driven by the most important people of all: those who use services. The meaning of some of the terms below will become clearer as the book progresses.

Care in the twenty-first century is characterised by:

- more emphasis on personalisation and person-centred care, and involving service users and carers in decision making (see explanation of personalisation below)
- a move towards more self-directed support, as part of the personalisation agenda, where service users and/or their representatives make choices about how support is provided
- much more focus on integration of services, a government policy in its own right and also fundamental to personalisation, for example the establishment of local Health and Social Care Partnerships (HSCPs)
- rigorous registration and training requirements across all professions
- increasing demands on care workers to develop a broader range of knowledge, skills and critical ability
- changes in the vocabulary of care, such as 'a person who uses services' or 'service user', with a social model of care placing the emphasis on the individual first rather than on issues or problems
- changes in the providers of care
- the continuing proliferation of institutional care for very frail older people, and also as a lifestyle choice for people who can afford it
- continuing financial restraints.

Figure 1.3 Care in the twenty-first century
(Source: Kennedy Care Group and Duke of Edinburgh's Award (DofE))

Two topics from the above introduction to Care in the 21st Century are both central and integrate discussion about the other areas. These are demography and personalisation which are more fully discussed below.

Demography

Demography, through the analysis of both quantitative and qualitative information about populations, provides us with a wealth of information that can inform practice and the planning of care provision. Some of the main demographic factors and changes are briefly discussed below. The statistical information provided is from National Records of Scotland (2014) unless otherwise stated:

- **Population growth**: Scotland's population in mid-2014 is the highest it has ever been at 5,347,600. This is a rise of 19,900 (0.4 per cent) people since mid-2013 and is part of a trend in rising population since 2009. There are three main reasons for this population increase: increased life expectancy resulting in more people over the age of 65, a slight rise in fertility, and inward migration exceeding outward migration.
- **Population ageing**: Scotland has an ageing population. Between mid-2004 and mid-2014 there was an increase of 17 per cent in the number of people aged 75 and over. The ageing of the population is also evident in the rise of 13 per cent in the 45–59 age group, and of 17 per cent in the 60–74 age group. This can be seen in Figure 1.4.

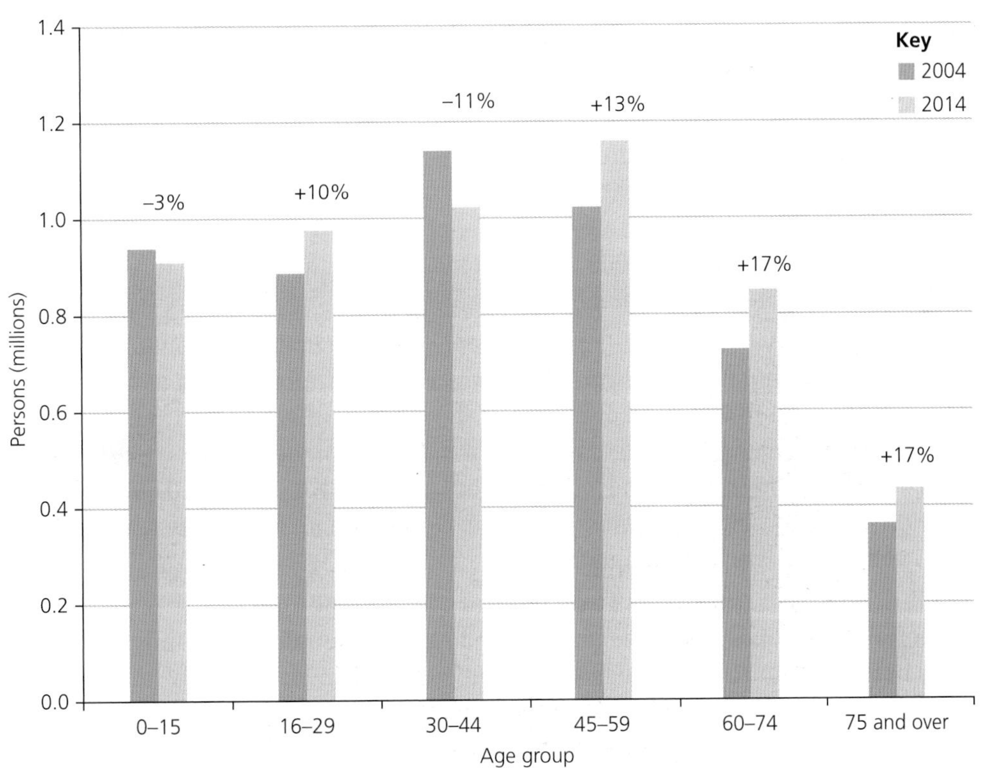

Figure 1.4 The changing age structure of Scotland's population, mid-2004 to mid-2014

An ageing population can have both negative and positive consequences. It has implications for what is known as the dependency ratio (the ratio of those working to not working in paid employment), the economy, demands on services and the amount of money from tax available to pay for services. Many government policies are aimed at reducing dependency and increasing independence in terms of economics, health and the provision of services.

One consequence of people living longer is a rise in the number of people with **dementia**. Currently approximately 86,000 people or 1.6% of the population of Scotland experiences dementia. This figure is expected to double between 2011 and 2031 as the number of people living longer increases. Since people with dementia are likely to need support for at least some of the time, this group is of particular importance in considering future service provision.

There are also **positive aspects of an ageing population**. People working for longer continue to contribute to the economy, including tax revenues, older people are important consumers, important carers and supporters of one another and in their roles as grandparents and family members.

Healthy life expectancy is increasing but not at the same rate as life expectancy and many government policies, as you can see in the section on policies later in this chapter, aim to tackle issues related to health in its widest sense to include physical, psychological and social factors. Although mortality, life expectancy and healthy life expectancy are all improving in Scotland as a whole, there are areas of deprivation where this is not the case. The section on inequality in Chapter 5 provides more information about this.

- **Fertility**: Although 3,500 more people were born than died in 2013, thus adding to the population increase, there is a falling birth rate in Scotland. This is attributed to a range of factors including educational qualifications, women in employment, views about gender equality, friendship networks and whether or not neighbourhoods are family friendly. The birth rate fluctuates from year to year and indications in 2015 are that the birth rate is continuing to fall and that the number of people being born continues to be insufficient to maintain the population at its current level.
- **Migration**: Migration is a major factor in the population increase. In-migration exceeded out-migration by approximately 17,600 between mid-2013 and mid-2014. Most migrants coming to Scotland come from other parts of the UK. Between mid-2013 and mid-2014, approximately 49,240 people came to Scotland from the rest of the UK, and approximately 39,660 left Scotland to go in the opposite direction, giving a net migration gain of approximately 9,600.
- Between mid-2013 and mid-2014, 33,200 people came to Scotland from overseas and 25,200 left Scotland to go overseas giving a net migration gain of 8,000, which represents about 1 in 700 (0.14 per cent) of the total population. Migrants to Scotland tended to be younger than the general population. The highest proportion of migrants are economic migrants from the EU. Refugees total approximately 20,000 in Scotland and there are 2,300 asylum seekers (Scottish Government, 2013), constituting in total only 3 per cent of the total population.
- **Lesbian, Gay, Bi-sexual and Transgender (LGBT) people**: There is increasing recognition of lesbian, gay, bi-sexual and transgender people as a demographic group in the population. Although there is no way of knowing exactly how many LGBT people there are in Scotland, Stonewall Scotland estimates the figure to be around 300,000, 5–7 per cent of the population. The Stonewall website (www. stonewallscotland.org.uk) provides evidence of both increasing acceptance of LGBT people in Scotland and continuing discrimination and harassment.
- **Families and family structures**: Families and family structures, an important demographic factor, are also changing with more single-person households (34 per cent of total households), dispersed families with younger people often living at some distance from older family members, small nuclear family units and multiple

family structures. The family continues to be important in people's lives in its many manifestations and is more fully discussed in Chapter 5.

Demography is a complex area and often changes that are expected to have a particular consequence may have several consequences, both expected and unexpected. For example, you may expect an increase in the number of older people to result in more people in residential care but in fact numbers have fallen over the past 14 years, alongside a rise in the number of people receiving free personal care at home. Changes in policy can also have consequences for the impact of demographic change.

Activity *Provision of care*

Discuss what you think the above demographic factors may mean for the provision of care in Scotland?

You should consider the possible impact of:

- population growth
- migration
- refugees and asylum seekers
- the ageing population with an increasing number of older people, especially people over 75
- LGBT people in the population
- family structures.

Activity *Demography*

Since demographic factors are changing all the time, bring yourself up to date by researching the main changes in the demographic structure of Scotland that you think are influencing the provision of care this year. You can find information about demographic factors at the National Records of Scotland website (**www.nrscotland.gov.uk**) and also at **www.stonewallscotland.org.uk** (in relation to LGBT issues) and at **www.scottishrefugeecouncil.org** (in relation to refugees and asylum seekers).

Personalisation

> *Personalisation enables the individual alone, or in groups, to find the right solutions for them and to participate in the delivery of a service. From being a recipient of services, citizens can become actively involved in selecting and shaping the services they receive. Personalisation means that people become more involved in how services are designed and they receive support that is most suited to them.*

(Self-directed Support Scotland available at: **http://www.sdsscotland.org.uk/resources/personalisation.php#sthash.iN6w1vH8.dpuf**)

Since personalisation is fundamental to understanding many of the changes that are taking place in relation to care practice further explanation is provided here. Personalisation is both an ideology and a policy. It has been promoted as Scottish policy through an agenda of person-centred and self-directed support (SDS) which aims to give people dignity and to optimise their participation in the care they receive. SDS is enshrined in legislation through the Social Care (Self-directed Support) (Scotland) Act 2013. Personalisation is further supported through other legislation including the Children and Young People (Scotland) Act 2014, the Public Bodies (Joint Working) (Scotland) Act 2014 and the Equality Act 2010, all described later in the chapter. As an approach it requires continuing changes in the way in which care is thought about and delivered. It requires:

- services to work together collaboratively in partnership to promote inclusive opportunities for people
- a self-directed and person-centred approach that focuses on the individual and meeting their needs
- the implementation of the options provided in the Social Care (Self-directed Support) (Scotland) Act 2013
- an inclusive and anti-discriminatory approach in universal and community services
- prevention or early intervention so that services are not just responding to crises.

The approaches discussed in Chapter 6 promote personalisation through person-centred, self-directed, strengths-based and outcomes approaches. The value base underpinning the National Care Standards, the Code of Practice for Social Service Workers and Anti-discriminatory Practice, essential to personalisation, are discussed in Chapter 2. Legislation and policy are discussed later in this chapter. As a theme, personalisation is both explicit and implied in much of the content of the book. You can find out more about personalisation from resources described at the end of this chapter, especially the resources from SSKS (Social Services Knowledge Scotland) and SCIE (Social Care Institute for Excellence). The practical application of personalisation in terms of self-directed support, whilst it is recognised as a good idea, is not universally considered to be advantageous to everyone. For other people it is life-changing, especially through managing their own budgets and purchasing support from personal assistants (PAs) who can be flexible in the care they provide:

> *I was 38 years old when MS struck. I need to remain feeling useful and engaged and managing my own funds and my PA input helps me to do so.*
>
> *The best is being able to get the sort of flexible support that means I can continue to be healthy and thereby remain fully engaged in work and the community where I live.*
>
> *For me, having control over my life means not having to stick to other people's routines. My PAs understand that they're here to support me, so they accept that they may do very different things each time they're on duty.*
>
> (Scottish Government, 2008)

For a more critical consideration of personalisation and self-directed support you can read the works of Cromer and Maclean (2011) and Peter Beresford (2013). Even its critics, however, see the ideal of personalisation as having the potential to transform the lives of service users and as the best thing we have if it is adequately resourced and can be implemented fairly and sensitively.

Developing professional skills and knowledge

One of the major developments in care over the last decade has been that of a broad range of training and learning opportunities. In most areas of care work there are now regulatory bodies, which have established qualifications criteria for registration that mean you will be required to become competent for the specific requirements for your role. This in turn will contribute to you becoming as good a care worker as you can be.

Table 1.2 Agencies responsible for regulating health and social care professionals in Scotland

Professional group	Regulatory body	Website
Social service workers (including care workers), qualified social workers and social work students on approved degree courses	Scottish Social Services Council (SSSC)	www.sssc.uk.com
Dentists and dental professionals	General Dental Council	www.gdc-uk.org
Doctors	General Medical Council (GMC)	www.gmc-uk.org
Opticians	General Optical Council	www.optical.org
Art therapists, podiatrists, dieticians, occupational therapists, paramedics, physiotherapists, practitioner psychologists, social workers in England, and others	Health and Care Professions Council, or for some roles SSSC if working in a care setting	www.hcpc-uk.org www.sssc.uk.com
Nurses, midwives	Nursing and Midwifery Council, or SSSC if working in a care setting	www.nmc-uk.org www.sssc.uk.com
Pharmacists	Royal Pharmaceutical Society (RPS)	www.rpharms.com

There are many routes you may be able to follow in order to achieve the necessary qualifications. Training providers are increasingly making access to training as flexible as possible in order to maximise opportunities for people from different backgrounds, and with varied prior experiences of learning, to move into a career in care. There are also many websites to enable you to develop your learning. Some of these are listed within and at the end of chapters of this book. The notion of portfolio-building has also been gradually introduced into the care sector in Scotland. This is an approach to learning that means that as you progress through your career you can add to your training and experience portfolio in a range of different ways.

A further development in this area has been the Scottish Credit and Qualifications Framework (SCQF), which places all qualifications in Scotland in a coherent framework to make it easier to determine the equivalence of qualifications and easier to transfer learning. There is now a commitment both to lifelong learning (the Continuous Learning Framework, see **www.sssc.co.uk**) and to updating professional skills and qualifications for all levels of worker. Another trend is the opportunity to take care qualifications in your place of work or partly or fully on a distance learning basis. This is designed to further ease access to learning for all by addressing the difficulties people in the care sector have often had in balancing work, domestic and family commitments, and learning needs. Scotland's Curriculum for Excellence is an important milestone in establishing the foundations for learning throughout life, with its emphasis on the 'four capacities': successful learners, confident individuals, responsible citizens and effective contributors.

Activity *Influences on individuals in becoming care workers*

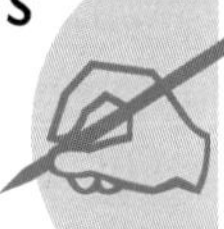

Read the case study of Andy below and identify the stages he went through and the influences on him in becoming a care worker. You should do the same for the two accounts that follow by students from Perth College UHI.

Andy

Andy left school with five Standard Grades (now National 4 and 5 qualifications) and subsequently worked on various building sites as a labourer for a couple of years. During his final year at school his parents had separated and he had remained living with his dad. This was not a very satisfactory arrangement but he didn't have much choice; his mum had gone to live with someone else. He subsequently moved to a shared flat with an old friend from school, Phil, who was working as a housing support worker with the local authority.

Andy never really fitted in on the building site or saw his long-term future as being there. He knew that he wanted something different. He and Phil volunteered with the local youth partnership in their time off and really enjoyed working with the young people. When the youth partnership organiser, John, showed Andy an advertisement for an open evening at a care and education centre entitled 'Men can care' he thought he might go along to see what it was all about. He found it really interesting but felt that he wasn't really ready to make such a big change in his life just yet. Instead, with John and Phil's encouragement, he took an introductory care course one evening a week, leading to a Higher in Care.

He was amazed when he passed the course with flying colours. He had been able to link his experience with the youth partnership, as well as his practical skills on the building site, to his assessments and John had provided valuable supervision and support.

The following year Andy applied to work at the care and education centre and was accepted on to their Modern Apprenticeship scheme as a care worker. This enabled him to take his SVQ3 in Social Services (Children and Young People), which he combined with an HNC in Social Care. He loved his work and felt that all his experience and learning had come together to enable him to make a really positive contribution to the lives of the young people at the centre. Many of them had experienced family difficulties and/or issues with the law and he felt a real **empathy** with them. A lot of his practical skills were useful too since the centre undertook a comprehensive preparation-for-work programme with the young people.

Below, two students from the National Certificate course in Health and Social Care at Perth College UHI contribute their accounts of how they came to the course.

Christine

My name is Christine and I am 23 years old. I would describe myself as a kind, caring, patient person. I am a good listener and I have a passion for helping people. Through school I took on extra responsibilities, such as being Primary 7 monitor, a junior prefect at the end of S3 and the start of S4, and a senior prefect in S5 and S6. I would also help people with learning difficulties. I was a volunteer for two years with Victim Support Scotland. During my time with Victim Support I worked with victims of minor crimes and domestic abuse. I helped the victims by arranging an appointment to come into the office and I would listen to them when they explained to me what they had gone through. I would give them options and support them as much as I could.

I would say I see myself as a people person. In my work at Baxter's Gift Shop and Restaurant we did events such as the Little Cooks Club, which was for children aged 5–12 years, and birthday parties and breakfast with Santa for the same age group. I got on to the course I am doing, the NC Health and Social Care, following encouraging results in the NQ Care and because I had really enjoyed that course. I am hoping to go on to do an HNC, then to progress on to the nursing college at Ninewells Hospital in Dundee. I would like to become a nurse. As part of my NC Health and Social Care course I am doing community involvement at a Macmillan Centre and I am enjoying every minute of it there. The staff and the patients make me feel part of the **team**. I can spend time with patients, doing activities with them like cross stitch, which is a skill I can share and that people seem to like doing. There's a friendly and welcoming atmosphere at the centre. My placement has made me more determined to become a nurse.

Stacy

I am Stacy, I am a 'mature' student at age 32. I come from the Highlands in Aberdeenshire, Ballater to be precise. My history? Aged 15 I was employed by a residential home, and at that time I feel I was far too young to be a care worker. Sadly, the staff there weren't very nice to me. I soon left and started working as a domestic cleaner within a different care home, where the staff were lovely. Because I had hands-on experience with the care side, I was asked if I could help with taking residents to the toilet when they asked me to do so. I happily obliged as I wanted to help my colleagues and the residents. One of the people I worked with was a resident called Molly. Molly used to tell me about her past, and seeing her face light up when she told me about past boyfriends or 'courting' really interested me and I thoroughly enjoyed talking to her, because she taught me so much. Sadly, Molly had somehow contracted an illness that I cannot remember, and when I went to go and see her in her room, just to keep her company and keep her room tidy, she died with me by her side. I was distraught but I was glad I was there when no one else was.

After this I took on a hotel cleaning job, followed by several retail jobs including management posts. I also took on the role of informal carer to my granny, who had partial sight at that time due to a stroke. I was her youngest granddaughter. I took very good care of my granny until she moved to a sheltered housing complex. She then told me to go and live my life. Eleven years later, I am still in Perthshire.

Following the birth of my son I enrolled on the NQ Intermediate 2 Health and Social Care at Perth College. In August 2014 I received the qualifying grades to get me on to my current course, NC Health and Social Care.

My placement is with CATH (Churches Action for the Homeless). They have several running projects, a charity shop, a homeless hostel, floating support and a day centre. I am really enjoying my time there. I am meeting new people all the time, and helping those in need of things we take for granted. I have been offered relief work as well, so it's definitely something I will be looking into in the summer time.

I generally enjoy helping others, even in a foreign language, as I know what it's like to be in a different country that has a different language as I lived in Germany for seven years. It's very overwhelming. Empathy is by far the biggest core condition in my view.

My advice for others ... Care is hard work and tears at your heartstrings. It's also very rewarding, however; life lessons can be learned. Listen to your **client**.

Care services

Formal and informal care

Care can be provided formally through organisations or informally to people known to the carer. **Formal** care can be provided by people who are paid to do a job or by unpaid volunteers; **informal** care is usually unpaid, though there are **statutory** allowances that can be claimed by informal carers (summarised to '**carers**') who provide substantial amounts of care. Informal care may be provided to people of any age who may be affected by physical or mental illness (often long-term), by disability, frailty or substance misuse. These people may be the carer's close family members, other relatives, partners, friends and neighbours. People providing unpaid, informal care to someone who is not a relative may be called **volunteers**, so that volunteering crosses the boundaries of formal and informal care. In *Caring Together: The carers' strategy for Scotland* this contribution is acknowledged and a strategy is set out to support carers now and in the future:

> *Carers play a crucial role in the delivery of health and social care provision in Scotland. The identified 657,300 carers in Scotland, 1 in 8*

of the population, are an essential part of the workforce, in its broadest sense, contributing savings to health and social care services in Scotland of an estimated £7.6 billion every year.

(COSLA and Scottish Government, 2010)

Being a **carer** is not an easy option. The hours are often long and fitted in around other responsibilities. Being a carer can involve a substantial loss of income from paid work, and the work can be stressful and physically and mentally arduous. It can also be very rewarding, though this depends greatly upon individual attributes and the quality of the pre-existing and current relationship. In recent years there have been some substantial improvements in the quantity and quality of support available to carers. These include: the provision of free personal care introduced in the Community Care and Health (Scotland) Act 2002, which has taken some of the stress from some carers who were providing up to 24-hour support; the introduction of **self-directed support**, which makes provision for direct payments for care; the reiteration of carers' rights to be assessed in their own right in a number of pieces of legislation, including the Community Care and Health (Scotland) Act 2002; a number of organisations that provide helpful services, such as Carers Trust Scotland (**www.carers.org/scotland**) and Alzheimer Scotland (**www.alzscot.org**). As is the case for users of services, however, there are not always adequate services to meet the needs of carers. Seventy-three per cent of people receiving Carer's Allowance for caring for someone for more than 35 hours a week are women. The 2011 census showed that among all carers, 58 per cent are female and 42 per cent are male. This includes young carers (Carers UK, 2014).

Volunteers also make an incredible difference to the well-being of the people with whom they work. Volunteering is defined by the National Council for Voluntary Organisations (NCVO, 2015) as:

... any activity that involves spending time, unpaid, doing something that aims to benefit the environment of someone (an individual or a group) other than, or in addition to, close relatives.

Central to this definition is the fact that volunteering must be a choice freely made by each individual. This can include formal activity undertaken through public, private and **third sector organisations**, as well as informal community participation and social action.

The Scottish Household Survey 2013 (Scottish Government, 2014) indicates that 28 per cent of adults in Scotland, more than 1.25 million people, volunteered through an organisation in the year of the survey. In 2012 volunteers living in Scotland contributed 162 million hours of help, estimated to contribute £2.6 billion to the Scottish economy. Of these, approximately 23 per cent volunteered in the area of health, disability and welfare, with 283,000 volunteers in this sector. You can find out more about volunteers and volunteering from the websites of Volunteer Scotland (**www.volunteerscotland.net**) and the Scottish Council for Voluntary Organisations (**www.scvo.org.uk**). Roy McGivney, who was interviewed for this book, is a good example of someone who volunteers. He volunteers as a counsellor of people with problems with alcohol, as an advocate and as a Children's Panel member. He states:

All I need in the world is to see people smile ... I love people, individuality, challenges ... I don't regard myself as a do-gooder ... I'm getting so much from it.

Formal care refers to care that is provided formally by or through an organisation, or through a formal agreement, and is received by people in a wide variety of settings, including their own homes. Support is usually provided by paid workers but may also be offered by volunteers formally appointed through an organisation. Formal care may be defined as caring for and with people in society, other than self or family, in an **agency** whose codes of practice are dictated and guided by legislation, policy and professional ethics, or care provided by individuals employed using self-directed support or employed and paid for by the individual in need of care. The main types of provider of formal paid care and the areas in which they operate are examined below.

Care services in Scotland

In 2013 there were 13,665 services regulated by the Care Inspectorate, used by approximately 320,000 people. In 2014 there were 189,670 social service workers employed in these services (SSSC, 2014b). The nature of this workforce is changing, with an increasing proportion employed in the private and voluntary sectors (41 per cent and 27 per cent, respectively) and a decreasing proportion in the statutory (also called public) sector (32 per cent) (see Figure 1.4), indicating a mixed economy of care. In the past, before the NHS and Community Care Act 1990, most services were provided by the statutory sector. Workers are employed in a range of areas, as illustrated in Table 1.1 on page 3. Eighty-five per cent of the workforce is female, though proportions of men and women vary for different parts of the sector.

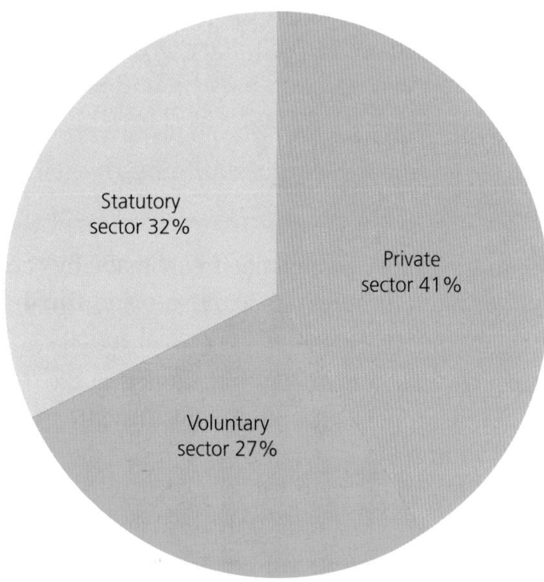

Figure 1.5 Scottish social services workforce

Key points about the social services workforce in Scotland:

- *The size of the workforce appears to have fallen slightly to 189,670 people. This accounts for approximately 7.4 per cent of Scottish employment.*

- *The largest employer type differs between local authorities, with services in the Orkneys, Shetlands and Western Isles (i.e. the three 'island authorities') being provided mainly by the public sector. In the majority of areas, however, the private sector is the largest employer.*

- *The three largest sub-sectors are housing support/care at home, care homes for adults, and day care of children. Together, these account for almost 76 per cent of the workforce.*

- *The median age of the workforce is highest in the public sector (47) and lowest in the private sector (41). Early years workers in the private sector have the lowest median age (28).*

- *The percentage of men working in the sector has fallen slightly to 15 per cent, though it is more than double this in criminal justice and residential children's services.*

- *The workforce is predominantly employed on permanent contracts (79 per cent). The median figure for the typical weekly hours worked by staff is close to full-time at 32.5.*

(SSSC, 2014b)

Activity *Statistics*

By the time you read this book some of the statistics above about care services in Scotland may be out of date. Use the internet to provide yourself with an up-to-date picture of care services in Scotland. Note that the voluntary sector is sometimes included as part of the third sector and is sometimes referred to separately. You may wish to consult these websites:

- Scottish Government: **www.scotland.gov.uk**
- Scottish Social Services Council: **www.sssc.uk.com**
- Care Inspectorate: **www.careinspectorate.com**

The statutory sector

The statutory sector, also known as the public sector, contains organisations that provide health services, social work services and increasingly joint or combined services, for example with housing, education and justice. They are known as statutory services because they perform some of their functions, or have been set up, under Acts of Parliament. Every Scottish local authority must by law provide a range of certain social work services. It used to be the case that Scottish local authorities were the direct providers of most of the services themselves. They had large Social Work Departments that ran a whole range of care provision, such as home helps, day centres for people with learning disabilities, intermediate treatment services for offenders, adoption services and fieldwork services. Since the National Health Service and Community Care Act 1990, such departments have adopted a mixed economy approach to the provision of care, and many services are now provided by and/or commissioned from the independent sector. The proportion of services actually provided by the statutory sector fell from 60 per cent in 1994 to 42 per cent in 2004 to 32 per cent in 2013 (SSSC, 2014b). One such service provider is Glasgow City Council, whose social work services ethos is set out in Chapter 6.

The third sector

The third sector comprises voluntary organisations, charities, community groups, social enterprises, co-operatives and individual volunteers. Some organisations have identities as more than one kind of third sector organisation and may also have one part of the organisation that is run separately as a for-profit, private sector organisation. The third sector and the private sector together are referred to here as the independent sector, though this term is also sometimes used to refer only to the private sector. The Hillcrest Group is an example of an organisation with multiple aspects. It is a registered charity with the following companies:

- Hillcrest Housing Association providing housing and support
- Northern Housing Association providing affordable rented accommodation
- Gowrie Care providing person-centred support services
- Hillcrest Maintenance Services providing maintenance for Hillcrest properties and a number of external organisations
- Hillcrest Enterprises performing a range of services from letting to managing properties for people with particular needs and developing new business opportunities
- Craigowl Communities helping people who have had difficulties in their lives to move into work and accommodation.

Hillcrest has aspects of being a social enterprise, a charity and a voluntary organisation run as a business.

The third sector is a growing sector in Scotland. Statistics still often refer to the voluntary sector which is providing 27 per cent of all care services (SSSC 2014). The third sector is also an area where new services are often developed in order to fill the gaps that statutory and private sector services don't cover or to provide creative approaches in the provision of service. Some of the first services for people with learning disabilities, for example, were provided on a local level by groups of volunteers such as parents who, in the absence of any provision, grouped together and ran their own services. At the same time such groups lobbied to get the statutory services to take notice of the difficulties experienced by the people they were caring for and created pressure for high quality services to be provided. Some of these groups grew up to become service providers themselves. One example is Enable, formerly known as the 'Scottish Society for the Mentally Handicapped', which was an amalgamation of local groups of parents all of whom worked very hard for the benefit of their family members. They opened and ran their own day centres and respite care units, some of which were eventually taken over and managed by local authority services. Enable continues as a campaigning group for this service user group and also functions as a direct provider of quality services through a number of affiliated service provision agencies.

Another example of a third sector provider is TRFS (The Richmond Fellowship Scotland). It is both a voluntary organisation and a charity. Joanne Gaughan of TRFS has provided the following account.

CARE IN PRACTICE

The Richmond Fellowship Scotland (TRFS)

The Richmond Fellowship Scotland (TRFS) was established in 1993 and provides personalised, community-based support services. All of the services work in person-centred ways to offer choice, promote inclusion and maximise ability. The organisation has grown considerably since its inception and now manages in the region of 190 services across Scotland in both rural and urban settings, employing more than 2500 staff. The organisation currently supports almost 3000 individuals and works with 28 local authorities. It is a people-focused organisation, motivated by the needs of individuals and communities, not by profit. Throughout its history TRFS has developed both various service models for individuals and an expertise in supporting people with a wide range of care and support needs.

The range of care and support needs includes the following:

- mental health difficulties
- learning disabilities
- physical disabilities
- sensory impairment
- autistic spectrum disorders
- complex challenging behaviour
- substance misuse
- age-related problems, including dementia
- alcohol-related brain damage (ARBD)
- homelessness issues
- offending issues
- forensic needs.

Service provision includes:

- intensive, individualised support packages
- small group living services
- floating support
- family support services
- services to young people in transition

- housing support and care at home
- respite services
- crisis services
- registered care homes
- shared lives services.

The organisation provides structured support that is designed to be flexible to respond to the individual's changing needs, to be unobtrusive and person-centred, while being measurable and accountable. We have been involved in supporting resettlement programmes for 23 hospitals and continue to develop new services and reconfigure existing services in response to individuals, planners and commissioners.

The private sector

The private sector is the other part of the independent sector and it continues to grow at a steady pace in Scotland, especially in the provision of residential care for older adults. This sector also makes a contribution in other parts of the care sector, as you can see from the example of Aspire Scotland below. Provision by this sector increased from 30 per cent in 1994 to 41 per cent in 2013 (SSSC, 2014b). Private sector services are run as businesses and need to make a profit to ensure viability. This can have both advantages and disadvantages. Successful businesses that plough back enough of their profits to provide an ethical and progressive service can be tremendously beneficial to the overall provision of care.

CARE IN PRACTICE

Aspire Scotland Ltd

Making a difference for all children, young people and families

Aspire Scotland Ltd is a provider of high quality care and education to some of Scotland's most vulnerable and 'needy' children, who also may have additional support needs. The impact of its work in respect of these needs is measured using the SHANARRI indicators (see pages 260–1).

As a provider of School Care Accommodation, Aspire is registered to deliver both care and education. Its school has been approved by the Registrar of Independent Schools and its residential houses have been registered by the Care Inspectorate. Its work is scrutinised by the sector's regulatory bodies – Education Scotland and the Care Inspectorate – with each residential house being inspected twice yearly and its school being inspected every four years via a joint inspection team from both regulatory bodies.

Local authorities place children and young people in the care of Aspire when they themselves are unable to provide the specialist assistance required to meet their identified needs. Normally the decision to place an individual in School Care

Accommodation is taken by the local authority itself and the grounds for such a placement are ratified by the Children's Hearings System. Such children are known as Looked After and Accommodated Children (LAAC).

Aspire Scotland Ltd has the firm conviction that each child is to be regarded as a unique individual. It works collegiately with a wide range of professionals and support agencies to ensure that the care and education plans constructed with each child are accurate and focused on agreed **outcomes**, which are reviewed regularly and discussed, in full, at post admission meetings, LAAC meetings and Children's Hearings themselves.

All providers have a responsibility to ensure that all those who work directly with children and young people are suitably qualified to do so. The Scottish Social Services Council (SSSC) and the General Teaching Council for Scotland (GTCS) insist that all workers be registered with them for the appropriate services, and both councils have a very clear 'code of conduct' to which registered workers must adhere. Currently staff are trained at least to Higher National Certificate (HNC) and SVQ (Scottish Vocational Qualifications) Level 3 in Social Services (Children and Young People), and to PDA (Professional Development Award) and degree level in the educational context.

Legislation and policy for care practice

Legislation refers to a 'law or set of laws suggested by a government and made official by a parliament' (Cambridge Dictionary Online). Legislation that applies in Scotland can be British, Scottish or European. The majority of key legislation relating to care is Scottish, with the key functions of health, social care, education and many other areas devolved to the Scottish Parliament. **Policy** in this context refers to national or local plans or agreements about what it is officially decided to do in particular situations, for example government policy about self-directed support, **safeguarding** or education.

Policy

Before proceeding to an account of current legislation, a sample of policy documents relevant to service users and the provision of care services in Scotland is outlined. Policies are continually evolving and you should try to keep yourself up to date through the Scottish Government website: **www.gov.scot**. Policies are much more readable than legislation and are often presented as strategies. A strategy is a high-level plan to achieve identified goals or outcomes.

Some of these policies have been incorporated into legislation. Where this is the case it is indicated in the text. Policies do not need to be incorporated into legislation to be put into action and indeed most policies are not. Where there are changes in legislation this usually means that existing legislation needed to be introduced or adapted to make services more efficient, to deliver new entitlements or to ensure the delivery of new policy objectives and directions that could not adequately be implemented through existing legislation.

Caring Together: The carers strategy for Scotland 2010–2015 (COSLA and Scottish Government, 2010)

The Scottish Government recognises the support provided by informal carers, often family members, to the people they care about and for, and the social and economic contribution that this makes to Scotland. This strategy aims to support carers of all ages, including young carers, to manage their caring responsibilities with increased confidence and in good health, and to have a life of their own outside caring. Actions include increased respite provision and support for carer organisations. The Carers (Scotland) Bill 2015 will consolidate existing rights as well as ensuring new rights for carers and young carers. Local authorities will have a duty and not just the power to support carers.

Available at: **www.gov.scot/Resource/Doc/319441/0102104.pdf**

Getting it Right for Every Child (GIRFEC) (Scottish Government, 2012)

GIRFEC is Scotland's programme to improve outcomes for all children and young people. It is included in policy, practice and legislation including the Children and Young People (Scotland) Act 2014. Essential elements are:

- making practice child centred
- working to the National Practice Model (this is outlined in Chapter 6)
- the introduction of 'The Named Person' and 'The Lead Practitioner'. The named person is the first point of contact for all children and young people. Where a child needs help, the lead professional will co-ordinate planning and support
- building confidence and the importance of training and learning.

Available at: **www.gov.scot/Topics/People/Young-People/gettingitright**

Scottish Government's 2020 Vision (Scottish Government, 2011)

The Scottish Government's 2020 Vision is that by 2020 everyone is able to live longer, healthier lives at home or in a homely setting and that we will have a healthcare system where:

- we have integrated health and social care
- there is a focus on prevention, anticipation and supported self-management
- if hospital treatment is required, and cannot be provided in a community setting, day case treatment will be the norm
- whatever the setting, care will be provided to the highest standards of quality and safety, with the person at the centre of all decisions
- there will be a focus on ensuring that people get back into their home or community environment as soon as appropriate, with *minimal* risk of re-admission.

Available at: **www.gov.scot/Topics/Health/Policy/2020-Vision**

Reshaping Care for Older People: A programme of change 2011–2021 (COSLA, Scottish Government, NHS Scotland, 2011)

This is a major document for the future care for older people. It has many of the features of the 2020 Vision, especially in terms of integration of services, and promotes a personalised agenda. The vision is that:

Older people in Scotland are valued as an asset, their voices are heard and older people are supported to enjoy full and positive lives in their own home or in a homely setting.

Among the main messages are:

- Older people should be seen as an asset, not a burden.
- There is a need for a shift in philosophy, attitudes and approaches with success measured in terms of enabling people to remain independent.
- Services should be outcome focused and personalised (see Chapter 6).
- Supporting and caring for older people is everyone's responsibility.
- It is important to align resources with more integration and partnership working.

Available at: **www.gov.scot/Resource/0039/00398295.pdf**

Mental Health Strategy 2012–2015 (Scottish Government, 2012)

The Mental Health Strategy also has the stated aim of being consistent with the 2020 Vision. The focus on 'prevention, anticipation and supported self-management' is central to taking forward mental health policy in Scotland. There are three main quality ambitions for Scotland that health and care must be:

- **person centred**: mutually beneficial partnerships between patients, their families and those delivering healthcare services which respect individual needs and values and which demonstrate compassion, continuity, clear communication and shared decision making
- **safe**: there will be no avoidable injury or harm to people from healthcare they receive and an appropriate clean and safe environment will be provided for the delivery of healthcare services at all times
- **effective**: the most appropriate treatments, interventions, support and services will be provided at the right time to everyone who will benefit and wasteful or harmful variation will be eradicated.

Available at: **www.gov.scot/Resource/0039/00398762.pdf**

New Scots: Integrating refugees in Scotland's communities 2014–2017 (Scottish Government, 2013)

The New Scots refugee integration strategy aims to ensure that refugees are offered safety in Scotland, afforded respect and given assistance to integrate into our communities. There were just over 20,000 refugees residing in Scotland in 2013 when the strategy was produced.

Available at: **www.gov.scot/Publications/2013/12/4581**

Play Strategy for Scotland: Our vision (Scottish Government, 2013)

The vision for this strategy is for Scotland to be one of the best places in the world in which to grow up, a nation which values play as a life-enhancing experience for all children. Also relevant to children is the Scottish Government's Early Years Framework 2008, the development of the Early Years Collaborative 2012 and the National Practice Guidance on Early Learning and Childcare 2014.

Available at: **www.gov.scot/Resource/0043/00437132.pdf** and **www.gov.scot/Topics/People/Young-People/early-years**

Scotland's Dementia Strategy 2013–2016 (Scottish Government, 2013)

The key outcomes for this strategy, which emerged from the National Dementia Dialogue as priorities were:

- more people with dementia living a good-quality life at home for longer
- dementia-enabled and dementia-friendly local communities, which contribute to greater awareness of dementia and reduce stigma
- timely, accurate diagnosis of dementia
- better post-diagnostic support for people with dementia and their families
- more people with dementia and their families and carers being involved as equal partners in care throughout the journey of the illness
- better respect and promotion of rights in all settings, together with improved compliance with the legal requirements in respect of treatment
- people with dementia in hospitals or other institutional settings always being treated with dignity and respect.

Available at: **www.gov.scot/Resource/0042/00423472.pdf**

Scotland's National Action Plan for Human Rights (Scottish Human Rights Commission, 2013)

Known as SNAP, this action plan sets out three outcomes to be pursued in Scotland:

- **Outcome 1**: better culture – People can understand and affirm human rights and organisations are enabled and accountable to put human rights into practice
- **Outcome 2**: better lives – Scotland effectively tackles injustice and exclusion, improving lives
- **Outcome 3**: better world – Scotland gives effect to its international obligations at home and internationally.

Available at: **http://www.scottishhumanrights.com/actionplan**

See Hear: A strategic framework for meeting the needs of people with a sensory impairment in Scotland (Scottish Government, 2014)

See Hear provides practical steps and recommendations for a framework of structured, coordinated, person-centred service delivery and support.

Available at: **www.gov.scot/Publications/2014/04/7863**

Self-directed Support: A national strategy for Scotland (Scottish Government, 2010)

Self-directed Support (SDS) is a term that describes the ways in which individuals and families can have informed choice about the way support is provided to them. It includes a range of options for exercising those choices. Through a co-production approach to agreeing individual outcomes, options are considered for ways in which available resources can be used so that people can have greater levels of control over how their support needs are met, and by whom. The choice may include:

- taking a direct payment
- having a direct payment managed by a third party
- directing the individual budget to arrange support from the local authority or from a commissioned provider
- a combination of these.

One aim of the strategy is to promote the personalisation of care, putting the individual in control of managing their care as much as they wish and are able to. Much of the strategy has been incorporated into legislation through the Social Care (Self-directed Support) (Scotland) Act 2014.

The strategy document provides many examples of implementation and can be viewed at: **www.gov.scot/Resource/Doc/329971/0106962.pdf**

The Keys to Life: Improving quality of life for people with learning disabilities (Scottish Government, 2013)

This strategy builds on 'The Same as You' (Scottish Government, 2000) to set out a vision for improved partnership working to deliver better outcomes for people with learning disabilities and their families and carers in the areas of life they have emphasised as important. There is a strong focus on tackling the health inequalities experienced by people with learning disabilities as well as other outcomes, such as independent living and keeping safe, to improve the quality of their lives. The principles of choice, control and independence are central. The strategy is consistent with personalisation and the implementation of self-directed support.

More information and linked resources can be found at: **www.keystolife.info**

Common themes of these documents and reference to Chapters 1, 2 and 6

These policy documents and several others make for very interesting reading and provide a lot of useful contextual information. They also have common themes, many of which are reflected in the content of this book, especially in Chapters 1, 2 and 6. These include:

- the promotion of dignity and a sound value base (Chapter 2)
- anti-discriminatory practice (Chapter 2)
- person-centred approaches (Chapter 6)
- the integration of health and care, and other forms of integration and partnership working (Chapter 1)
- an emphasis on outcomes (Chapter 6)
- personalisation, which includes all of the above and also an emphasis on self-directed care, collaboration and prevention or early intervention (Chapters 1, 2, and 6).

Legislation

Below are details of some of the major pieces of legislation affecting care services in Scotland. It is essential that you make yourself aware of legislation as some of it places a duty on you as an individual to carry out your care practice in particular ways. What follows is intended as a general introduction to the various types of legislation relating to care in Scotland and is by no means a comprehensive guide. It is important for you to keep up to date with the changes in legislation relevant to your practice.

Scottish and UK legislation can be found at **www.legislation.gov.uk**. It can be heavy going to look at the official version of a piece of legislation. Often it is better to go to the website of an agency that monitors or implements the legislation, as this will give you a summary of the key features and examples of how it is currently put into practice. Alternatively, you can refer to a guide to legislation such as Maclean (2015) (listed in Suggested reading at the end of the chapter), which simplifies components of Scottish legislation relevant to care practice, and the implications for the individual, carers, families, communities and society.

Children and Young People (Scotland) Act 2014

This Act includes provisions that:

- from August 2014 the amount and flexibility of free Early Learning and Childcare would increase from 475 to a minimum of 600 hours per year for 3- and 4-year-olds, and 15 per cent of Scotland's most vulnerable 2-year-olds; from August 2015 this will extend to 27 per cent of the most vulnerable 2-year-olds
- free school lunches would be provided to all children in Primary 1–3 by January 2015
- better permanence planning for looked-after children to ensure all 16-year-olds in care have the right to stay in care until the age of 21 from 2015; to extend the support available to young people leaving care for longer (up to the age of 26), and to support the parenting role of kinship carers
- elements of the Getting it Right for Every Child (GIRFEC) approach will be enshrined in law, ensuring there is a single planning approach for children who need additional support from services, providing a single point of contact for every child and providing a holistic understanding of well-being
- new duties will be created in relation to the UNCRC and to strengthen the role of the Children's Commissioner
- existing legislation that affects children will be strengthened, including a number of amendments to the process for school closure proposals under the Schools (Consultation) (Scotland) Act 2010.

Scotland's Commissioner for Children and Young People: **www.sccyp.org.uk**

Immigration Act 2014

An act to:

- make provision about immigration law, making it more difficult for immigrants without legal documents to enter the UK or to remain in the UK, and limiting provisions for appeal and the right to a private family life
- limit, or otherwise make provision about access to services, facilities and employment by reference to immigration status (includes provisions to charge for NHS services)
- make provision about marriage and civil partnership involving certain foreign nationals (aimed at increasing deterrents to 'bogus' marriage).

The main aim of the Act is to deter so-called 'illegal' immigrants from coming to the UK and to allow the Home Office more easily to identify and remove 'illegal' immigrants. There are fears that the measures in the Act will increase the likelihood of hostility towards migrants, including refugees who are here legally and people seeking asylum hoping to gain refugee and eventually citizenship status.

Only some aspects of this Act have so far been implemented. Legislation relating to immigration is not a devolved matter and is passed by the UK Parliament. The 2014 Act is preceded by many other pieces of legislation related to immigration still in force. These include:

Asylum and Immigration Act 1996

Under this Act it became a criminal offence to employ anyone unless they had permission to live and work in the UK.

Immigration and Asylum Act 1999

This Act removed benefits from asylum seekers and created the National Asylum Service to house them, taking pressure off local authorities.

Nationality, Immigration and Asylum Act 2002

This Act created the first English test and citizenship exam for immigrants and introduced measures against bogus marriages.

Asylum and Immigration Act 2004

This Act introduced a single form of appeal and made it a criminal offence to destroy travel documents. It limited access to support for those told to leave the UK.

Immigration, Asylum and Nationality Act 2006

A five-tier points system for awarding entry visas was created under this Act. Those refused work or study visas had their rights of appeal limited. The Act brought in on-the-spot fines payable by employers for each illegal employee, which could include parents taking on nannies without visas.

UK Borders Act 2007

This Act provided the UK Border Agency with powers to tackle illegal working and automatically deport some foreign nationals imprisoned for specific offences or for more than one year. It gave immigration officers police-like powers, such as increased detention and search-and-entry roles. The Act brought in the power to create compulsory biometric cards for non-EU immigrants.

Borders, Citizenship and Immigration Act 2009

This Act amended the rules so people from outside the European Economic Area had to have residential status for eight years before being eligible for naturalisation. Those seeking naturalisation through wedlock had to be married for five years first. The Act also allowed immigration and customs officers to perform some of each other's roles and imposed a duty on home secretaries to safeguard children.

All of these pieces of legislation have made it increasingly difficult to enter or to remain in the UK without official travel and/or employment documents or visas.

UK Government: **www.gov.uk**

Joint Council for the Welfare of Immigrants: **www.jcwi.org.uk**

Marriage and Civil Partnership (Scotland) Act 2014

An Act which:

- allows same-sex couples in Scotland to marry from 16th December 2014
- enables people with civil partnerships to convert these to marriage
- enables transgender people to remain married or in civil partnerships when they change their gender. Previously they were obliged to divorce before a gender reassignment.

Stonewall: **www.stonewall.org.uk**

Public Bodies (Joint Working) (Scotland) Act 2014

This Act ensures the integration of health and social care. It will put in place:

- nationally agreed outcomes, which will apply across health and social care, and for which NHS boards and local authorities will be held jointly accountable
- a requirement on NHS boards and local authorities to integrate health and social care budgets
- a requirement on partnerships to strengthen the role of clinicians and care professionals, along with the third and independent sectors, in the planning and delivery of services.

Partnerships will be jointly accountable to ministers, local authorities, NHS board chairs and the public for delivering the nationally agreed outcomes.

Scottish Government: **www.scotland.gov.uk**

Social Care (Self-directed Support) (Scotland) Act 2013

This Act gives people a range of options for how their social care is delivered and embodies the aims of the personalisation agenda. It requires councils to give people four choices in relation to how they can get their social care. The choices are:

- Option 1: direct payment
- Option 2: the person directs the available support
- Option 3: the local authority arranges the support
- Option 4: a mix of the above.

The Act also provides authorities with a power to support unpaid carers and with duties to provide information to help people make informed choices.

Self-directed Support in Scotland: **www.selfdirectedsupportscotland.org.uk**

Children's Hearings (Scotland) Act 2011

The Children's Hearings System is Scotland's unique care and justice system for children and young people. It aims to ensure the safety and well-being of vulnerable children and young people through a decision-making lay tribunal called the Children's Panel. Children's Hearings were first established through the Social Work (Scotland) Act 1968 and the system has been considerably revised in the 2011 Act.

The 2011 Act seeks to:

- strengthen the place of children
- deliver better support for children

- deliver better support for panel members
- ensure national consistency
- modernise processes.

Children's Hearings Scotland: **www.chscotland.gov.uk**

Equality Act 2010

The Equality Act 2010 legally protects people from **discrimination** in the workplace and in wider society. It replaces previous anti-discrimination laws with a single Act, making the law easier to understand and strengthening protection in some situations. It sets out the different ways in which it is unlawful to treat someone.

The main pieces of legislation that have merged are:

- Equal Pay Act 1970
- Sex Discrimination Act 1975
- Race Relations Act 1976
- Disability Discrimination Act 1995
- Employment Equality (Religion or Belief) Regulations 2003
- Employment Equality (Sexual Orientation) Regulations 2003
- Employment Equality (Age) Regulations 2006
- Equality Act 2006 (Part 2)
- Equality Act (Sexual Orientation) Regulations 2007.

As well as the provisions of previous Acts, this Act makes it illegal to discriminate directly or indirectly on the grounds of age or against people with mental health impairments in relation to public services and functions, access to premises, work, education, associations and transport.

The protected characteristics under the Act are:

- age
- disability (including physical and mental impairment)
- gender reassignment
- marriage and civil partnership
- pregnancy and maternity
- race
- religion or belief
- sex
- sexual orientation.

Equality and Human Rights Commission: **www.equalityhumanrights.com**

Public Reform (Scotland) Act 2010

This Act made changes to the organisation of public services in Scotland with the aims of simplifying them and making them more accountable. Among the provisions are:

- an increase in information available to the public about certain expenditure and activities of public bodies

- the establishment of the Social Care and Social Work Inspectorate Scotland, known as the Care Inspectorate
- provision for increased scrutiny by service users
- an increase in collaboration and joint working.

Scottish Government: **www.scotland.gov.uk**

Adult Support and Protection (Scotland) Act 2007

The main aim of this Act is to protect from harm people who are regarded as 'at risk'. At risk in this instance refers to people aged 16 or over who:

- may be unable to safeguard their well-being, rights, interests, or their property
- may be harmed by other people
- because of disability, illness or mental disorder are more at risk of being harmed than others who are not so affected.

The main provisions of the Act are:

- a requirement for councils to make necessary enquiries and investigations to find out if action is needed to stop or prevent harm
- requirements for specific organisations to co-operate with councils and with each other about adult-protection investigations
- assessment orders providing a power of right of entry to settings where **abuse** is suspected
- the creation of banning orders and removal orders so that perpetrators of abuse are removed from settings and banned from re-entering them
- establishment of Statutory Adult Protection Committees, operating on a multi-agency basis, to further develop strategic inter-agency working and collaboration.

Mental Welfare Commission for Scotland: **www.mwcscot.org.uk**

Protection of Vulnerable Groups (Scotland) Act 2007

This Act created the Protection of Vulnerable Groups (PVG) Scheme, which requires the PVG registration of all those who work, whether in a paid or an unpaid capacity, with children and young people or with protected adults. This is achieved by Disclosure Scotland maintaining a list of people who are barred from working with children and young people and a list of people who are barred from working with protected adults. This includes not only paid workers but also volunteers, board members, church stewards and Sunday school teachers, Scout, Guide and Duke of Edinburgh's Award leaders and volunteers, and anyone else who falls under the jurisdiction of the Act. The Act makes it an offence for an organisation to:

- offer regulated work to someone who is barred
- fail to remove a person from regulated work if they have been notified that they have been barred.

Scottish Government: **www.scotland.gov.uk**

Protection of Children and Prevention of Sexual Offences (Scotland) Act 2005

This Act introduced a range of measures to strengthen the protection of children from sexual harm and abuse. It created a new offence related to the 'grooming' of children for the purposes of committing sexual offences. It also contains a number of other significant measures, such as making it an offence to purchase from someone aged under 18 any services at all that could be construed as sexual, and introduced Risk of Sexual Harm orders.

Children in Scotland child policy information: **http://childpolicyinfo.childreninscotland.org.uk**

Smoking, Health and Social Care (Scotland) Act 2005

This Act aims to protect the general public from the harmful effects of passive smoking by making it an offence to smoke in public places. A few exemptions to the law are made, mainly on humanitarian grounds, so that people who have no choice about their main residence are still able to smoke, if they so desire. Exemptions include residential accommodation, designated rooms in adult care homes, adult hospices, designated rooms in psychiatric hospitals and units, and designated rooms in offender accommodation premises.

Action on Smoking and Health (ASH) (Scotland): **www.ashscotland.org.uk**

Mental Health (Care and Treatment) (Scotland) Act 2003

This Act came into force in October 2005 and is primarily concerned with the provision of care for people with mental health difficulties. It provides for the continuation of the Mental Welfare Commission and details the duties of local authorities to provide care and support services (although they do not have to do this directly). It creates a number of new roles for professionals who have to carry out certain duties, such as Mental Health Officers in Social Work and Approved Medical Practitioners. It also makes stipulations regarding hospital detention and compulsory treatment orders. All people working in mental health services have to abide by ten **principles** of good practice, such as participation and the least restrictive alternative.

Mental Welfare Commission for Scotland: **www.mwcscot.org.uk**

Community Care and Health (Scotland) Act 2002

The main provisions of this Act are:

- the introduction of Free Personal Care for older people over the age of 65, regardless of income or whether they live at home or in residential care
- the creation of rights for informal or unpaid carers, with the intention of providing adequate support services to ensure the continuation of care-giving in the community. The Act recreated rights to a separate carers' assessment, and the responsibility of Health Boards to produce 'Carer Information Strategies', which must be submitted free of charge to carers.

Alzheimer Scotland: **www.alzscot.org**

Freedom of Information (Scotland) Act 2002

Under the Freedom of Information (Scotland) Act 2002 (FOISA), a person who requests information from a Scottish public authority that holds information about him or her is entitled to be given it by the authority, subject to certain conditions and exemptions. Public authorities are also required to be proactive in publishing information. FOISA is enforced and promoted by the Scottish Information Commissioner.

Scottish Information Commissioner: **www.itspublicknowledge.info**

Regulation of Care (Scotland) Act 2001

This Act established two main regulatory bodies for social services in Scotland: the Scottish Social Services Council and the Scottish Commission for the Regulation of Care (SCRC). A new body, the Care Inspectorate, was later created under the Public Services Reform (Scotland) Act 2010 and took over the functions of SCRC and other inspection bodies. These bodies carry out the functions detailed below.

The Scottish Social Services Council (SSSC) is the organisation responsible for registering individuals who work in social services and also for regulating their education and training. This registration is intended to increase the protection of people who use services by ensuring that workers are trained, have the right qualifications for the job and are regulated properly. It is also involved in the development of training and workforce development, and acts as the Sector Skills Council. Staff and services are expected to meet agreed standards of conduct and practice, which are laid down in the Code of Practice for Social Service Workers and the Code of Practice for Employers of Social Service Workers (see Appendix 2).

Scottish Social Services Council: **www.sssc.uk.com**

The Scottish Commission for the Regulation of Care (the Care Commission) was the independent regulator of care services in Scotland. Its functions are now performed by the Care Inspectorate (see Public Reform (Scotland) Act 2010).

Care Inspectorate: **www.careinspectorate.com**

Adults with Incapacity (Scotland) Act 2000

This Act allows Sheriff Courts to appoint guardians to make decisions on behalf of those who are not able to do so. Guardians may have to account to the Public Guardian, Mental Welfare Commission or supervising Social Work Departments. The Act stipulates that anything that is done on behalf of an adult with incapacity is required to benefit him or her, to take account of the person's wishes and those of the nearest relative, carer, guardian or attorney, and to achieve the desired purpose without unduly limiting the person's freedom.

Mental Welfare Commission for Scotland: **www.mwcscot.org.uk**

Data Protection Act 1998

This Act protects the rights of individuals in relation to data obtained, stored, processed or supplied about them. The Act requires that appropriate security measures are taken against unauthorised access to, or alteration, disclosure or destruction of personal data and against accidental loss or destruction of personal data. The Act applies to both computerised and paper **records**. Breaches are investigated by the Information Commissioner.

Information Commissionner: **https://ico.org.uk/**

Human Rights Act 1998

This Act incorporates most of the articles of the European Convention on Human Rights into UK law. Many of these have to be tested in UK courts, and some have significant implications for care work, such as the right to respect for private and family life, and the right to freedom of expression.

Equality and Human Rights Commission: **www.equalityhumanrights.com**

Carers (Recognition and Services) Act 1995

Section 2 of this Act enables local authorities to assess the needs of carers, as well as individuals thought to be in need of **community care** services. The Community Care and Health (Scotland) Act 2002 has enhanced assessment and other provision for carers.

Carer's Trust Scotland: **www.carers.org/scotland**

Children (Scotland) Act 1995

This is the main piece of legislation relating to the welfare and protection of children in Scotland. It is broadly seen as a well-balanced Act that promotes the rights of children while attempting to ensure their protection where necessary. The Act puts children first. Each child must be treated as an individual who is encouraged to form and express views on matters affecting them and has the right to be protected from all forms of abuse, neglect and exploitation.

Action for Children: **www.actionforchildren.org.uk**

National Health Service and Community Care Act 1990

This Act introduced massive changes in the way social care services were delivered in the UK. It introduced into social care the whole notion of care in the community, needs-led rather than service-led provision, a mixed economy of care and market forces. It gave special duties to local authorities as the 'lead partner' in collaboration among agencies, one of their roles being to publish a three-yearly plan of needs and proposed services in their area. While much of the original provision has been superseded by subsequent legislation, many of the principles of the Act are retained in current policy and action in the care sector.

Scottish Parliament: **www.scottish.parliament.uk**

Health and Safety at Work Act 1974

This Act outlines the responsibilities of employers and employees in relation to developing safe working practices and creating a safe environment. For example, employers have to provide suitable training, and employees have to operate machinery properly; in a care setting this might relate to using hoists and other lifting aids.

Health and Safety Executive: **www.hse.gov.uk**

Rehabilitation of Offenders Act 1974

This Act allows some criminal convictions to become spent and ignored after a fixed period of time. Its main relevance to care work is that there is an 'exceptions order' to this Act that means that no offences are ever regarded as spent in regard to obtaining employment in this field.

SACRO: **www.sacro.org.uk**

Social Work (Scotland) Act 1968

This Act was the main platform for the creation of Social Work Departments to provide social work services in Scotland. It required each local authority to provide advice, guidance and assistance to people in need of care and attention arising out of infirmity or age, or those suffering from illness or mental disorder. Some aspects of it still apply today. It also created the Children's Hearings System.

Scottish Government: **www.scotland.gov.uk**

Legislation in context

One of the key ways in which society responds to social problems is through the creation of laws (legislation). When you reach Chapter 5 (Social influences and sociology) it will be useful to think about legislation from the perspective of different sociological theories, viewing law as a social influence. Functionalist theory emphasises the positive functions of legislation in maintaining balance in society and seeking to redress inequality in so far as it maintains balance. Conflict theorists maintain that legislation reflects the values of the ruling political party. From a symbolic interactionist perspective all parties are now generally more responsive to public opinion than they have been in the past, and the symbolic meaning of legislation is derived from an interaction between people and legislators. The Scottish Parliament, in particular, consults widely with a number of representative groups before deciding on any new legislation. In terms of social constructionist theory the interplay of language, knowledge and power are important, and using feminist theory it is important always to ensure that legislation provides consideration of the implications of legislation for women. You can see what issues the Scottish Parliament is currently consulting on at: **www.scottish.parliament.uk/gettinginvolved/current-consultations.aspx**

Most pieces of legislation go through quite a long process before they finally become an Act of Parliament. Special groups may have met and prepared reports that outline the need for change and detail proposals for parliament to consider. For example, the Scottish Parliament Health and Sport Committee examined the available evidence in relation to self-directed support, which led via the Stage 1 report (2012) to the Social Care (Self-directed Support) (Scotland) Act 2013; the Millan Committee (2001) set out the points that were developed into the Mental Health (Care and Treatment) (Scotland) Act 2003; the Griffiths Report (1983) led via two White Papers to the NHS and Community Care Act 1990.

What makes a good care worker?

Moira has provided care to several members of her family who required care services at various times. She had the opportunity to see, as a relative and carer, the quality of the care that they received. Here is what she said about what she thought was needed most:

> *A few key qualities care workers must have are respect, continuity of care, empathy and trustworthiness. They should provide the highest quality of care possible to ensure families/friends have the confidence that their relative/friend is in very capable hands and their needs are being met. They should encourage participation in activities in order to retain some form of independence and dignity where possible.*
>
> *On a personal level I think it's crucial that the care worker has the history of the person's life before providing care. This helps to build a relationship between care worker and client, which is crucial in my opinion.*

When a group of care students was asked what personal qualities care workers should have they suggested the following:

- patience
- empathy
- **congruence**
- endurance
- being able to listen
- being mentally well
- being able to delegate
- open-mindedness
- taking the trouble to gain knowledge of the person and the conditions that affect them.

Activity *What makes a good care worker?*

Moira's account and the students' suggestions provide an opportunity for you to begin to think about what may contribute to making a good care worker.

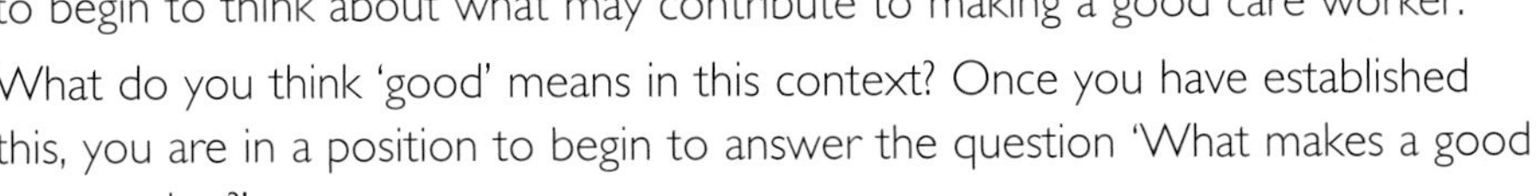

What do you think 'good' means in this context? Once you have established this, you are in a position to begin to answer the question 'What makes a good care worker?'.

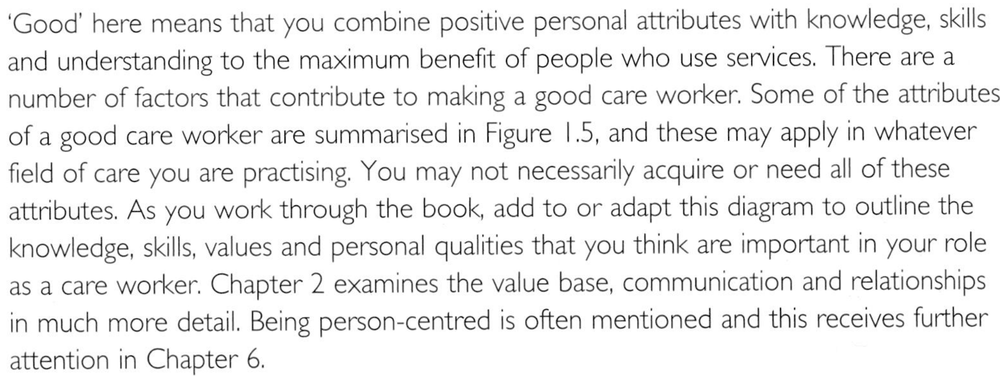

'Good' here means that you combine positive personal attributes with knowledge, skills and understanding to the maximum benefit of people who use services. There are a number of factors that contribute to making a good care worker. Some of the attributes of a good care worker are summarised in Figure 1.5, and these may apply in whatever field of care you are practising. You may not necessarily acquire or need all of these attributes. As you work through the book, add to or adapt this diagram to outline the knowledge, skills, values and personal qualities that you think are important in your role as a care worker. Chapter 2 examines the value base, communication and relationships in much more detail. Being person-centred is often mentioned and this receives further attention in Chapter 6.

Remember that in this area of work you never really stop learning. You have to be honest enough to admit sometimes that you don't know all the answers, that there may be different possibilities from which to choose, that you may need to go to find out something, that you are not the expert you thought you were, and that you need to listen more to the people who use services to find out what it is they are really communicating to you.

Knowledge
Needs
Care services
Legislation
Human development
Psychological theory
Social influences and **sociology**
Positive care practice

Skills
Communication (verbal and written)
Building professional relationships
Ability to be critical and reflective
Ability to work as part of a team
Ability to work with initiative
Ability to be person-centred

Values
Commitment to social justice
Appreciation of the worth of all individuals
Appreciation of the boundaries of **confidentiality**
Promotion of anti-discriminatory practice
Support for rights and choices
Acknowledgment of differences
Support and understanding of inclusion

Personal qualities
Sensitivity
Warmth
Patience
Empathy
Enthusiasm and sense of humour
Imagination and adaptability
Dependability and reliability
Confidence

Figure 1.6 Attributes of a good care worker

Activity *Attributes*

1 Reflect on your own attributes in relation to Figure 1.5. Award yourself a mark for each one on a scale of 1 to 5. Add up your total. The maximum possible score is 140. If you are anywhere near this then you are either reading the wrong book, too arrogant for your own good, or you cheated! Keep a note of your score and check yourself out again as you progress in your studies and gain more experience.

2 Refer to the MacDonald/Ahmed case study in Chapter 7. Bob and Alice are support workers at Riverside, the addiction network that Joe MacDonald attends; Nadia is a support worker at The Birches, the home for older adults where Senga MacDonald is the manager; Aisha Bibi is now a social worker.
   - What attributes do you think these workers need in their work?
   - Take four of these attributes and give an example of how you think each one can be put into practice by one of the workers.

3 How do you think the identified attributes contribute to personalisation?

SUMMARY

This chapter has invited you to reflect on what care means and has provided a context for your development as a care worker. In looking at this context, care work in the past and the present has been studied. Institutionalisation has been examined in terms of its consequences for the individual and how it can be avoided. The main providers of care in the statutory, third and private sectors have been described, together with some examination of legislation and policy for care practice, including the personalisation, self-directed support and integration agendas. Finally, as a way of leading towards the subsequent chapters of the book, the attributes that make a 'good' care worker have been considered.

Suggested reading

Books and reports

Harris, J. and White, V. (2013) *Oxford Dictionary of Social Work and Social Care.* **Oxford: Oxford University Press.**
More than just a dictionary. This book introduces you to contemporary challenges in social work and social care and serves as a springboard for further study.

IRISS (Institute for Research in Social Services) Imagining the future of support and social services in 2025. Available from: www.iriss.org.uk.
This report outlines different possible scenarios for the future of social services in Scotland.

Maclean, S. (2015) *Social Care and the Law in Scotland*, **9th edition. Lichfield: Kirwin Maclean Associates.**
A clear and up-to-date little book outlining all the most useful legislation for care workers.

Ross, D. (2013) *Scotland: History of a nation,* **new edition. Edinburgh: Lomond Books Ltd.**
An interesting book to read to increase your understanding of the history of Scotland.

Scottish Government (2008) *Personalisation: A Shared Understanding.* **Edinburgh: Scottish Government.**
Provides a clear definition, understanding and value base for personalisation as an over-arching concept for care resulting from a Scottish Government consultation. Emphasises that personalisation should result in services that are person-centred, flexible and joined up.

Websites and media

Community Care www.communitycare.co.uk – you can register to receive updates and articles at this website, for example:
Blair, J (2013) How Scottish personalisation legislation will affect social work, *Community Care,* May 15 2013 available from: www.communitycare.co.uk/2013/05/15/how-scottish-personalisation-legislation-will-affect-social-work-practice/

SCIE (Social Care Institute for Excellence) www.scie.org.uk – lots of good practice guidance, including social care TV. Be careful about the legislation though, since much of it is English and does not apply in Scotland. SCIE provides an introduction to personalisation, 'Personalisation: a rough guide', available at: www.scie.org.uk/publications/guides/guide47

Self-directed support www.selfdirectedsupportscotland.org.uk – explains self-directed support and provides useful links.

SSKS (Social Services Knowledge Scotland) www.ssks.org.uk – the gateway to a wealth of information and learning materials useful to care workers. For example, you can access information about personalisation and self-directed support, working with people from early years to older adults, criminal justice, drugs and alcohol.

CHAPTER 2
Values and principles

> *A decent quality of life where people can live with dignity and respect is a basic human right. For millions today and many millions more in the future, only effective care and support has the power to translate that right from an aspiration into an everyday reality.*
>
> (Equality and Human Rights Commission, 2014)

Introduction

This chapter includes material for Care: Values and Principles (Higher). It also covers information that will be useful for learners studying Care: Values and Principles at National 4 and 5 levels, Scottish Vocational Qualifications SVQ2 and SVQ3 in Social Services (Children and Young People) and Social Services and Healthcare, and for HNC Social Care and HNC Health Care.

By the end of this chapter you should be able to:

★ understand and explain the importance of values and principles in promoting positive care practice

★ understand and apply care values and principles

★ explain the meaning of discrimination and anti-discriminatory practice

★ consider the link between the meeting of need and the application of values and principles

★ explain the role of communication in the caring relationship

★ analyse caring relationships in terms of care values and principles and communication.

The value base

In all areas of care practice, a commitment to the values and principles of care is essential. Values and principles provide the foundations for good practice. A **value** is defined as 'that which is worthy of esteem for its own sake, that which has intrinsic worth' (Oxford English Dictionary). **Principle** is defined as 'a rule of conduct, especially good conduct' (Oxford English Dictionary). The principles of care are derived from two core values: respect for the worth and dignity of every individual, and according social justice to and promoting the social welfare of every individual. Social justice means that everyone has the right to fair and correct treatment in society. Welfare should ensure that those who are in need of care have the opportunity to improve their personal situation through the promotion of their right to services and benefits.

Activity *Values statements*

Listen to the people in your environment and write down any statements you hear that don't accord with these values. You may hear statements like:

> *'I don't mind people from other countries but I don't like asylum seekers. They just come here to get benefits.'*
>
> *'That old man on the corner never speaks to anyone. He's just ignorant.'*
>
> *'She's gone downhill since her husband left her. She seems drunk all the time and neglects her appearance. That's not the way to deal with her problems. Best to leave her to her own devices.'*

All of these statements make discriminatory assumptions. They don't value the individual or accord them social justice.

- To get an idea about what asylum seekers go through you could read *This Is Where I Am* by Karen Campbell (2013). It tells the story of an asylum seeker in Glasgow and his befriender.
- The 'old man' may be deaf and this is why he avoids contact. He would actually welcome someone trying to communicate with him.
- The woman in the third example may be experiencing depression and need help, not criticism.

There is a lovely Cheyenne saying: 'Do not judge your neighbour until you walk two moons in his moccasins.' This is a good place to start.

The necessity of having a value base with a set of guiding principles has been outlined many times. Scotland's National Care Standards (Scottish Executive, 2001, and a current update being undertaken in 2015), the Code of Practice for Social Service Workers (SSSC, 2002), as well as a quantity of Health and Social Care legislation, all emphasise the importance of values and principles. As far back as 1946 the Universal Declaration of Human Rights, published after the Second World War, gave prominence to 'fundamental human rights, the dignity and worth of the "human person" and equal rights for men and women'.

The principles of care

The main principles considered in this chapter are those set out in Scotland's National Care Standards. These are the principles of:

- dignity
- privacy
- choice
- safety
- realising potential
- equality and diversity.

These principles are also reflected in the Codes of Practice for Social Service Workers and Employers, which are reproduced in full in Appendix 2. They underpin personalisation and a person-centred approach to care practice.

Figure 2.1 The principles of care

Activity – *National Care Standards and Codes of Practice*

- Acquire a copy of the National Care Standards relevant to your workplace. This can be obtained from the Scottish Government website **www.scotland.gov.uk/Topics/Health/Support-Social-Care/Regulate/Standards** or if you need a paper copy you can request this from **scottishgovernment@booksource.net** Examine your practice and ensure that it reflects these standards.
- Read the Code of Practice for Social Service Workers in Appendix 2. While this reflects the principles of the National Care Standards there are some additional responsibilities, especially in relation to **accountability** and professional **development**. These are considered in Chapter 7.

Dignity

Everyone has a right to:

- be treated with dignity and respect at all times
- receive respect for their chosen relationships.

The application of this principle involves individualisation and respect for each particular person, whoever he or she may be. It also involves empathy, **acceptance** and encouragement from the care worker to heighten the **self-esteem** of the person. Individualisation is the recognition and understanding of each person's own qualities, distinctive character and personality. It is based on your right to be treated not just as *a* human being but as *this* human being, with all of your specific needs and personal preferences.

Activity *The dignity challenge*

Imagine a person who is receiving a care service. This may be:

- John, a gay man who has HIV/**Aids**
- Grace, from the travelling community, who needs home care in her caravan
- Aaid, who has learning difficulties and often loses his temper
- Anne (see the case study below), who has dementia
- Sekou, a refugee who has lost his eyesight.

Now ask yourself the following questions, imagining that you are assisting this individual.

1. Is valuing this individual central to my philosophy of care?
2. Do I uphold his/her dignity at all times?
3. Would I take action if I thought a colleague wasn't upholding the individual's dignity?
4. Am I polite and courteous to this individual?
5. Do I put respect for dignity into all my practical tasks?
6. Do I respect his/her **beliefs** and values?
7. Do I try to consider all of this individual's needs and preferences?

Try to discuss this; note any areas with which you have difficulty and why you think this may be the case.

Resources you may wish to use include:

SCIE (Social Care Institute for Excellence) Social Care TV: *Dignity in Care*.
www.scie.org.uk

CASE STUDY

Dignity: Stacy and Anne

Stacy states:

My Aunt Anne, who has dementia, is in a care home. When I went to visit her she was dressed in jeans. I was really shocked as she would always wear skirts. She would never wear jeans. I discussed this with the staff, saying that she wouldn't have chosen to wear jeans. I asked them if they could dress her in her own clothes and always in a skirt. They complied with this and did see how much it mattered. But before I said anything I got the feeling they didn't see that it mattered because my aunt has dementia.

Privacy

Everyone has a right to:

- **have their privacy and property respected**
- **be free from unnecessary intrusion.**

Everyone has the right to privacy, to have his or her own 'space'. It is not difficult to imagine how it would feel if someone accompanied you to the bathroom and insisted on staying, or barged in without permission when you were in your own bedroom, or listened in on your telephone conversations, or discussed your financial affairs with you in front of others. If you consider the humiliation and embarrassment this would cause *you* then you will appreciate the need for care workers to give service users the privacy that is their human right. Sometimes, when a care worker knows a service user very well, the care worker may assume it is acceptable to look through a bag, look in drawers or open a letter without permission. Such behaviour is disrespectful, however, and ignores the right to privacy.

Activity *Privacy*

Challenge yourself with the following questions:

1. Do I actively promote privacy, including the protection of modesty?
2. Do I avoid assuming that I can intrude without permission into someone's personal space?
3. Do I enable people to use quiet areas or rooms when they express a wish for privacy?

CASE STUDY

Chris

Chris, a student on placement in a care home, had to assist a care worker one morning in waking up service users and then helping them to wash and dress. Chris was horrified when the care worker boldly walked into each person's bedroom without knocking, switched on the lights and proceeded to help them out of bed. Chris did not follow suit. He knocked on the doors first and then, when told to enter, went up to the person and kindly spoke to her before switching on the light, allowing time for *her* to decide when she wanted to get out of bed. Chris was criticised for his actions by the care worker and told that they did not have time for this. Realising that this was common practice in the home, Chris discussed his concerns with his supervisor. The supervisor, without hesitation, discussed this practice with the manager of the home. It was agreed that this type of practice was not acceptable and that training for staff would be put in place. It is only by not accepting poor practice and by good example that long-standing, poor, 'well, that is the way that we do it', practice will change.

Confidentiality

Confidentiality means maintaining the right to privacy of information and is an extension of the privacy principle. It is not only an ethical obligation on the care worker but is also necessary in order that the service user trusts and confides in the worker. The principle of confidentiality appears deceptively simple. You may think that it can be equated with secrecy but this is not the case. It is about the appropriateness of sharing, transmitting or storing information about a service user, where a number of competing factors may influence decisions about the information usage.

It may appear to present a dilemma for the care worker when a service user offers to tell him or her something of a confidential nature. In this instance the worker should explain to the service user that what is told to them may have to be shared with their line manager. Confidence needs to be instilled in the service user that this would be done solely in his or her best interest. For example, a very vulnerable young person with autism told a care worker about a man who was sending texts to her of a sexually explicit nature. She didn't want to tell her parents and didn't want anyone else to know, but the care worker explained that she couldn't keep this a secret because the law and her organisation said that she must report information like this. The young person was relieved in the end to be protected.

Suggested methods of maintaining confidentiality are by gaining permission from the service user if information has to be shared with other professionals, by keeping all records in a secure place when not in use, by restricting access to records, by keeping confidences unless there are limitations imposed by law or agency policy, by not talking about service users or their carers behind their backs or to others who are not members of the care team.

It is wise not to talk about any area of work in caring to anybody other than those involved, whether it is about service users, their carers, their family or any incident. Prevention is better than cure. Even to discuss an issue using different names is not recommended, as some people will probably be able to recognise who or what is being talked about. There could be times when you are in a place or talking to people whom you would never associate with your workplace or a service user, when in fact they do have connections. How many times have you started to talk to someone when you have been away somewhere, only to find out that they know someone you know or are even related to them? As the familiar saying goes, 'It's a small world.' One student overheard on a bus two care workers talking in a derogatory way about the relatives of a service user. She knew the relatives and knew that they had experienced terrible stress before their parent had gone to live in a home.

You may find it interesting to read the article 'Proof! Just six degrees of separation between us' at: **www.theguardian.com/technology/2008/aug/03/internet.email**

This explains research by Microsoft that analysed 30 billion communications. It was found that any two complete strangers in the world can be connected on average by just 6.6 links. This gives food for thought and means that there are probably fewer than seven links between you and the Queen, the Dalai Lama or Madonna.

Activity *Confidentiality*

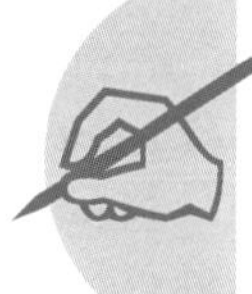

Challenge yourself with the following questions:

1 Do I actively promote confidentiality?
2 Do I know about and follow my agency's confidentiality policy?
3 Do I respect the privacy of people's documents and correspondence?
4 Do I follow the rule that **only** the people who need to know, get to know?

Choice

Everyone has a right to:

- make informed choices, while recognising the rights of other people to do the same
- know about the range of choices available
- get help to fully understand all the options and choose those that are right for them.

Applying the principle of choice is fundamental to the personalisation agenda outlined in Chapter 1, with providers of care offering choice about the ways in which needs can be met, whether people are living in their own homes or any care setting. Choice encourages **independence**. Independence may be defined as having 'opportunities to think and act without reference to another person, including willingness to incur a degree of calculated risk'.

Many service users are or were previously accustomed to, and capable of, making decisions and choices for themselves. Others, for example people who were severely institutionalised as a result of spending many years in hospital, may never have had the opportunity of being independent. Irrespective of service users' circumstances it is the care worker's duty to ensure that those in his or her care are enabled and empowered to maximise choice and independence.

Choice can in many situations result in an element of risk. This is embodied in the following quote from the principles of practice of one home for older adults:

> *Responsible risk taking is regarded as normal. Excessive paternalism and concern with safety may lead to infringements of personal rights. Those who are competent to judge the risk to themselves are free to make their own decisions so long as they do not threaten the safety of others.*
>
> (The Retail Trust, Glasgow)

Choice **empowers** people who might be seen as powerless and vulnerable in some aspects of their lives. Giving service users choices, which is a form of control over their own lives, empowers them. It also involves making sure service users are given sufficient information to enable them to make informed choices, that is choices based on a sound understanding of their situation and any options that may be available. Too often the service user is not given the power of choice because of inconvenience, apathy or over-protection. This type of practice is in complete contrast to the key factors stated in government reports and legislation, such as Getting it Right for Every Child (Scottish Executive, 2006), the Patient's Rights (Scotland) Act 2011, and the Social Care (Self-directed Support) (Scotland) Act 2012.

Examples of this principle in practice are:

- a person who is blind choosing a direct payment to manage their own support
- a resident in a care home choosing to go to bed when it suits her rather than when it is convenient for the night shift workers
- a young person who is being looked after in a children's home choosing to travel to school on public transport rather than in the local authority bus
- a person with learning difficulties choosing to cook his own meal
- an individual with a long-term mental health issue refusing to engage in treatment.

Finally, the following quotations make points about choice and the ways in which this is empowering:

> *Service users want two other issues to be prioritised … First is that choice becomes a reality, with people able to live their lives how, where and with whom they want and with the right to the support they want, instead of relying on what scraps of services are thrown their way. Second, they want choice and control taken out of the hands of managers and clinicians who think they know what's best …*
>
> (Beresford, 2007)

> *Self-directed support is about allowing people who receive care to choose and manage their support. SDS measures – such as direct payments – have the potential to be life changing …*
>
> (Multiple Sclerosis Society, Your care, your choice (Scotland) campaign, 2014)

Activity *Choice*

Reflect on your own practice in relation to choice and ask yourself the following questions:

- Do I avoid making assumptions about what people want and what is good for them?
- Do I give people as much choice as I can?
- Do I give people the opportunity to influence decisions about their choices as much as possible?
- Do I understand and know about the choices available to people through self-directed support and personalisation?

Safety

Everyone has a right to:

- feel safe and secure in all aspects of life, including health and well-being
- enjoy safety but not be over-protected
- be free and protected from exploitation and abuse.

It is the duty and moral obligation of the care worker to enable service users to feel safe and secure and to protect them from any form of abuse. Abuse includes behaviour intended to exploit, dominate and/or damage another person. There are several forms of abuse, including physical abuse, emotional abuse, financial abuse, sexual abuse, and neglect. Safeguarding and protection from harm and abuse are more fully discussed in Chapter 6.

In many situations the service user's reasons for being in need of care are due to one or more forms of abuse. Rightfully, then, they should not be exposed to the same painful treatment by those who are supposed, and legally bound, to ensure in them a feeling of safety and security. Unfortunately abuse in many forms still rears its ugly head in the care sector and we should be justly horrified by examples in the media, such as:

> *A care home worker is accused of assaulting patients at a care home in Dunblane, which cares for adults with learning difficulties and complex behavioural problems, between March 2008 and March 2010 …*
>
> (*The Scotsman*, 28 August 2012)

> *Winterbourne View: Care workers jailed for abuse. … Judge Ford said no attempt was made to provide a caring environment … [and that] the home had been run with a scandalous lack of regard for patients and staff …*
>
> (BBC News, 26 October 2012)

You may be stressed, you may be working long hours, some of the tasks you have to perform may be unpleasant, and some of the behaviour you have to cope with may be challenging, but the first thing any care worker should learn is that neither this, nor anything else, is reason to abuse another person. By virtue of their need for care, people who use social services are in a vulnerable situation where they cannot meet all of their needs themselves. Care workers have to protect the rights and dignity of those in this situation. Any perceived abuse by a care worker should be reported in accordance both with organisational policies and procedures and with government guidance and legislation. **There is no excuse for abuse.**

Activity *Safeguarding*

Reflect on your own practice and ask yourself the following questions:

1. Do I do everything possible to promote the health and well-being of the people with whom I work?
2. Do I provide a safe environment without over-protecting people?
3. Do I place enough importance on ensuring that people are as safe as possible from abuse?
4. Would I report abuse immediately if I saw it happening?
5. Would I take action if I heard about abuse from another source?
6. Am I sufficiently aware of all forms of abuse: physical, psychological, emotional, financial, sexual, neglect and discrimination?
7. Do I know my agency's policy on abuse and reporting abuse?

Realising potential

Everyone has a right to have the opportunity to:

- achieve all they can
- make full use of the resources that are available
- make the most of their lives.

Care workers should be committed to providing more than just basic care and should enable service users to lead rich, fulfilling lives in which they are encouraged to achieve their ambitions and goals and to realise their maximum potential.

The following guidelines aim to assist care workers in this task. Care workers should:

- support a personalised approach and the use of self-directed support in enabling people to realise their potential
- make themselves knowledgeable about the service user's previous life events and lifestyle by consulting them or someone else, such as a relative, who knows them well, and by consulting any available care plans and notes. In this way the worker becomes aware of the service user's expectations and wishes in relation to independence, as well as having an appreciation of the significance of the service user's past life
- help and encourage the service user to think and act as independently as possible
- encourage, enable and participate, if required, with the permission of the service user
- assist in ensuring a suitable physical environment, which has an appropriate, assessed level of safety and risk for the service user to do as much as possible for him/herself
- monitor the service user's achievements and ensure that there are opportunities for progression
- praise achievements
- offer and make the service user aware of services outside their own residence or local environment
- offer information on training, educational provision such as further education colleges, choices of outings and holidays, choices of creative and leisure activities.

Activity *Realising potential*

Peter's case study below was written by a support worker in a resettlement unit for people who have been released from prison. Read the case studies of Peter and George, and answer the following questions.

- How did the support workers and other staff help or hinder Peter and George to reach their potential?
- What values and principles did they use, or fail to use?

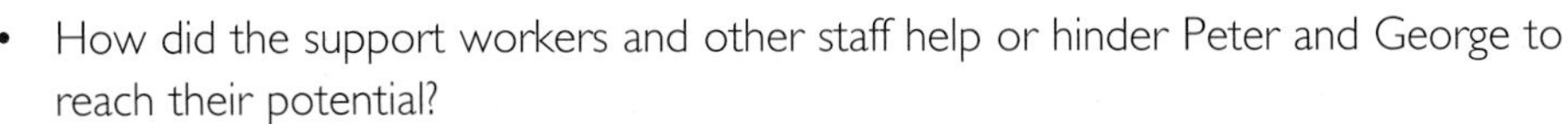

Peter

Peter grew up on a large council estate. He lived with his mother and father and four brothers and sisters. His father was continually unemployed and his mother had a part-time job. Life was not easy for Peter when he was growing up as he

was the eldest and was expected by his father to provide for the family. He first started to drink when he was 14 and had become addicted to alcohol by the time he was 18. Peter, who generally had a pleasant and amicable personality, would 'lash out' when he was drunk. Eventually he lost his job and, after being arrested many times for fighting, breach of the peace and assault, was given a six-month sentence in prison and then released into a resettlement unit.

When Peter arrived at the unit he was very embarrassed and angry with himself that he had become an alcoholic. He was also fearful that he might end up like some of the older residents in the unit, who he felt had no future. Fortunately the unit he was living in had very dedicated staff who accepted others for whom they were and provided wonderful encouragement and support. Peter's support worker built up a good relationship with him. Over time, Peter, who was the youngest in the unit, found himself helping other residents in the unit. After a year, Peter moved into his own flat, which was not too far from the unit. He was actively seeking employment and rather than having nothing to do he offered to work voluntarily in the unit.

It was soon realised that Peter had many good qualities and skills in caring, and he was offered part-time paid work in the unit. The manager arranged training for Peter, and not long after that he was accepted on to the HNC in Social Care. Peter now says: 'My aim is to support people the way I was supported and encouraged to realise my potential. I know how they feel and how when others believe in you it gives confidence, optimism and happiness to your life.'

George

George had lived in a 'long-term' hospital for the largest part of his life and had been discharged from hospital to live in the community. He had lived in his present house with the support of paid support workers for almost a year and enjoyed travelling into the city to shop. Because of the expense of bus travel, however, he was limited in how often he could do this. When a student support worker realised George's plight, he made inquiries about why George did not have a concessionary travel card. Unfortunately, George's right to this benefit had been overlooked by his support workers. Their negligence had caused George to be deprived of his leisure pursuits and he had been limited in his number of trips into the city. His right to receive a concessionary travel pass should have been made known to him when he originally moved into his own home. The support workers involved failed to ensure that George's support needs were fully met, and he was deprived of the opportunity to live his life to the full. Care workers should ensure they know and find out about all available benefits, resources and facilities. This should include exploring options in relation to self-directed support.

Activity — *Reflect on your own practice*

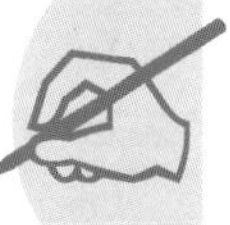

Reflect on your own practice and challenge yourself with the following questions:

1. Do I try to find out about the past and present lives of the people with whom I work, so that I know what their strengths and interests are or have been?
2. Do I encourage people to think independently and to follow their interests?
3. Do I assist in providing the best possible environment for people to reach their potential?
4. Do I try to provide opportunities for people to reach their potential?
5. Do I give enough praise and encouragement?
6. Do I know enough about the opportunities available, both within and outside the care environment and in relation to personalisation and self-directed support?

Equality and diversity

Everyone has a right to:

- live an independent life, rich in purpose, meaning and personal fulfilment
- be valued for their ethnic background, language, **culture** and faith
- be treated equally and cared for in an environment that aims to be free from bullying, harassment and discrimination
- be able to complain effectively without fear of victimisation.

Equality is not a straightforward concept in care practice, unlike the mathematical meaning of equality where three plus three is equal to six. Equality in care practice really means treating people with fairness, without **prejudice** or discrimination. It is not something you have a choice about. It is the law that people are treated equally in terms of not being discriminated against and of having their right to social justice upheld. The Equality Act 2010 is UK legislation that protects people from discrimination on the grounds of:

- age
- disability
- gender reassignment
- marriage or civil partnership
- pregnancy or maternity
- race
- religion or belief
- sex
- sexual orientation.

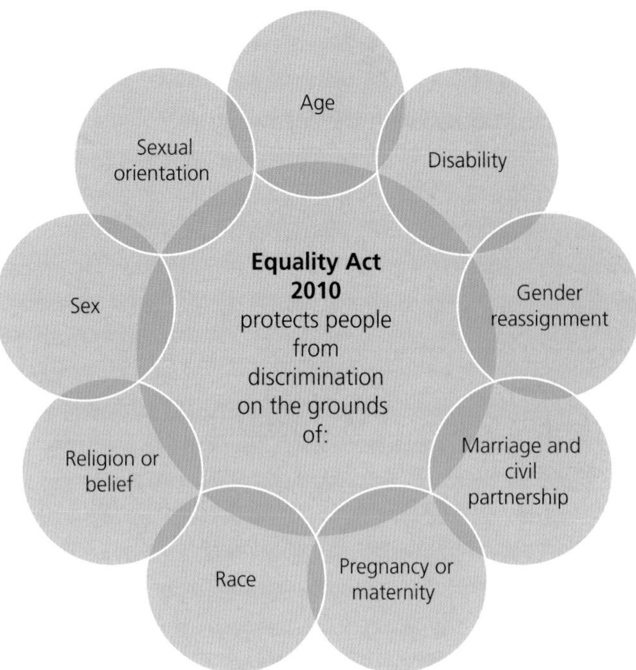

Figure 2.2 The Equality Act 2010

Care providers have a duty to uphold the provisions of the Act. The Equality and Human Rights Commission (EHRC) is the UK government body set up to promote the legislation, to challenge discrimination and to protect and promote human rights: **www.equalityhumanrights.com**

Diversity literally means difference. The promotion of equality encompasses respecting and valuing diversity. Valuing diversity goes beyond promoting equality, however, and supports the view that differences among people should be seen as assets to be appreciated. Promoting equality and valuing diversity are essential aspects of anti-discriminatory practice, which is considered in the following section and, from a sociological perspective, in Chapter 5.

SCIE (Social Care Institute for Excellence) has produced many resources that can help you to further your learning in relation to equality and diversity: **www.scie.org.uk**. Among these are some interesting and helpful case study videos on Social Care TV, including a series on working with gay, lesbian, bisexual and transgender people.

Activity *Equality and diversity*

Reflect on your own practice and challenge yourself by asking the following questions:

- Do I act fairly in relation to everyone?
- Do I appreciate and value diversity and encompass everyone in this?
- Am I aware of and familiar with the law and my agency policy in relation to equality and diversity?

Activity *Value base*

Copy the list below and tick the things that you value:

- living in your own home
- being free to come and go as you please
- living in a rented flat with other people
- having to ask permission to leave your own home
- living in a hospital ward
- having worthwhile employment
- having to repeatedly apply for state benefit
- choosing how you spend your money
- going on holiday abroad
- sharing underwear and clothes with other people
- going to the seaside for a week once a year
- spending the day doing 'arts and crafts'
- doing work for which you do not get paid
- going to college
- going to the hairdresser
- being neat and well dressed
- winning an athletic event
- passing your driving test
- having your teacher, hairdresser and doctor come to see you only at your place of work
- having the right to marry if you wish
- not being able to eat or drink without help
- having your needs discussed by other people at a meeting
- being told the truth about a medical condition you have
- going out for a drink with your friends.

Consider the statements you have *not* ticked and think why you do not value them. It may be because they do not give you choice, because they do not give you privacy and/or because they take away your dignity or your right to equality.

Discrimination and anti-discriminatory practice

> *Discrimination is … a sociological and political phenomenon as well as a psychological one, hence the need for a holistic approach …*
>
> (Thompson, 2012)

Introduction

As a care worker it is essential that you develop a clear understanding of discrimination and anti-discriminatory practice. Anti-discriminatory practice is underpinned by the value base explained above. It rests upon the values of respect for the dignity of all individuals and the promotion of social justice and welfare, and on the principles set out in the National Care Standards and the Code of Practice for Social Service Workers (see Appendix 2), especially those relating to equality and diversity. An understanding of anti-discriminatory practice requires an understanding of the concepts of **discrimination**, **prejudice** and **stereotyping**, and the development of a variety of strategies to combat these.

Few people would deny that discrimination exists, but there is still disagreement and confusion about exactly what it is, why it exists and what can be done to change things. Discrimination is a complex subject, and one that is prone to a hostile response because people feel threatened when their views are challenged. In Chapter 5 discrimination is considered sociologically, in terms of the social influences of and on it. In this chapter you are introduced to concepts about discrimination as a basis for understanding anti-discriminatory practice.

What is discrimination?

- Discrimination is treating someone differently. Although it can be positive or negative, it is negative discrimination that is being discussed under the heading 'discrimination'.
- Discrimination is the unequal and unfair treatment of an individual or group.
- Discrimination is based on prejudice towards people who are seen as being different.
- Prejudice is learned from picking up negative **attitudes** from our families and from society.
- Discrimination is built into the way we run our social, political and economic institutions.

What is prejudice?

A prejudice is an attitude about an individual or a group, based on judgements that are often founded on ignorance, fear or speculation, rather than on fact. Prejudice – the pre-judging of someone – can be either positive or negative. You can be prejudiced in favour of, or prejudiced against, a person. Everyone has prejudices: once we become aware of what they are for us, we can begin to do something about them.

The way prejudice works in relation to discrimination is that a negative, biased and intolerant attitude against someone is maintained, even in the face of contradictory evidence. These prejudices are often based on negative **stereotypes** of a group.

To answer your questions on this important topic, we have Jim Smith!

Figure 2.3 When one group is disadvantaged, another is advantaged (© Andrew Parry and Robin Maclean)

A stereotype is a label that is applied to all members of a group. A quality or characteristic is taken as applying to all members of the group, for example that people with Down's syndrome like music, girls don't like playing football, gay men like to travel, Scottish people are pessimistic. People within the group are not seen as individuals with unique needs and interests. They are treated as if they are the same as everyone else in that group.

Apart from being based on a lack of correct information, prejudices and stereotypes such as these disadvantage people because negative assumptions are made about them based on one aspect of their identity. People are not seen as a 'whole person', but are categorised according to one feature – having a disability, or being of one **gender** or sexual orientation or ethnicity rather than another – and they are related to on that basis alone. That one aspect of their identity defines them in the eyes of the prejudiced person. Assumptions are made about their abilities and interests based on these stereotypes and prejudices. This limits their opportunity to construct their own feeling of positive self-esteem, because they so often meet with negative or misinformed reactions, and this limits their opportunities to participate equally in society.

Activity *Lifeline*

On a piece of paper, write 'Who am I?' at the top. Answer this question twenty times with as wide a range of responses as you wish: I am female, I am small, I have brown hair, I'm a joker, I am a grandfather, I have a hearing impairment, I help out at the youth club, I am Chinese, I am fat, etc. The list might contain descriptions of what you look like, what you do or an aspect of your personality.

Place a large piece of paper sideways and draw a line with your date of birth at the left-hand side and today's date at the right-hand side. For each of the twenty responses to the question 'Who am I?', write or draw on the paper when you first became aware of that part of your identity. Things like 'I am a grandfather' will be easy to date, but you might need to think about exactly when you first became aware of your ethnicity or your gender. The purpose of this activity is to reflect on exactly when you developed your sense of what makes up your individual identity. Discovering and creating an identity throughout your life is an active process for everyone.

Prejudice and stereotypes don't occur randomly. They reflect the divisions within any society, whereby those who have power are able to define what is good or bad, and what is acceptable or not. Power is the ability to control or to influence other people. Prejudice reflects the power that the dominant group has over other groups. Where there is prejudice, when one group is disadvantaged, another group is advantaged. Conflict theory, examined in Chapter 5, is of relevance in considering this, and the point about the power of dominant groups is returned to later in this chapter.

How are prejudices developed? The process of **socialisation** (the way in which we develop our values, attitudes and ideas) will be dealt with in more detail in Chapters 3 and 5, but it is touched on here because it is central to the process of developing prejudice. The messages you pick up, firstly from your family (agents of **primary socialisation**) and later from friends, school and the media (agents of **secondary socialisation**), influence the way you see the world.

Prejudice exists partly because we are brought up with negative pictures of certain groups, which are often based on views developed many generations ago. The negative message still exists today because it is ingrained in legal, political, educational and other structures in society. Not everyone brought up with these negative images agrees with them or acts on them, however. Once people are able to make up their own minds about issues, they can reject the attitudes and behaviours they have been socialised to accept. Some people, however, even if they can see that the values they have learned are wrong, still continue to hold them. This may result from pressure from friends or family to 'fit in with the crowd'. People who have low self-esteem and a need for acceptance by others are more likely to conform to values they don't hold, in order to remain part of the crowd. People who have higher self-esteem are able to disagree and not fear the consequences of disapproval, because they have a stronger sense of their own identity.

Prejudice is learned during the process of developing identity, and we tend to accept unconsciously that this is 'just the way things are': it is part of our culture. As care workers, however, it is important that we don't assume that it is only gay people who have to think about their sexuality, or only black people who develop a sense of belonging to an **ethnic group**. We have all had to make choices about our sexuality, and to construct our own sense of what being a member of a certain racial group means to us. Some people who belong to the 'mainstream' may not have had to give much conscious or active thought to how their identity has been created; it just seemed 'normal'. Anyone who is outside the 'mainstream', though, will have had to give more active thought to their identity because aspects of it may have been stigmatised or devalued in our society.

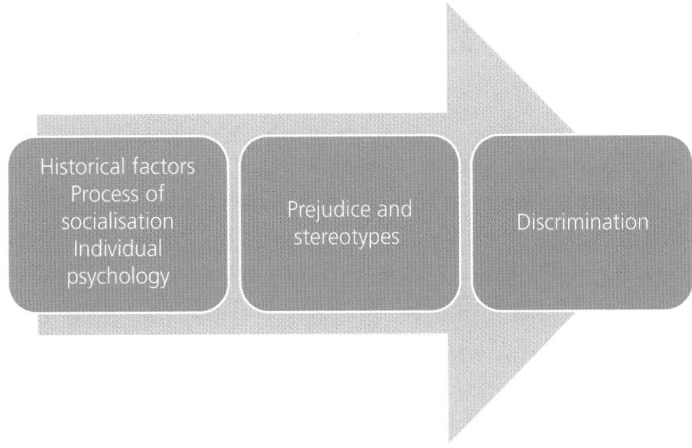

Figure 2.4 Causes of discrimination

Types of discrimination

Discrimination can occur in a number of different ways. It is important not to get too caught up in defining what type of discrimination any particular situation is. If it's negative, it's wrong and it should be challenged, whatever type it is. In a care setting, the main reason for trying to categorise the type of discrimination is so that you can work out the best way to challenge it. If it is a one-off person-to-person situation, where it just needs to be pointed out to the person that they are being rude or dismissive, and they accept this, then no further action may be needed. If it turns out that the person doesn't think it is wrong and in fact has picked it up as being acceptable from someone else in the organisation, it then needs to be tackled at an organisational level.

Conscious discrimination

Conscious discrimination occurs when a person knows they are acting negatively and wants to disadvantage someone. In a care setting, as well as being contrary to care values and principles, this would be against equal opportunities policy and breaking the law. The person should be reported and, depending on the situation, may receive supervision, training or disciplinary action. If the discrimination persisted they could lose membership of their professional organisation and have their professional registration taken away.

Activity: Conscious discrimination: Joan

Joan, a care worker, has developed a hierarchy of people she really likes to work with and those she has decided she doesn't like. She ensures that she spends longer with the people she likes. Gordon is one of the people she doesn't like very much. When he asks for assistance to go to the toilet or for an extra cup of tea, she ignores him. You are one of her colleagues and observe this behaviour on several occasions.

What do you do?

Unconscious discrimination

Unconscious discrimination occurs when a person discriminates against someone without realising that they are discriminating. It can be seen in the everyday behaviour and language that people routinely use, without being aware that they may be infringing someone's rights or disrespecting them. Many actions disadvantage people because they perpetuate stereotypes of people being weak and helpless. This is the 'Does she take sugar?' syndrome, where people talk to the person who is supporting an individual rather than to the person herself. The unconscious prejudice is shown through thinking that the person who needs support is also unable to think or talk on their own behalf.

As a care worker, it is possible to fall into another version of this patronising behaviour. Under the guise of 'helping' someone, you may do or decide things for them that they could do independently. This creates a dependency on the worker and keeps a power imbalance in the worker's favour. The following quotation illustrates these processes in relation to older people.

> *Older people can find they are having decisions made for them (for example, by professionals or relatives) without consultation or their rights are being overlooked or they are being patronised, for example in the way they are referred to ('the old dear'). These are examples of … 'infantilisation' …*
>
> (Thompson, 2012)

The language we use is one of the most obvious ways in which we unconsciously show prejudice. Many of the words, phrases and expressions we use are insulting to, or undermining of, others without us being aware of it. For instance, shortening a 'difficult-to-pronounce' Asian name to a Western nickname can be seen as an attempt to make the person part of the group, but underlying this assumption is the fact that people can't be bothered to find out and use the proper pronunciation. Examining and changing the words you use is more than just window dressing. Although it is apparently a small step, it is something you as an individual can start thinking about, and acting on, immediately. It is a symbolic step, because you notice it and so do others around you. The theory of symbolic interactionism considered in Chapter 5 enables you to examine the use of language or unconscious discrimination from a sociological perspective.

Language is an important representation of our thoughts and feelings, therefore it is important to consider what message is given by the words we use. Changing the term 'disabled toilets' to 'accessible toilets' gives a different message to everyone. It emphasises the attributes of a building, not of a person. A number of organisations for people with a disability have changed their name because they wanted to portray a more positive and modern picture of their work. The Spastics Society renamed itself Capability Scotland and the Scottish Society for Mental Handicap changed its name to Enable.

Our use of language changes all the time, and terms that were once commonplace are now rarely used. Most people would agree that it is unacceptable to call someone who is mentally ill a 'moron', or someone with learning disabilities an 'imbecile', but these terms were once the normal medical terms. This is not about political correctness, but about being aware of the effect of your words on those around you. Two of the qualities required to be a good care worker are respect and sensitivity. Appropriate use of language is one of the ways in which you can display these qualities.

Levels of discrimination

There are many levels on which discrimination can occur. Discrimination can take place at personal, cultural and structural levels. Institutional or organisational discrimination includes discrimination at both cultural and structural levels. In reality, these levels are not separate as our personal views are influenced by the culture in which we live and the organisations we encounter, but it is useful initially to look at the way in which each level operates independently. It is important to analyse at what level we believe discrimination occurs, because then we will know at which level to challenge it. It is of little use treating a broken leg with a sticking plaster, and it is equally pointless trying to tackle large-scale structural or cultural inequalities with only small-scale personal solutions.

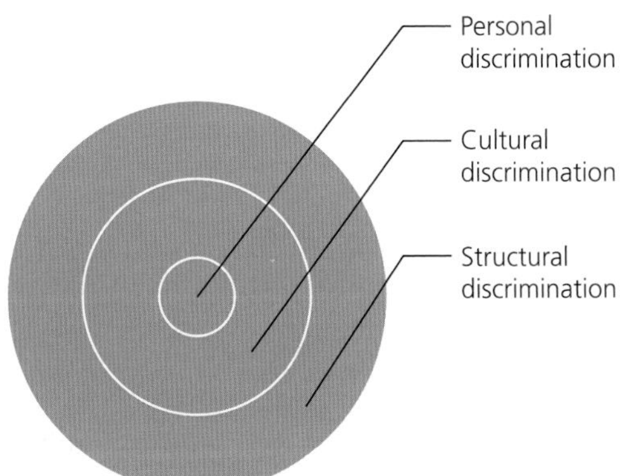

Figure 2.5 Levels of discrimination (based on Thompson, 2012)

Personal discrimination

When someone attacks a black person because of his colour, or bullies a child with learning disabilities, or sexually harasses an employee, he or she is individually discriminating against that person. Although this individual behaviour exists because that person may have been brought up in a culture that devalues certain groups, it is still individual discrimination because it is that person acting alone. It doesn't need to be literally only one person. If a small group of people harasses or intimidates someone, this can still be described as an example of personal discrimination, because the essence is that they are operating independently and not as part of a wider structure. There is no official backing for their behaviour.

Individual responsibility for discrimination also occurs when we see an act of discrimination and don't seek to stop it or change it. We say 'I don't want to get involved', or 'It's not my problem, someone else will do something about it.' Discrimination continues to exist, however, precisely because people don't challenge it. It is not just the perpetrators who keep groups oppressed by acting against them, it is also the people who do nothing to stop it or change it. The system of discrimination is perpetuated by individual people doing nothing to challenge it. In care settings this might mean not reporting an incident of bad practice, or failing to support someone who is experiencing harassment.

Cultural discrimination

Cultural discrimination is discrimination that is supported by the norms, values and practices of society or of particular cultural groups. It is embedded in cultural practices, such as norms of family life that often disadvantage women, school assemblies that only praise sport, or academic achievement that often disadvantages young people gifted in other areas, or religious rituals and practices that exclude some groups. These cultural practices are often backed up by historical accounts and by the media, thus perpetuating cultural discrimination. Cultural discrimination can manifest itself in jokes and cartoons, for example older people as the objects of cruel humour. It is closely linked to **institutional discrimination**, which has both cultural and institutional aspects.

Structural discrimination

The way society operates can disadvantage certain groups. Sometimes this is enshrined in law, but often it is due to the way society has developed historically. Similar instances of discrimination can occur in so many different places that it can be said to be part of the 'normal' functioning of that part of society. It is not just a few people, and it is not just the occasional organisation: it is structured into the way that society operates. This topic is considered in more depth in Chapter 5, when deprivation and inequality are examined, but it is also briefly considered here in the following examples.

People with a disability continually come up against negative messages that they are not suitable romantic partners. Segregated education, for example, can limit their interaction with non-disabled children and reinforces negative stereotypes about people with a disability being asexual. Opportunities to interact socially with others, let alone chances to be sexually intimate, are all too scarce for many people with a disability. It is challenging enough for some members of society to accept that people with a disability have sex, and even more difficult for some to contemplate that they might engage in same-sex relationships. Special education and other segregated systems create informal networks that often have values that do not accommodate difference.

There is an under-representation of a number of groups, such as ethnic minorities, in key positions in society. Some individuals in these groups, however, have managed to break through the invisible barrier – the 'glass ceiling' – having managed to escape from the 'sticky floor' that keeps so many people from oppressed groups in unpromoted posts.

There is also evidence of structural discrimination in relation to age. Although the information below relates to the NHS, **ageism** takes place at a much wider level across many aspects of caring for people. Findings presented in an RCN report outlined in *The Scotsman* (Whitaker, 2014) state:

> *Despite older people often having the most complex needs, the evidence suggests that they regularly suffer from a severe shortage of nurses and healthcare support workers ... Today's evidence shows that currently one nurse cares for around nine patients on older people's wards. The RCN says this is not enough to provide basic, safe care, which requires a minimum of one nurse to seven patients.*
>
> (*The Scotsman*, 20 March 2012)

If this just related to one organisation providing care, it could be regarded as institutional discrimination. Since the NHS is so large and so pervasive in society, however, and since the provision of health and care services goes beyond the NHS, the failure of these services to adapt to the evolving needs of a changing population could also be seen as 'structural ageism'. You will see from the further example below that ageism can also be regarded as cultural discrimination.

Institutional discrimination

Discrimination is institutional when it operates within the rules, regulations and practices of an organisation or related organisations. It is also sometimes referred to as organisational discrimination and has aspects of both cultural and structural discrimination as well as being practised at a personal level. When an instance of personal discrimination is backed up by the culture and structure of an organisation, or when it happens so often that it is part of everyday practice, it can be seen as being institutional discrimination. It is part of the way an organisation or institution is structured and part of its culture.

Rules and regulations

Discrimination occurs because it is built into the rules and regulations of an organisation. For example, a white woman was told on starting her job as a receptionist with a van hire company that it was not the company's policy to hire vehicles to 'coloureds or Asians'. She resigned and took her case to an employment tribunal, claiming she had been asked to carry out discriminatory instructions.

Everyday practices within an organisation

Most organisations have rules and regulations that forbid discrimination, but nonetheless discrimination still occurs. That is because the culture of the organisation allows certain poor practices to occur, and people don't do anything to challenge it. There has often been no formal discussion among the people involved about what is happening – it is just 'the way things are done around here' and there is strong pressure to fit in or to leave.

Activity *Cultural discrimination in an organisation*

Identify the ways in which organisational cultures allow discrimination to continue in the three examples below.

Sex discrimination

In 1986 Jean Porcelli won a landmark case that established sexual harassment in the workplace as a form of sex discrimination under the Sex Discrimination Act (SDA). Yet today sexual harassment remains all too common, according to the Equal Opportunities Commission (EOC).

Jean Porcelli worked as a school science technician for Strathclyde Regional Council; she brought her case after experiencing a sustained campaign of harassment from two male colleagues, some of which was sexual in nature. Initial harassment included stealing her keys, disturbing her experiments and emptying out her desk drawers. It soon escalated to rubbing up against her, blocking her path in stairways and corridors, and threatening her with physical violence.

Speaking on the twentieth anniversary of the case, Jean Porcelli said: 'It disheartens me that sexual harassment still happens – sadly my own daughter has experienced it. And I can certainly understand why so many women are reluctant to come forward – I know I paid a great price, both personally and professionally. Despite changing jobs, I was labelled a "troublemaker" until the resulting stress and ill health eventually prompted me to take early retirement. In my day, there was no shortage of managers – and even my union officials – who told me to sit down, keep quiet and get on with my job, a response some women still experience today. I hope employers – prompted by the new EOC guidelines – will take a strong leadership role, and in another twenty years' time we'll be telling a very different story.'

(Equal Opportunities Commission, 2006 (adapted) -- note that the Equality Act 2010 has now replaced all of the separate legislation relating to discrimination and that the Human Rights and Equality Commission has now replaced the Equal Opportunities Commission.)

This would have been an example of personal discrimination if the council had followed their own procedures and backed Mrs Porcelli's complaint. The fact that the council and unions chose not to support her, however, meant it became institutional or organisational discrimination, because now it was the organisation as a whole that supported the discrimination, not just a few individuals within it.

Age discrimination

Research from the Royal College of Surgeons suggests that, across a range of common conditions, people over the age of 65 are less likely to receive treatment. While the research indicates there may be a number of reasons for this, the authors suggest a patient's chronological age is a significant factor, with treatment decisions made on assumptions about old age rather than a comprehensive and objective assessment of the individual. This supports previous studies, which have concluded that inadequate hospital care for older people condemns many to death (NCEPOD, 2010). Poor care provision for those over the age of 65 has also been identified in social care provision to older people in their own homes. An inquiry by the Equality and Human Rights Commission (2012) found many incidents of older people's human rights being breached because of the way care was delivered by paid carers.

(Galpin, 2012)

Racial discrimination

A committee of MSPs has said it is 'appalled and horrified' by the discrimination suffered by Gypsies and travelling people in Scotland. The Equal Opportunities Committee said there had been repeated failures on access to health and social care for the travelling community. Its report said very little had changed for travellers over the past 15 years. The Scottish Government said there should be no barriers to Gypsies/travellers accessing health care. The committee's Gypsy/Traveller and Care report found that the average life expectancy for male members of the travelling community was just 55. Many encampments were of poor quality and located beside landfill sites or under electricity pylons, the committee said.

If we were to substitute any other ethnic minority instead of Gypsies/travellers in our report there would be uproar at the obvious racial discrimination.

(BBC News website, 24 September 2012)

How do the different levels of discrimination interact?

Developing an awareness of the structural, cultural and institutional aspects of discrimination helps to change the focus of discussion away from the personal limitations of individuals and towards the barriers they face in society. At these levels, it can be seen that disadvantage is not just a random, individual problem, but is systematic and embedded in the day-to-day rules and practices of culture and the institutions that make up society.

The personal, cultural and structural levels interact in a different way for every individual. We share some similarities in the wider structural and cultural influences we experience but, even at these levels, we develop a unique interaction with the society and cultures in which we live. This individual relationship with our surroundings continues throughout our lifetime in the experience we have in the institutions with which we come into contact and the family, education, work, media and peer group we experience.

The effects of discrimination

The net result of the various levels and types of discrimination is that someone is disadvantaged, denied an opportunity or refused access to something. Whether this happens once or repeatedly, it can have an effect on that person's identity. Their self-esteem is diminished because of the negative treatment, they may feel disempowered, they may be less likely to claim or demand their rights; their potential to achieve what they are capable of may be reduced and a cycle of discrimination may be repeated. A person with learning disabilities who is frightened to walk down a street because they are being taunted and bullied may miss the bus to college; a woman who is harassed at work takes long-term sick leave due to stress-related illness; a gay person, who has disclosed their sexuality to a colleague who now avoids him, is concerned that he will be isolated within his team and not gain the promotion for which he has just applied.

The result of not being accepted, not having your concerns taken seriously or not being listened to, can be a feeling of alienation. Alienation is a sense that you don't belong to society and that you are often excluded from participation in mainstream activities and events. People who are discriminated against don't have the same rights as other people, or are constrained from asserting their rights.

Another way of looking at this is the invisibility of some groups in sections of society: their needs are just not recognised or addressed. Their experience is marginalised; they feel as if they have no voice, no platform, and no one to listen when they try to express themselves. This can lead to groups feeling as if the services that are supposedly for their benefit represent just another way in which their experience is undervalued. When you read Chapter 5 you should be able to analyse these experiences in terms of symbolic interactionist and social constructionist theories.

Activity Discrimination

Discuss and make a list of the types of discrimination that you have observed in your everyday life. Think about the levels at which this discrimination occurs and the actions you might take to counter discrimination.

Activity Assumptions of normality

If one in ten people is gay, then in a class or workplace of 30 people, statistically there are three gay people. Research the statistics that can be applied to other aspects of identity that are not immediately visible, for example the percentage of people with mental health problems or epilepsy, or who experience some form of sexual abuse.

It is probable that you and/or some of the people you live and work with will fall into one or more of the categories in the Activity above, but because of the general 'assumption of normality' – that everyone is the same – people who are different may not feel free to talk about their experience openly. They may fear that people will misunderstand their situation because of negative stereotypes and prejudice, or that they will become stigmatised and that people will avoid them or make jokes at their expense.

The next time you are talking about any of these issues, ask yourself whether, if you knew that someone in the room was gay, had been raped, or had experienced mental health problems, you would talk about things in the same way? Would you make the same 'innocent' jokes and comments? Is the way you make assumptions about the normality of people you work with one of the factors that perpetuates their silence, and therefore their continued invisibility?

All the examples of discrimination in this chapter are of real-life situations and show not only the variety of negative effects of **oppression** but also the desire to fight back. A lot of people in the examples have stood up against discrimination and taken a variety of approaches to seek redress for the negative treatment they have experienced. They have spoken out, found support, and used the law and other tools in an effort to change their personal situation, and this often has had the effect of making the discrimination less likely to occur for other people in other situations. They have taken individual action or joined together in groups to campaign against the discrimination they faced. Figure 2.6 illustrates the effects of discrimination and the processes for challenging it.

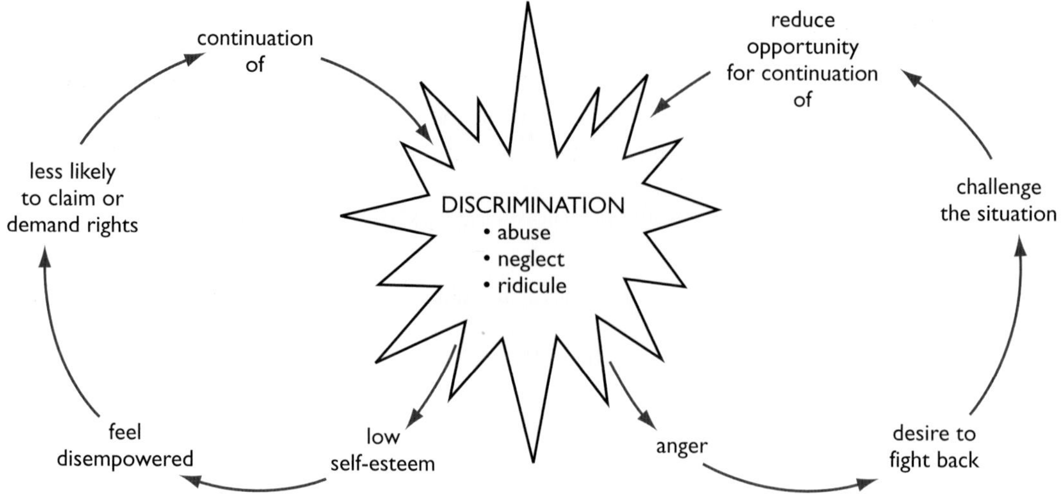

Figure 2.6 Effects of discrimination

Discrimination in a care setting

In a care setting, both service users and workers can be affected by discrimination. Some of the factors that affect each group are examined below.

Discrimination against service users

Care services are in an uneasy position when it comes to discrimination. They are part of the social service, benefits, housing and health systems in which people may have experienced institutionalised oppression, but part of their function is to help these same people to challenge this discrimination and assert their rights.

Discrimination still exists in community-based services, however, because many people with disabilities or mental health problems still do not have access to resources that would enable them to live an autonomous life. The Social Care (Self-directed Support) (Scotland) Act 2013 aims to provide more choice to people about how their care is funded and provided. In a world of limited resources, fairness and equity are dominant principles and great care must be taken to allocate resources fairly, equitably and without discrimination. Care workers have a role to play in advocating for the rights of service users, which requires knowledge and understanding of available resources.

The role of the care worker implies a certain amount of power and, in any situation of power, abuse may occur. It is possible to behave in a way that devalues, suppresses or dismisses the beliefs or needs of the service user. Not all examples of poor practice in care work are necessarily also examples of discrimination, but when the misuse of power by workers is based on a denial of the rights of certain people, then it can be seen as discrimination.

Discrimination against staff

Staff in care services can experience discrimination from colleagues, their organisation or service users. As a potential employee, a care worker can face discrimination during the recruitment and selection process and, once they have a job, they can face discrimination when applying for promotions. Workers can experience harassment and bullying from colleagues and service users. Violence against staff by service users in care settings is an increasing problem. Some women workers have been sexually assaulted by service users, and some ethnic minority workers have been racially abused by service users. As a worker, you still have the right to be respected as an individual and to expect your rights to be recognised by colleagues and service users.

CASE STUDY

Discrimination against male nurses

Andrew Moyhing, a 29-year-old former student nurse, left the profession over concerns about how male nurses were treated. He was told that a female member of staff would have to chaperone him while using an ECG machine with a female patient, but witnessed female staff providing intimate care to male patients with no chaperone present. This was based on the stereotype that all men are sexual predators and that therefore female patients automatically need extra protection when being treated by male nurses. The Equal Opportunities Commission (EOC) helped Andrew take his case to an employment tribunal as they wanted to highlight the problems that men experience from outdated stereotypes when they seek employment in areas previously considered as 'women's work'. The EOC has now been replaced by the Equality and Human Rights Commission (EHRC) which continues to raise the issue of male nurses requiring chaperones.

Anti-discriminatory practice

> *Anti-discriminatory practice challenges people's values and their taken-for-granted assumptions in constructing their own sense of reality. Such a challenge can prove very threatening and destabilising. If not handled sensitively, exposure to anti-discriminatory ideas and values can be so alien and threatening as to arouse considerable resistance and barriers to change … our focus needs to be on educating and convincing, not on bullying.*
>
> (Thompson, 2012, p.193)

Anti-discriminatory practice is not about treating everyone the same; it is about challenging and not tolerating discrimination, and about recognising and celebrating people's differences. It involves negotiating with service users how best to meet their needs, assert their rights, and challenge the inequalities they face. It includes challenging and countering oppression through what is also known as anti-oppressive practice. The different levels of discrimination have been examined; consideration will now be given to the ways in which discrimination can be challenged at the three levels of personal, cultural and structural, and also at the institutional, organisational level, which contains aspects of all of these.

Personal strategies

There are a number of things any individual can do to combat discrimination. Strategies include increasing your self-awareness to ensure that you are less likely to discriminate unconsciously and more likely to challenge discrimination when you see it.

Increase your self-awareness

The most immediate action you can take is to examine your own attitudes and behaviour. The first step to being a good care worker is the development of self-awareness, because you can change only those aspects of your attitudes and behaviour that you have recognised. Workers need to become alert to the ways in which they present themselves to, and respond to, service users. Increased self-awareness reduces the likelihood of unconscious discrimination. Becoming more aware of your value and belief systems is essential for competent care practice and is addressed elsewhere in this chapter.

Challenge prejudice and discrimination when it occurs

This requires you to be clear in your own mind about what discrimination is, and to develop interpersonal skills so that you can tackle situations assertively. Challenging discrimination is not the same as confrontation. If you are prepared and informed there are non-aggressive ways to discuss your views with people. A lot of training courses use role play to help people plan and prepare how they would tackle difficult situations. This gives you a chance to 'try things out' in a supportive atmosphere, so that you are more able to deal with the problem in real life.

The secret to success when challenging discrimination is to choose the best time and place to raise the issue. It is impossible to counter every statement or action you see that is directly, indirectly, consciously or unconsciously discriminatory. It is also too easy to think that the time is never right, because there is always the potential for hassle when you raise it as an issue. If you choose not to tackle a phrase or an action, however, you are colluding with the discrimination: you are part of it, you are part of the culture of acceptance. Things will never change if you just leave it up to other people, or to Parliament, to make a difference. If people did not allow phrases and actions to pass by unchallenged, a culture of non-acceptance would develop. There would be zero tolerance of discrimination. In this way anti-discriminatory practice would become institutionalised – it would be the accepted way of doing things in an organisation, the routine and regular way of dealing with things. This has already been established in some organisations and workplaces, in which individuals had the strength of their convictions to start challenging bad practice.

Activity *'I'm not prejudiced, but what about ...?'*

When talking about prejudice and stereotypes, people often start sentences with 'I'm not prejudiced, but what about ...?' and go on to speak negatively about a group, based on prejudices they have picked up from newspapers, TV, etc. An example would be, 'I'm not prejudiced, but what about young women who get pregnant just to get a house – they shouldn't go to the top of the council house list.' Or, 'I'm not prejudiced, but I know Pakistani grocers who sell cigarettes to underage kids and the police are too scared to get them into any trouble in case they say it's **racism**.' Why are these statements prejudicial? They are based on assumptions rather than fact; they generalise about a particular group of people when the same may be true about lots of other groups of people; they focus on one aspect of identity (young women who get pregnant, Pakistanis); they are intended as an excuse for prejudice.

It is important to note that, when discussing prejudice with other people, the point is not to score points or be more politically correct than someone else, but to become aware of the kind of assumptions that are being made and the evidence on which they are based. Since prejudice is usually based on lack of knowledge you could ask, 'What evidence do you have for what you have just said?' or, if it is accepted that in a society where discrimination is structured into all levels, we will all have a number of unconscious prejudices, you could say, 'Everyone has some prejudices. What are yours, do you think?'

What other comments might you use to counter the prejudices shown in the above statements?

Cultural strategies

Changing behaviour and practices at a cultural level is much more difficult than changing the behaviour of single individuals at a personal level. It involves changing shared ways of thinking and behaving that may be embedded in aspects of socialisation and considered as 'normal'. As mentioned above, however, personal strategies can have an impact on culture where the personal is extended to such policies as zero tolerance of discrimination. If enough people are operating a personal strategy of zero tolerance of discrimination, it can become a cultural strategy. Achieving this involves showing the irrationality of discriminatory behaviour through increasing knowledge and awareness and through changing behaviour and attitudes. Cultural discrimination can also be tackled through changes to structures, as discussed in the next section. Things like legislation and policy, the way services are structured and delivered, and the way language is used, are all ways in which cultural discrimination can be tackled. The **agents of socialisation** discussed in Chapter 3 are important in delivering anti-discriminatory messages: the family, education, work, the media, and religion.

As an example, disability is examined. Practices, language and attitudes in relation to people with disabilities reflect cultural strategies in relation to people with an impairment. For clarification, an **impairment** is the condition a person has, and a

disability is the effect this impairment has on them. We still use the term 'disability' to refer to an impairment, however. This aspect of language hasn't changed but the way in which the term 'disability' is thought about is changing. This has come about gradually, partly through a change from a medical model to a social model. The medical model views disability as an illness, as stopping people from doing the things that 'normal' people are able to do. It separates them from society by the labels it applies and the way in which they are treated. The application of a social model is a cultural strategy. It focuses on the way society impedes the ability of people with an impairment and disables them. The emphasis is on the individual as a person first, rather than the disability being the determinant of that individual's identity. Society is the disabling factor, not the person or the disability. In Chapter 5 you will be able to see this process in terms of theories of symbolic interactionism and **social constructionism**.

Activity *Cultural strategies in relation to disability*

Discuss and/or write about what you see as cultural strategies in relation to disability.

You may have thought about: the way the media portrays people with disability through popularising such events as the Paralympics as part of their prime time coverage; the acceptance of equal access to public places for people with disability; the general acceptance of adaptations to buses and other forms of public transport to accommodate wheelchairs; children with disability being accepted into mainstream opportunities; changes in the way in which people with an impairment are seen, as people first.

We are beginning to see these cultural changes, which are emphasised through the word 'acceptance', as normal. This doesn't mean that discrimination in relation to disability has gone away; unfortunately it hasn't. But it does indicate a cultural shift – brought about to some extent by changes in personal attitudes and behaviour, to some extent by structural and institutional/organisational change, and to some extent by the effects of these shifts in behaviour, attitudes and structure, reinforced through agents of socialisation such as the family and education.

Another example of a cultural strategy is the 'Taking action to end stigma' campaign jointly directed by the Mental Health Foundation (MHF) and the Scottish Association of Mental Health (SAMH), with funding from the Scottish Government and Comic Relief. This campaign builds on the previous 'See me' campaign. Billy Watson, Chief Executive of SAMH, said of the campaign:

> *Every year one in four people in Scotland will experience a mental health problem and it is imperative that we work towards eliminating the stigma and discrimination that currently exists.*
>
> *We are delighted to be working with MHF to deliver this new national programme. We will build on the legacy of the 'See me' awareness-raising campaign. We will focus now on transforming behaviour; we will directly involve people affected by stigma and discrimination and bring about positive and long-lasting change in Scotland.*

For the past year, Lynsey has volunteered with SAMH to support their work and raise awareness of mental health. Lynsey said:

> *I've experienced mental health problems for most of my life and was hospitalised for ten months, so I know how it feels to deal with the stigma of mental ill health.*
>
> *I've lost friends and have felt alienated by people who don't understand that, despite my illness, I'm still the same person.*
>
> *I know first-hand that with the right facts and information, the stigma of mental ill health can be reduced, which is why this new campaign is crucially important for the one in four Scots living with mental health problems.*

The new programme will help communities to find local approaches to reducing mental health stigma and discrimination. It will target places where the greatest impact can be achieved, including the workplace, and education, health and social care settings. It will aim to ensure that having a mental health problem is no longer viewed as something that should be hidden and that people who experience mental health problems feel empowered and confident to talk about the issue without facing discrimination.

Structural strategies

Personal and cultural strategies are reinforced through structural strategies that can result in structural change. **Legislation and pressure groups** are major ways in which this can take place. There is usually considerable pressure from individuals and groups before any piece of legislation is passed. Legislation very often reflects a cultural shift and then reinforces it. Legislation goes through a process of consultation and debate before it is finally passed, and efforts are made to avoid any unforeseen consequences that could be contrary to human rights. Indeed, this is a prerequisite of current legislation.

One example of such legislation was the passing of the Adult Support and Protection (Scotland) Act 2007. Long before this legislation was passed there were concerns that very vulnerable adults did not have the protection from harm and abuse that children had. Abuse can be seen as a discriminatory act. It involves a misuse of power by one person or group in relation to another, resulting in disempowerment and oppression.

A key obstacle to introducing the legislation, and with it new statutory requirements and powers, was achieving a balance between individual human rights and the State's responsibility to intervene. Examples of a lack of protection were brought to light, however, including the severe abuse over a number of years of a woman with learning difficulties in the Borders. This resulted in an inquiry into practice in the Borders by the then Social Work Services Inspectorate, which revealed failings in the protection of adults affected by learning disability and led to a recommendation to introduce new legislation (SWSI, 2004). Age Concern (now Age UK) also contributed evidence of the abuse of older people who had no satisfactory protection under the current statutory measures. Since the introduction of the legislation, local authorities have established training, adult protection committees and outcomes evaluation. Adult protection is now embedded within social services structures as a strategy for tackling abuse.

Activity *Legislation*

Identify another piece of legislation that you think provides a structural strategy for anti-discriminatory practice. Discuss the changes brought about by this legislation.

A description of legislation relevant to care can be found in Chapter 1. The Scottish Parliament cannot develop its own equal opportunities legislation: that is one of the powers reserved for Westminster. The issues that are the responsibility of the Scottish Parliament – education, social work, transport, health and housing – however, still provide an opportunity to make an impact on the inequality and disadvantages that people face.

Pressure and campaigning groups

Thompson (2012, p.xv) adopts a holistic perspective on anti-discriminatory practice, seeing it as 'a broad undertaking that needs to incorporate sociological, political and economic concerns above and beyond narrow legal requirements'. Many pressure and campaigning groups provide a focus for both one-off and long-term challenges to discrimination. Sometimes they are campaigning for a change to legislation, but often they are trying to raise awareness of an issue and encourage people to become more informed. Many groups have projects that work to challenge stigma and prejudice, such as the Mental Health Foundation and Scottish Association of Mental Health programme 'Taking action to end stigma' (see above), the Poverty Alliance 'Stick your labels' campaign, and the charity Show racism the red card (SRTRC), which uses top footballers to campaign and educate against racism.

People might mobilise a group overnight to highlight a particular incident of racial violence, while many organisations run campaigns for many years to highlight inadequacies in the law and campaign to change the way they are treated. Many of these groups are well funded and very powerful, for example Amnesty International UK. They provide statistics and information for MPs to use when issues are discussed in Parliament. Many groups also provide services, such as informing people of their rights in relation to existing law, for example the Govan Law Centre (**www.govanlc.com**), an independent, community-controlled law centre.

Institutional/organisational strategies

Employers are responsible in law for acts of discrimination carried out by employees, whether or not they are with the employer's knowledge or approval. Employees can be personally responsible for discriminatory acts if the employer mounts a defence to show that they took all reasonable and practical steps to prevent the discrimination. Employers are responsible if they instruct employees to act in ways that discriminate. Within an organisation, there are many actions that can be taken to prevent and challenge discrimination and to promote equal opportunities for staff and service users. These include positive action, having a clear equal opportunities policy, diversity training and promoting anti-discriminatory practice. These actions are aimed at the culture, structure and personal behaviour within the organisation.

Positive action

Positive discrimination is not allowed by law, except in the case of people with disabilities, and in some other very specific situations. This means that an employer cannot give a job to or promote someone solely on the basis of their gender or race. Positive action is allowed under the Equality Act 2010, however, which has embraced sections 47 and 48 of the Sex Discrimination Act (1975) and sections 37 and 38 of the Race Relations Act (1976). Certain groups are more likely to be unemployed or in lower-grade jobs because of the discrimination they have faced, not only in a specific job but owing to, for example, poor access to education in the past, or lack of response to their needs. The main aim of positive action is to make **equality of opportunity** more of a realistic possibility. Even if racial discrimination, for instance, could end immediately, many people from some ethnic groups would continue to experience the effects of discrimination and disadvantage from the past. They would still not be 'on a level playing field' or able to compete equally with those who have not been systematically disadvantaged over a period of time.

In a work setting, positive action can take the form of encouraging people from certain groups to apply for vacant posts. Employers might put 'Applications especially welcome from members of ethnic minorities' or 'People with disabilities are currently under-represented in our workforce' in an advertisement. The job can still be awarded only on the basis of merit of the applicants, but the message is intended to encourage under-represented groups to apply. The Equality and Human Rights Commission, for example, states on its employment page that it has a Guaranteed Interview Scheme (GIS) in place for applicants with a disability if they achieve 60 per cent of the short-listing score.

An employer might advertise in newspapers and magazines aimed at gay people or members of an ethnic group, or talk to community groups to convey the positive desire to increase the diversity and representation of a variety of groups in their workforce. They might organise training specifically aimed at groups under-represented at certain levels, for example 'Women in management' or 'Men can care' courses. The purpose of such training is to equip people with skills and abilities that they have not had the opportunity to develop in the past, so that they are qualified on merit to be appointed or promoted. Workplace awards such as 'Investors in People' emphasise this need for training and the utilisation of existing staff as being good for morale and commitment to the organisation.

Equal opportunities policy

Positive action measures are just one piece of the equality jigsaw in the workplace. If the measures aren't embedded into a clear equal opportunities policy, which is applied and monitored effectively, they will be little more than window dressing. A lot of organisations have a written equal opportunities or diversity policy, which states behaviour that is not acceptable, outlines avenues of complaint and provides strategies for **monitoring** and evaluating the policy.

It is crucial for any care organisation to have a written policy in order to safeguard the rights of workers and service users. Most established organisations should have a policy and all new organisations have to develop one as a prerequisite for obtaining funding and registration. It is important, however, that these policies are not meaningless pieces of paper, full of fine principles that cannot be implemented or measured, that have been decided only by management.

It is good practice to have a process of consultation when developing or changing an equal opportunities policy in order to give all workers and service users a sense of ownership of the policy (i.e. they helped to draft it and so have a sense of responsibility for implementing and monitoring it too). They will have thought about the reasons why certain things are included and how they might need to change to conform to the requirements. Management will have had to listen to all points of view and to make some attempt to integrate them into a policy that is acceptable to everyone who has a stake in the process. There is a parallel here with good care planning, because it involves consultation with all relevant stakeholders and is not determined solely by orders from above.

How will anyone know if the equal opportunities policy has made a difference? Organisations are now bound by legislation to promote equality, so there has to be some form of measurement from year to year to see if there has been any progress. An organisation might include statistics in its Annual Report or in commissioned research reports on such outcomes as: have under-represented groups had more success in gaining promotion? Does the mix of service users reflect that of the target population? Has training had an impact on the number of reports of discrimination? It might also include some more subjective data on the quality of the service and levels of satisfaction that staff or service users feel they receive. This could be obtained by questionnaires, interviews, group discussions, personal development meetings with staff and re-assessment of care plans with clients.

Diversity training

Another way organisations can promote equality in the workplace is to provide suitable training on diversity. Best practice is to make this compulsory for all staff, including senior management and part-time workers, so that every employee is knowledgeable and informed about the range of diversity issues in general, and specifically those that relate to their role in the organisation. Organisations such as Stonewall Scotland, Leonard Cheshire Disability and Regional Equality Councils work with employers to provide relevant training and support.

Anti-discriminatory practice

The commitment to equal opportunities in an organisation extends much further than developing and implementing a policy. A commitment to anti-discriminatory practice can be shown in many ways. It can be demonstrated with service users in everyday practice by promoting independence, maintaining dignity, supporting choice, respecting beliefs and valuing opinions. Many care agencies have published a 'Charter of Rights' that specifies the rights and choices a service user can expect (see Chapter 6). These rights include the right to confidentiality, the right to take risks and the right to make relationships.

Care organisations implement policies and practices to encourage the active participation of service users and staff, thus giving them a voice and some power in the decision-making process. These include: service user committees and service user involvement in the recruitment and selection of new workers; regular training and supervision sessions giving staff the opportunity to update their skills and knowledge, and providing an opportunity to discuss any problems they may be experiencing.

Anti-discriminatory practice is also about visibility. It is about promoting positive images of people in publications and leaflets about your organisation, and it is about having a representative workforce and range of service users. Anti-discriminatory practice has an impact on the way services are delivered. It has to address the wider issue of redistribution, not just of scarce resources such as funding or accommodation, but of the power imbalance that exists between workers and users, staff and management, funders and providers of services.

Barriers to achieving equality in an organisation

There are a number of barriers that a care organisation may encounter when trying to achieve equality. For example:

- insufficient funds to implement changes or provide staff training
- resistance or hostility from some staff or service users to changes
- lack of information for new staff and service users about policies and how they work
- ineffective policies with no monitoring mechanism
- fear of 'political correctness' impinging on people's behaviour
- a culture of inequality.

An organisation should be aware of these potential problems and use the above strategies to try to address them when developing their anti-discriminatory policies, procedures and ways of working.

Effective communication

So far in this chapter a sound value base and a commitment to anti-discriminatory practice have been shown to be vital for positive care practice. Another essential factor is effective communication.

Communication can be defined as the imparting or exchanging of thoughts, opinions or information by speaking, writing, signing or using some other medium. **Effective** can be defined as meaning communication that is successful at producing a desired or intended result. From these two definitions, adapted from the Oxford English Dictionary, it is apparent that communication is more complex than just speaking to a person. The ways in which care workers communicate conveys to service users how they value that person.

Think of someone in your life whom you admire and find it easy to speak to, perhaps a friend or a relative. It is likely that the reasons why you find them easy to speak to are that you know that person well and they know you well, they accept you, they are warm and understanding, they listen to you and they do not criticise or judge you. Bear this in mind when communicating and building a relationship with service users.

Effective communication in care work involves many features, including:

- a caring, valuable relationship
- listening skills
- non-verbal communication
- using appropriate language
- using the right pace and tone.

A caring, valuable relationship

Forming and sustaining a caring, valuable relationship is the main essence of effective communication between a service user and a care worker. Without a good relationship there will be no mutual respect. This is likely to result in failure to meet the needs of the service user. The ingredients necessary to form relationships are the practice of all the values and principles, knowledge of human behaviour, knowledge of the person, all of the other features of effective communication and also that bit extra – **the 'oomph factor'** (contributed by Ellen Lancaster in Miller, 2007, pp.64–65).

The oomph factor

The ingredients that bind together the oomph factor are as follows:

- **Enthusiasm**: this is ardent interest and eagerness, and includes encouraging and having a belief in others. Care workers need to be energetic and find inspiration in what they are practising. If there is a day when the carer does not feel 100 per cent then it is best to apologise and explain this to the service user without going into too much detail. The service user will then realise that any reserve is not because of them.
- **Dedication**: this is consistent support and commitment to the well-being of the service user. Try to be reliable. When you do have to be away, always explain that you are not going to be there and state when you will be back.
- **Vocation**: this emphasises the professionalism of care work and that it is not 'just a job'. Your heart really has to be in care work, with the individuals you work with as the focus of your attention.
- **Genuine interest**: this includes being interested in all people, knowing people's likes and dislikes, frustrations and expectations, and also being truthful.
- **Enjoyment and humour**: these involve the worker in showing and feeling genuine pleasure in what they are doing and sharing successes or even failures, however great or small. What a difference a smile makes, and that pleasantness needs to be evident from the minute you start work until you finish. A real challenge!
- **Positive self-disposition**: this emphasises that the care worker should be confident and happy with him/herself in what he or she is doing, and should strive to share this confidence and happiness with the service user. If the care worker does not feel this way then the service user will sense it. There may be a time when the care worker does not feel happy. He should then reflect on and evaluate his own life to decide whether there are changes that need to be made.

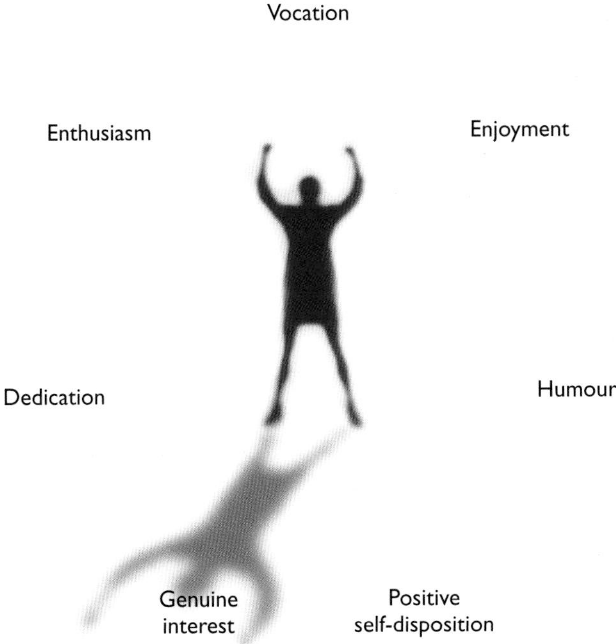

Figure 2.7 The oomph factor: 'I love what I do!'

Carl Rogers: empathy, congruence and unconditional positive regard

In addition to these attributes, other factors are essential in establishing helpful relationships. Carl Rogers (1902–87) emphasises three core conditions for promoting good relationships (Rogers, 1991): empathy, congruence and unconditional positive regard. These help the service user to have self-esteem, to make choices and to solve problems.

Empathy

Rogers saw the idea of empathy as 'the ability to experience another person's world as if it was your own world'. Service users may have completely different experiences from the care worker so it is important to try genuinely to understand a service user's thoughts and feelings. Through the care worker's expression of empathy and the opportunity of talking freely, many service users experience great relief at being able to share their feelings without getting a negative reaction from the care worker. This process is sometimes referred to as 'ventilation'. It can lower anxiety and can, if the care worker provides empathy, be sufficient in itself to let the service user find their own solution to their problem.

Also, when service users feel that the care worker has empathy they will be more likely to talk about themselves, which will enable the care worker to learn more about that person and to understand their views. Understanding can grow from a conversation that conveys empathy with the service user.

Congruence

Congruence is genuineness: being totally sincere. Being sincere is paramount. It means that care workers have to be honest and open, be themselves and be giving to others. There is no room for acting or using language that confuses the service user. This only gives the impression that the care worker is superior to others. When a person talks to a friend or relative there may be no barriers if each is relaxed, natural and genuinely interested. When a care worker talks to a service user it should be just the same. It is essential that a care worker conveys a little of what kind of person they are and shares information that may help the service user to feel relaxed and comfortable. In some situations this might encourage service users to be more forthcoming with information about themselves.

Like any other skill, forming a supportive relationship with a service user improves with practice, and care workers should continually evaluate themselves. It is necessary for care workers to develop reflective practice and to accept feedback from colleagues, supervisors and most importantly the service users. It is possible to tell if communication is effective by the response of service users. They will show trust, be honest with the care worker and show that they enjoy the care worker's company. Without these kind, humane ingredients the relationship will be doomed and very difficult to redeem.

Unconditional positive regard

Unconditional positive regard means accepting someone unquestioningly as having worth, whoever they are and whatever they may have done. It is conveyed through showing both acceptance and warmth. This will ensure that the service user feels valued as an individual. A service user may be feeling helpless, threatened or embarrassed, or that they are a nuisance. The care worker may reflect warmth by **non-verbal communication**, such as:

- a warm smile (facial expression)
- open, welcoming gestures
- a confident manner – this reassures the service user that they can be helped
- offering physical help – for example, offering a guiding arm to an elderly or distraught person
- general appearance
- calm and gentle gestures and movements.

The care worker may also reflect warmth by **verbal communication**, such as:

- a friendly tone of voice and not speaking in a patronising way
- using friendly words that show respect, for example, instead of saying 'tell me', ask 'Would you like to tell me?' or 'Can you tell me …?'
- expressing a wish to help
- explaining clearly what the care worker is trying to do
- giving reassurance about confidentiality
- showing clear understanding of what has been achieved and what can be achieved.

In developing the skill of showing unconditional positive regard it is important to be yourself, to be natural and genuine. If you pretend to be interested, warm or understanding then the service user will sense this and it will jeopardise the whole relationship.

Listening skills

> *Trying to get them to listen is ... well, let's just say it's a Herculean task and I aren't no Hercules.*
>
> (Beresford and Branfield, 2004)

> *Listen and pay attention, otherwise it can go in one ear and out of the other.*
>
> (Roy McGivney, personal communication, 2014)

Listening is as important as communicating verbally. It shouldn't be a Herculean task for a service user to get a care worker to listen. Listening should not be 'passive' but active, and this involves more than just hearing; it involves also paying attention, concentrating on what the person is saying, responding to what has been said and then acting on it. To be a good listener involves practising all the values, principles and attributes in caring, as well as being attentive, using prompts and using appropriate questions, as explained below. When I interviewed Roy McGivney, an advocate and Children's Panel member, he put listening and paying attention right at the top of his list of what is important in relating to people.

Being attentive

Being attentive means actively listening and concentrating on what is being said, as well as being aware of what is *not* being said by sensing that the service user is perhaps shy, feeling awkward, embarrassed or unable to express how they feel. They may show signs of these feelings by silence, eye movements, nervous movements like wringing their hands or turning a ring on their finger. Facial expressions, posture and other forms of **body language** all give clues to a person's feelings. The care worker should try to understand these signs and allow the service user time to relax and feel confident to talk.

Using prompts

Service users who may be shy, nervous or hesitant about talking for various reasons may need encouragement from the care worker. This can be done by, for example, nodding at appropriate times to show acceptance and understanding, making eye contact to show that attention is being given, and using words and sounds, such as 'oh', 'really', 'mmm', to show you understand what is being said and are happy to listen further.

Using appropriate questions

Questions may be asked to clarify what the service user has said and to establish more information. To encourage service users to talk it is better to use **'open' questions**, which invite answers that are longer and more involved; these questions usually start with words like 'how', 'why', 'what', 'when', 'where'. For example, rather than asking a young person 'Do you like your new school?', which would probably be answered with 'yes' or 'no', it would be better to ask 'What do you think of your new school?' The care worker is then likely to learn more information about how the young person feels about the school. Using open questions provides an opportunity for the service user to say what they are thinking and/or feeling.

Non-verbal communication

Non-verbal communication comprises appearance, gestures and movements. There are four main ways in which non-verbal communication is used: eye contact, posture, facial expression and physical contact.

Eye contact

Eye contact is very useful to show that the care worker is paying attention to the service user when they are speaking; it also conveys sincerity and genuineness. It would not be appropriate to stare continually at someone, however: it is best to be natural.

Posture

When two people are talking they generally feel more comfortable if they are at the same level. If a care worker were to tower over a service user, the service user might feel intimidated, or that they cannot move away. The care worker should be sufficiently relaxed to be friendly and calm. Positioning of seating is important: it is better to be facing the service user and leaning slightly forward, showing willingness to listen. Such mannerisms as hands in pockets, playing with hands or running hands through hair should be avoided as these would be distracting to the service user. Sitting behind a desk presents a barrier between the service user and the worker and should be avoided.

Facial expression

The expression on a person's face can often convey how that person is feeling and can be used effectively to communicate feelings. Therefore it is essential that the care worker shows warmth and friendliness. It is difficult to communicate with someone who shows no emotion in their face and it can be very unsettling. Of course, the expressions that the care worker shows should be appropriate; they should not, for example, show signs of laughing, sneering or superiority.

Physical contact

When a service user is distressed or frightened, a care worker might show understanding and empathy by giving a child a hug or an older person a reassuring arm around their shoulder. The care worker has to be careful, however, that their familiarity is not misinterpreted. It can be difficult to know when physical contact is appropriate or inappropriate, but just because this is the case does not mean that it has to be avoided altogether. Remember that attachment is very important to children as they develop, and that warmth and genuineness are very important in developing helping relationships. It is keeping to agreed boundaries that is important. This is a controversial issue and appropriate physical contact should be discussed and agreed at team meetings. You should always know your agency policy in relation to this subject.

Using appropriate language

Each service user is an **individual** with their own social background, culture, character and abilities. For these reasons it is necessary for care workers to adapt and tailor their language and communication to suit each individual service user. The choice of words, the length of what is said, the content and the communication methods used are all important. Too often care workers, without thought, use 'jargon' – such as 'goal setting', '**empowerment**' or 'interaction' – which will only confuse the service user.

The **age** of a service user has to be considered. An older person, for example, should never be spoken to as if they are a child, by using childish words. This is patronising and shows no respect for the person. Similarly, when speaking to a child, language should be appropriate to the age of the child. It is useful to check, in an appropriate way, that what is being said has been understood.

When working with service users who have a **hearing impairment** you should find out how this person prefers to communicate. It may be useful to have some familiarity with sign language. If signing is the usual mode of communication and you are not a fluent signer, the individual has a right to an interpreter when there are formal matters to discuss. Remember, however, that an individual may not sign but may lip read, or may have only limited use of signs because of an additional learning difficulty.

When working with someone who has a **visual impairment**, it may be helpful to describe objects and situations. Every individual and situation will be different and the worker needs to be adaptive and sensitive to these differences.

Care workers may work with service users who speak a **different language**. This should not cause a barrier in communication, nor should the service user be made to feel inferior because they do not speak English. An interpreter will be required if there are difficult issues to talk about, but it is unlikely that an interpreter can be present on every occasion. The care worker could make an effort to learn the service user's language, or at least a few words of it. In many care situations there are other workers and/or service users who have a knowledge of different languages and can help out on a day-to-day basis.

Service users who have a **learning disability** need the care worker to be patient and capable of using words that they will understand. The length of what is being said should take into account the service user's ability to understand. It may be advisable to repeat what has been said so that the service user understands. Adults should not be spoken to in a patronising or childish way, and time should be given for service users to express themselves. To aid communication, facial expressions, gestures and appropriate touch may be useful. You may enhance communication through using visual aids such as pictures and story boards.

The 'Care in practice' case studies below provide examples of communication and of ways of enhancing communication with service users. When you undertake the Activities later in the chapter you may wish to refer back to these case studies to see how communication took place.

CARE IN PRACTICE

Eric and Jennifer

Eric is a support worker, working with adults who are deaf and blind. Here he talks about working with Jennifer.

'At present I support Jennifer, who is 21 years of age and has complex learning difficulties including partial deafness and partial blindness. Before commencing support of Jennifer I read her Personal Passport and her Care Plan, which stated that she communicates through gestures, i.e. pointing and facial expressions. I then requested some observation shifts so that I could observe how she communicated with other people in her surrounding environment. I was told that she had no verbal communication at all but appeared to understand simple words. Jennifer seemed to spend most of her time crumpling pages of magazines and putting them in a plastic bag. Over time I built up a relationship with Jennifer by using communication skills, speaking to her in simple language, sitting opposite her at the right level and showing friendliness in my face. As Jennifer's trust and confidence began to build up with me I started using simple communication skills with her, asking her to take off her own jacket and showing her by taking off my own jacket. After several weeks Jennifer would happily take her jacket off when requested.

'Jennifer and I went out one day into a supermarket. While out, Jennifer preferred to hold my hand as she can see only short distances. When I got the trolley Jennifer let go my hand and pointed to it. I went to give her my hand again and she pushed it away, pointing to the trolley again. I went through the process of getting eye contact with her and asked her clearly at a pace and level she could understand what it was she wanted. Jennifer then put both her hands on the trolley and began to wheel it around the supermarket. She communicated to me that she was really enjoying this activity by laughing and clapping her hands. I passed this information on to her other key workers and family, and now she enjoys weekly shopping trips with her father and mother, which is helping to build up the communication in her home environment.'

Eric also realised that Jennifer loves music, especially when it is played loudly. Jennifer is now able to choose and enjoy things that she likes to do, thanks to the support worker who used good values and communication skills, treated Jennifer as an individual and respected her wishes.

Usha

A student who took up part-time employment as a care worker in a home for elderly people noticed that an Indian woman, Usha, who was in the home for a period of assessment and respite, seemed very unhappy and isolated. When she asked another care worker about Usha she was told that English was her second language. The staff had assumed that there was no point in speaking to her as she would not understand. They believed that she was in the home for a short time and they did not have the time to communicate with her. They had attended to her physical needs, washing her, dressing her, giving her meals, but they had not attempted to communicate with her. When they did have to speak to her they had used inappropriate language, such as 'You sit up', 'Me feed you'.

The student approached Usha with a smile and introduced herself. She found that Usha understood what she was saying, and she continued by telling Usha her name and a little about herself. The student realised that the other staff had assumed that because English was Usha's second language she would not understand what they were saying. By not speaking quickly or shouting and by being patient and repeating some words, the student had been able to communicate with Usha. If there were words that Usha did not understand then the student had used facial expressions and hand gestures. Some of the other staff noticed the attempt made by the student and they too made more effort to speak to Usha. The student found that after a few days Usha seemed happier and had made friends with other service users.

Using the right pace and tone

The **pace** of the communication used by a care worker should, like the language used, take into account the age, ability and culture of the service user. There would be no point in talking on and on very quickly if in fact the service user was still trying to understand what was first said. The **tone** of voice that is used by the care worker should also be appropriate to who is being spoken to. They should not 'talk down' to service users, and there is no place for abruptness. The tone should be friendly and warm, irrespective of who is on the receiving end. Civility costs nothing and goes a long way. For example, 'What do you want?' with the emphasis on 'what', would be better replaced with 'What would you like?', said in a warm and friendly tone with an emphasis on 'like'. The first question and tone would make the service user feel that it was a bother for the care worker, whereas the second reflects that the care worker is genuinely interested in those to whom they are talking. There are times when the tone of voice has to be different, for instance when the service user has received disturbing news, and then the tone should be comforting. Care workers have to be sensitive about what they say and how they say it and this should stem from a good understanding of and interest in the person with whom they are working.

Communicating without using language

For some service users with a learning difficulty, dementia, serious illness or disability, language may not be the best way of communicating and alternatives must be found. The use of pictures and story boards has already been mentioned. The case study of Susan below provides a good example of how alternative means of communication can be utilised.

CARE IN PRACTICE

Susan

This case study was contributed by The Richmond Fellowship Scotland (TRFS).

'Susan had been in hospital for more than four years when we began to work with her to make the transition to a new home. Change causes Susan high levels of anxiety and can lead to incidents of verbal and physical aggression.

'Susan uses limited verbal communication so we worked with the Speech and Language Therapist and the ward staff who knew her well to create pictorial formats to help her understand the changes ahead. We created a photo album showing the progress of the renovation of her new home, as well as things that she would like and be interested in in the immediate area around her home. This was updated regularly with new photographs.

'Susan was also supported to create a "mood board" to help her pick colours and fabrics that she liked, so that she was able to make choices about the décor and furnishings in her new home. The choices she made (for example, a red sofa) were purchased and photographs were taken to show the progress. Susan was helped to pick out specific personal belongings, which were taken to the house and then photographed in the rooms.

'This preparatory work meant that when Susan first visited her new home and then began to spend time there her levels of anxiety were reduced. She felt familiar with her environment and had a sense of ownership.'

Writing, recording and storing information

Another communication skill is that of writing things down. Keeping records, writing reports and communicating in writing – through notes, letters, emails and other media – present other ways of working with people. This can help to ensure there is continuity in their care and that care workers, with service users, make a relevant professional contribution to the care process. Records play a part in collaborative and partnership working as well as in promoting a person-centred approach by maintaining the focus on service users and carers. Written information can also play a part in protecting people from danger, harm and abuse by recording risk factors and what should and should not happen in the care process. Some of the records kept include records of tasks, contributions to care plans (including what people say about their needs, wishes and dreams) and one-page profiles (discussed in Chapter 6), which summarise the service user's answers to at least three questions:

- What do others like and admire about me?
- What is important to me? (what I like, what I don't like)
- What is good support for me?

One-page profiles are a good way for people to introduce themselves to one another and to keep the most important issues at the forefront of the care process.

Activity *Records*

When writing things down, what are the most useful things to remember?

You may have thought of some of the following points or other completely different ones:

- Bear in mind the purpose of what you are writing and keep to the point.
- Ensure that the views you record are the service user's, not yours (unless you specifically state that they are yours).
- Remember the value base and ensure that records promote dignity and justice, and are in no way discriminatory.
- Keep records up to date.
- Write clearly and concisely. If you have trouble with writing, work at this skill because it is very important to service users that records on their behalf do them justice.
- Bear in mind confidentiality and use the principle of 'need to know'. Records should be seen only by those who need to know and should be stored securely, whether they are paper records or on a computer.
- Keep people informed. Often an email can make the world of difference and doesn't take long to write.
- Remember carers, including families, and their needs, as well as service users. While your main focus is on the service user, carers often play a huge part in the caring process and should be respected and informed as appropriate and agreed in the planning process.

There are also some more official protections that apply to written records and communications. The Care Inspectorate requires that agencies have policies and procedures that apply to written records and that staff comply with these. The provisions of the Data Protection Act 1998 and the Freedom of Information Act 2002 (FOISA) (see Chapter 1) must be adhered to. This means taking great care to protect information and also great care about what you communicate in writing. This includes the emails you write that relate to your work. Under FOISA these can be requested if someone has a legitimate reason to see them.

Finally, to be successful as an effective communicator, whether verbally or in writing, care workers need to be flexible and aware of their own ability to communicate, and to use the necessary skills to work successfully with service users. Where effective communication is practised the service user will feel accepted and understood and will know that their needs have been recognised. Effective communication is an important way of helping to promote independence, ensure equal opportunities and empower service users.

Example: written communication

An organisation working with young people develops care plans online in partnership with the young people. All of the young people have access to their own care plans and can make contributions online about how they are getting on in relation to agreed outcomes (see Chapter 6 for more information on outcomes). Staff also make contributions, seen by the individual young people, and this collaborative process between young people and staff has made a huge difference to how the young people feel about themselves and their achievements. It has also played a part in the development of relationships and their language and computer abilities. Young people do not see one another's care plans unless they wish to share aspects of these with others. There is confidential help available to the young people in terms of entering their contributions.

Barriers that impede communication

In many of the examples in this chapter there were barriers to communication. Care workers need to be aware of such barriers as these may deter or prevent a service user from expressing their needs, wishes and feelings. Failure to understand and detect these barriers will affect communication and make it impossible for the care worker to understand and respond to the needs of a service user.

Activity *Barriers to communication 1*

Identify three of the most frequent barriers to communication that you face or that you think are the most important to tackle in care work. Discuss these with friends or colleagues.

You may have thought of the following:

- Personal barriers:
    - nervousness, distress, embarrassment and/or anger
    - feeling uncomfortable
    - feeling that problems are too personal to discuss
    - fear of being ridiculed, misunderstood or that a confidence won't be kept
    - fear of being abused or neglected
    - lack of self-esteem
    - speaking a different language, including sign language
    - feeling inferior
    - being unable to express feelings
    - discomfort with age difference.

- Impairment barriers:
  - a hearing impairment
  - a speech impairment
  - a visual impairment
  - two or multiple sensory impairments
  - a learning difficulty
  - dementia or Alzheimer's disease.
- Environmental barriers. Consider where communication is taking place, for instance:
  - Is the meeting place the choice of the service user?
  - Is it safe and comfortable?
  - Is it private and quiet?
  - Is it free of any interruptions?
  - Is it appropriate, with suitable lighting (especially for those with visual impairment)?
  - Are the seating arrangements positioned in a friendly way?
  - Is the care worker sitting in full view (especially for those with hearing impairment)?
  - Is there refreshment available that is appropriate for the service user?

The care worker who is sensitive to these aspects enhances their competence in achieving effective communication with those with whom they are working.

Activity — *Barriers to communication 2*

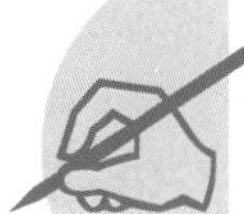

Work with a partner for this activity.

Imagine you are unable to speak, write or walk following a stroke. You are able to understand what people say to you. Work out how you would:

1. Tell your partner that you are hungry.
2. Tell your partner you need to go to the toilet.
3. Tell your partner you want to go out.
4. Explain to your partner that you are uncomfortable and want to be moved.

What were your feelings during this activity?

What did your partner do that was most helpful?

What could she have done that she did not do?

How did your partner feel?

Can you suggest a method of communication that would be useful in this situation?

Activity Barriers to communication 3

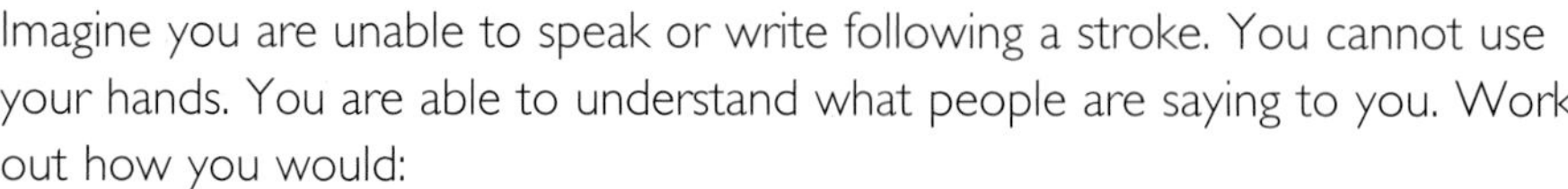

Work with a partner for this activity.

Imagine you are unable to speak or write following a stroke. You cannot use your hands. You are able to understand what people are saying to you. Work out how you would:

1 Tell your partner that you are thirsty.
2 Tell your partner you would like the TV on.
3 Tell your partner you want a friend to come and visit you.
4 Explain to your partner you are concerned about how hard they are working to look after you.
5 Tell your partner that you are worried about the future.

What were your feelings during this activity?

What did your partner do that was most helpful?

What could she have done that she did not do?

How did your partner feel?

Activity Barriers to communication 4

Read the following case studies and write down what factors may impede communication in each situation, and how you could maximise communication with each service user. For example, which methods you could use, which you should avoid and what else might help. Think about what or who might also be of assistance to you.

1 Hayley Anderson (age 35)

Hayley has spent periods of time in hospital for depression. She now lives in her own flat and is supported by community support workers, who are based in premises nearby. When Hayley is depressed she self-harms but knows she can call on her support workers.

2 Antonio Biagi (age 55)

Antonio has had Alzheimer's disease for two years and lives with his wife. A care worker visits him twice a week for three hours to give his wife time to herself.

3 *Amir Patel (age 16)*

Amir is deaf and blind. He lives at home with his mother and father. He attends a resource centre twice a week. He uses the deaf/blind touch alphabet to communicate.

4 *Frankie Hughes (age 23)*

When Frankie was released from prison he was ordered by the court to reside at a resettlement unit, where he has his own flat within the unit. He had been on drugs since he was fifteen years of age. He has been off drugs since entering prison and he is hoping to find employment.

5 *Natalia Kuger (age 17)*

Natalia is an asylum seeker who arrived in Scotland six months ago after fleeing her own country, where she was physically abused. She speaks limited English. She is at present living in a hostel for young women.

6 *Margaret McKinnon (age 72)*

Margaret lives alone in her own home. She has recently suffered a stroke, which has left her with her right arm paralysed. She is unsteady on her feet and her speech is affected. She needs a care worker daily to help her with household chores and shopping.

Strategies for effective communication

1 Hayley Anderson:

- Be non-judgemental.
- Accept Hayley for who she is and show her she is valued.
- Support Hayley to express her feelings.
- Allow her time and space.
- Use positive body language.
- Use gestures and touch.
- Do not treat her like a child.
- Work closely with the Community Psychiatric Nurse and other relevant professional people.

2 Antonio Biagi:

- Sit facing Antonio and at the same level.
- Speak clearly without raising your voice.
- Use simple sentences.
- Try using photographs, pictures or objects.
- Learn from Antonio and his wife what things he likes to do, e.g. listening to music, being read to, gardening.
- Read up on new approaches in care of people with Alzheimer's disease (**www.alzscot.org**).

3 Amir Patel:

- Sit close to Amir and let him know if you have to move.
- Learn and use the touch alphabet on his hand to communicate. Touch is important and reassuring.
- Give Amir assistance in eating and drinking by putting a cup or food in a comfortable position in his hand.
- Encourage Amir to communicate with you, and pay attention to what he communicates.
- Talk to Amir's mother and father and find out how they communicate with him and how they know how he is feeling.

4 Frankie Hughes:

- Be non-judgemental, accepting Frankie and his ambitions.
- Be encouraging, enthusiastic, genuine, helpful.
- Help Frankie to find out about benefits and grants to pay for training.
- Support him to find out about training and employment.
- Ask him what support he needs.
- Give him praise when he accomplishes even a small thing like making an enquiry by himself.
- Be consistent.
- Ensure that you are fully informed about resources that may be useful to Frankie.

5 Natalia Kuger:

- Be welcoming and friendly with kind gestures.
- Ensure that you have an interpreter present for decision-making discussions.
- Speak slowly and use facial expressions, signs and pictures to communicate.
- Make an effort to learn some phrases in Natalia's language, e.g. 'good morning', 'how are you', 'thank you'.
- Offer to accompany her to English classes initially.
- Introduce Natalia to others in the hostel, especially those who may speak her language.
- Suggest to Natalia that you show her round the city.

6 Margaret McKinnon:

- Introduce yourself and ask Margaret how you can support her.
- Remember that Margaret is mentally aware.
- Do not treat her like a child.
- Be patient and listen to her.
- Be cheery and let her know what is going on in the community.
- Offer to contact her friends.
- Discuss options for outings or other opportunities.
- Find out about community transport.
- Make arrangements with Margaret for how you will enter her home.
- Always make sure that you leave her home in a safe condition, e.g. that there are no objects, papers or furniture that may obstruct Margaret moving about.
- Find out about utensils that are available for those with the use of only one hand, or make a referral to an occupational therapist (OT) for assessment if Margaret agrees to this.

Gerard Egan's three-stage model of helping

Gerard Egan, who was born in Glasgow and is now a professor at Loyola University of Chicago, first presented a model of helping, which gives emphasis to the importance of communication and relationship skills, 30 years ago. His book *The Skilled Helper* is now in its tenth edition (Egan, 2014) and Egan's ideas have gone through several revisions over the years. He underlines the importance of 'keeping the client in the driver's seat throughout the helping process', and makes the assumption that, with a little help to identify and talk through things that concern them, most people can reach their own satisfactory solutions. Egan stresses that helping should mainly be about life-enhancing outcomes for clients (as a counsellor and psychologist he uses the term 'client' rather than 'service user'). He presents a staged model of helping, with tasks to be undertaken at each stage:

1 **Exploration**: helping clients to tell their stories

Tasks:

1A Help clients tell their stories.
1B Help clients tell the real story.
1C Help clients tell the right story, working on issues that will add value to their lives.

2 Helping clients to **set problem-managing goals** and plans to accomplish these:

Tasks:

2A Help clients discover possibilities for a better future.
2B Goals, outcomes and impact: help clients move from possibilities to choices.
2C Help people commit themselves.

3 Planning the way forward:

Tasks:

3A Help clients develop strategies for accomplishing their goals.

3B Help clients choose best-fit strategies.

3C Help clients formulate viable plans.

These stages and their associated tasks are followed by **implementation**: making it all happen.

This process is illustrated below through an examination of the work with Aisha Bibi (see 'Case study: A tale of two families' in Chapter 7) at the Westgate Clinic, to which she was referred by her doctor for the first time after her husband died ten years ago and for the second time five years ago, a year after her son Nabeil died aged 21. Nabeil had a severe physical disability and lived in supported accommodation but was doing well at art school. The account below refers to Aisha's second referral.

Stage 1

At the Westgate Clinic Aisha was allocated a worker who used communication skills (Rogers' empathy, congruence and unconditional positive regard) to enable Aisha to explore her situation and to look at what was going on in her life. The worker listened to what Aisha said and helped her to understand that she was still grieving for her son and that this was a completely 'normal' process; Aisha also realised that losing her son had brought back to her how much she missed her husband and that she was unsure about how to face the future. The worker didn't offer any advice to Aisha but just asked open questions, such as 'Tell me about how you have been feeling this week', 'Tell me what life is like for you at the moment', 'What do you think may be making you feel like this?' and 'What would you like life to be like?' In this way Aisha was helped to tell the story of her current life, to explore all of the factors that could have a bearing on her current feelings and to begin to look at what life could be like.

Stage 2

During the second stage Aisha was helped to look at her situation in different ways so that she could work towards some decisions about her future. It was at this stage that the worker suggested that it was going to be very difficult for Aisha to make much progress because she still needed to mourn the loss of her son. Aisha joined a bereavement group at the clinic for six weeks and this helped her to meet other people who were experiencing loss. She talked a lot about her son and her husband and began to feel that she could now tackle discussions about her future. The group also helped her to see that the independence of her remaining son, Tanveer, was something she would need to build into her new way of life and that this presented opportunities for her as well as losses. She returned to her discussions with the worker with some new perspectives about her situation and having dealt with a lot of her feelings of loss. When Aisha stated that she thought she would like to set herself some goals and make some choices about her future, the worker rephrased this for her and helped her towards stating what her life might look like. Aisha was able to make the suggestion that she would like to go back to work after taking the past year off, and perhaps eventually gain further qualifications, as well as to support her son Tanveer with whatever decisions and choices he made. The worker encouraged her to make a commitment to taking at least one step towards her return to work.

Stage 3

At this stage Aisha was helped to make a plan of actions to work towards and the ways in which she would achieve the outcomes in the plan. The worker subsequently supported Aisha on a monthly basis as she took steps to return to work at Barnardo's, her previous place of employment, in a phased way until she was ready to return on a full-time basis. She offered encouragement to Aisha in her long-term plan to gain further qualifications but left this action for Aisha to complete after her **counselling** had finished. She left Aisha the option of returning for further sessions if she felt she needed help again at a later stage. Before she completed the counselling sessions Aisha also tackled areas of her personal life, re-joining a social group for outings and conversation that she had stopped attending when Nabeil died. She had dreaded her return to the group but found that everyone was very welcoming. She was soon enjoying some of the activities, especially the weekend walks. At all times it was Aisha who 'was in the driving seat', who made the decisions, and the worker who offered support.

Activity *Communication skills*

Imagine that you are a worker in one of the following units, described in Chapter 7:

- the McTavish Unit
- Queen's View
- the Five Trees Nursery
- 6 and 8 Newton Road

Discuss in small groups or write down:

- the interpersonal skills that a care worker needs to develop in this setting
- the barriers that there may be to communication with this group of service users
- ways of overcoming at least two barriers.

SUMMARY

This chapter has introduced you to the value base for care upon which practice is based. It has explored the principles of the National Care Standards, introduced you to the Code of Practice for Social Service Workers, and established the foundation for a consideration of discrimination and anti-discriminatory practice. Essential components of interpersonal skills associated with communication, including relationship skills, 'oomph', listening skills and non-verbal communication, have been explored. Barriers to effective communication have been examined. You have been introduced to Gerard Egan's model of helping, which rests on effective communication and relationships.

Suggested reading

Books

Egan, G. (2014) *The Skilled Helper*, **10th edition. Pacific Grove, California: Brooks Cole.**
This book provides an opportunity to look at Egan's theory in more detail. Includes lots of examples.

Rogers, J. (1990) *Caring for People: Help at the frontline*. **Milton Keynes: Open University Press.**
A warmly written, practical and relatively short introduction to care practice. Unfortunately there aren't any later editions, but there's some clear guidance for practice in this book.

Thompson, N. (2009) *People Skills*, **3rd edition. London: Palgrave Macmillan.**
A clear and useful text to enhance your communication and interpersonal skills. Deals with self-awareness, time, stress, information management and being creative, among many other topics.

Thompson, N. (2012) *Anti-discriminatory Practice*, **5th edition. Basingstoke: Palgrave Macmillan.**
A really interesting and thorough discussion of the historical background and theoretical bases of anti-discriminatory practice. A variety of areas of discrimination are discussed, with chapters specifically on gender and **sexism**, ethnicity and racism, ageism and alienation, disability and social handicap, sexuality and heterosexism, and faith and religious discrimination.

Websites and media

Avenue Media Solutions www.avenuemediasolutions.com – has a range of DVD resources in which Neil Thompson has participated, including: *Equality and Diversity*; *Language and Discrimination*; *The Equality Act 2010*.

Helen Sanderson Associates www.helensandersonassociates.co.uk – a helpful website that encourages person-centred thinking. There is useful information, examples, videos, etc.

National Care Standards www.nationalcarestandards.org/322.html – resources to support the NCS including a video of a play, *Carry on Caring*.

SCIE (Social Care Institute for Excellence) www.scie.org.uk/publications/elearning/index.asp – a range of resources that relate to the topics in this chapter, e.g. the resource 'Getting to know you', which outlines creating a one-page profile.

SSKS (Social Services Knowledge Scotland) www.ssks.org.uk – useful resources including a very good paper on using talking mats as an aid to communicating with people with dementia.

SSSC (Scottish Social Services Council) www.sssc.uk.com – useful resources in relation to the Codes of Practice for Social Service Workers and Employers, RPL (Recognising Prior Learning) support materials, and the Workforce Solutions portal to assist learning and development.

YouTube www.youtube.com – provides some interesting and enlightening clips about care work. For example, an extract from the Amanda Waring film based on the poem 'What do you see, nurses, what do you see?'.

CHAPTER 3

An introduction to human development and behaviour

Life is a bunch of straws. You pull some long ones. You pull some short ones. Maybe you got born into a family with money. Maybe you got born into a family on the brink of existence with barely enough to eat. You don't get the choice. Maybe you got good health, a fully working body, or maybe at the roulette of your creation you picked up a genetic condition like me ...

(Rebecca Atkinson, The Limping Chicken website, 29 September 2014)

Introduction

In this chapter you will look at human development and behaviour, and the interconnected strands that make up these processes. These are considered under the headings social, physical, emotional, cognitive, cultural, and spiritual (SPECCS). To set the scene there is reference to the **nature/nurture debate**, and to the importance of the underpinning concepts of attachment and separation, transition and loss, **resilience**, and socialisation. Human development is examined in terms of the stages and **transitions** of a lifespan approach, from birth through to older adulthood and the end of life.

This chapter covers material for the Higher and National 4 and 5 units Care: Human Development and Behaviour. It provides the foundation for the application of psychological and sociological perspectives and theories outlined in Chapters 4 and 5. It also provides important underpinning knowledge and understanding for Scottish Vocational Qualifications SVQ2 and SVQ3 in Social Services (Children and Young People) and Social Services and Healthcare, and for HNC Social Care and HNC Health Care.

By the end of this chapter you should be able to:

- ★ define human development
- ★ define human behaviour
- ★ understand the nature/nurture debate
- ★ understand and explain some basic developmental concepts that underpin and influence development and behaviour: attachment and separation; resilience; transition and loss; socialisation

- ★ understand and explain the strands of human development: social, physical, emotional, cognitive, cultural and spiritual (SPECCS)
- ★ understand and apply a lifespan perspective in relation to different life stages
- ★ begin to consider why the knowledge and understanding gained is important to care practice.

This chapter is about all of us: you, me and everyone else. One major source of information is you yourself and those with whom you live and work. These are not the only sources of information, however. In a multicultural and varied world your analysis needs to be wide-ranging in order that you can take account of the influence of cultural, socioeconomic and other factors. You provide a good starting point, but remember that your development will be taking place in the context of a unique set of **genetic**/biological influences and a particular combination of personal, social, economic and cultural circumstances, which will all exert an enormous influence on your development. Most of the generalisations made in this chapter refer to human development in Western Europe in the twenty-first century. Anthropologists, sociologists, psychologists and, more recently, neuroscientists have shown, however, that this is only one view of human development. Some of the examples in this chapter are drawn from other cultures to illustrate that we cannot make global assumptions about the nature of human development.

Development can be seen as a gradual unfolding, as an increase in complexity involving change and movement. Where there is change there is also transition, passing from one stage or situation to another. There is also loss and gain connected with change, and transitions are associated with both of these in varying proportions. Development involving increasing complexity (e.g. speech going from babbling to talking clearly in whole sentences) can be distinguished from growth, which is an increase in size that can be measured (e.g. height, weight).

Behaviour refers to how people conduct themselves, in both the way they do things themselves and in their relationships with others. Development and behaviour are very much interconnected and, though they are not the same thing, they exert influences upon one another. Some behaviour patterns are typical of certain stages in development, while other behaviours reflect personal traits that, although they may alter in many ways during the life cycle, are characteristic of a particular individual and are woven into the way that a person does things throughout life.

Activity *Your development and behaviour*

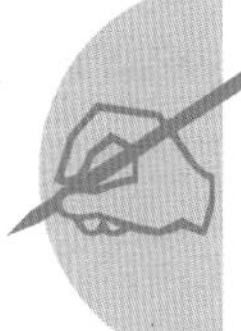

To make a start in the study of human development and behaviour, examine how you have developed since you were born. List the high and the low points, the times of change and the times of stability. Think about what the influences were on your development and behaviour. Your list may mention such things as:

- I was premature.
- I was born with a congenital heart condition.
- I started school.
- I won the swimming championship.

- I broke my arm.
- I began my Higher Care course.
- My granny died.
- I spent three weeks in hospital for heart surgery.
- My brother left home.
- I got a holiday job.

You may come back to your list as you read the chapter and add a few things. You may consider how some of the things you have listed are things you have chosen to do, how some of them were out of your control, how some of them were expected and some unexpected. You may also consider how you coped with or reacted to the things you have listed. This will begin to show you how complex human development and behaviour are and how they are determined partly by nature (your biological inheritance) and partly by nurture (the environment in which you grow up), how sometimes the individual has to adjust to growth, transitions, illnesses, and that this is all part of development.

The nature/nurture debate

Nature or nurture, is that the question? This long-standing debate about whether and by how much your development and behaviour are determined by nature or nurture is not really a question of either/or, but of both acting together in varying degrees. There are some things that you are born with: aspects of personality, appearance, sometimes a genetically inherited illness such as cystic fibrosis, or an impairment such as deafness. Parents will often tell you that there are elements of an individual child's personality that are there at birth, are observable in the first weeks of life and continue to manifest themselves as the child develops. They attribute these to **nature**, to biological inheritance. And then there is the influence of environment on development (**nurture**).

Studies of twins provide some evidence of the extent to which nature and nurture play a part in elements of development. The on-going Twins Early Development Study (TEDS), based at King's College London, is trying to disentangle the complexities of nature and nurture with the help of over 10,000 families (see **www.teds.ac.uk**). The data indicate that both genetic and environmental factors are important in nearly all areas of behavioural development. In an examination of the effects of genes on cognitive abilities it was found that genetic influence increased throughout childhood, with genes responsible for fundamental ability but environment being responsible for performance in relation to that ability. New developments in neuroscience indicate that aspects of the environment in which a child develops, including their emotional environment, for example in terms of attachment and resilience, can have an impact on the brain. This in turn can have an impact on other areas of development. All of this has huge implications for families, care and education in terms of providing the optimum environment for people to develop and change.

Activity *Nature or nurture*

Imagine three babies are born today in a large city hospital in Scotland:

- Amber is born to Mandy, a 19-year-old single mother with an almost non-existent support system. Mandy has a privately rented tenement flat near the city centre. She had to give up her job during pregnancy since she couldn't keep up with the long hours and physical demands of being a sales assistant. Amber is her first child.
- Hugo is born to June, who is married to Fred. Fred is a supportive husband. They have a house in a reasonably affluent suburb of the city. June hopes to go back to work as a teacher after her maternity leave. Hugo is her second son.
- Gloria is born to Catherine, who is a lesbian in a stable relationship with her partner, Liz. They both work as administrators for the local authority. They plan to continue working and to raise Gloria together in their small rented flat on the outskirts of the city.

Discuss and/or write about the extent to which you think nature and nurture will influence the development and behaviour of Amber, Hugo and Gloria.

As you read Chapters 4 and 5 you will have further opportunity to consider both genetic and environmental influences on behaviour. Chapter 4 provides an opportunity to look at influences on behaviour from a psychological perspective and Chapter 5 enables you to look at some social influences using a range of sociological perspectives and theories.

Developmental concepts

Later in this chapter we will consider the strands of development (page 122). Before doing this it is useful to consider some concepts that underpin any discussion of human development and behaviour. These are the concepts of:

- attachment and separation
- resilience
- transition and loss
- socialisation.

These concepts are relevant to a consideration of all stages of development, from birth to old age. From a care practice point of view, they also have implications for 'positive care practice' (discussed in Chapter 6).

Attachment and separation

Attachment

> *Attachment refers to an emotional link between two or more people. It begins in infancy but is repeated throughout the lifespan in various ways … Attachment … is a basic condition for life.*
>
> (Nicolson, 2014)

Attachment is vital to get you off to a good start in life. An understanding of it is essential for good, competent care work. While attachments can occur at any time in a person's life, the first attachments have been shown to be of particular relevance to human development and behaviour. Ideas about attachment were first made popular by John Bowlby in his work *Child Care and the Growth of Love* (Bowlby, 1953).

Bowlby was asked by the World Health Organization to investigate the effects on children's development of being brought up in orphanages. Having seen the negative impact of emotional deprivation he initially placed emphasis on the importance of the attachment of a baby to his/her mother in healthy development. In later work (Bowlby, 1988), however, he emphasised that this attachment relationship was transferable to other relationships, for example with the child's **siblings**, father, other relatives and friends. He built on the work of Mary Salter Ainsworth (1978), who developed thinking in relation to secure and insecure attachments and distinguished three different styles of attachment with differing consequences for the development and behaviour of the individual. Ainsworth's attachment styles are:

- **secure attachment**, when an individual feels safe and secure with whoever is/are the main providers of care. This provides a sound basis for becoming a secure, happy and independent person
- **anxious, resistant attachment**, which is less straightforward since it involves anxiety when the caregiver is absent but little reassurance when the caregiver returns. The attachment is uncertain and may give rise to excessively clingy and cautious behaviour, with anxiety about relationships
- **anxious–avoidant attachment**, which occurs when the individual avoids the caregiver because he or she expects to be rejected. This can result in suspicion of others and sometimes the betrayal of trust because that is what the individual expects will happen to them.

Activity *Attachment*

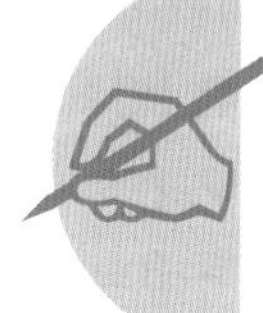

Try to find opportunities to observe children with their main caregivers, either in family or care situations. Make a record of your observations in terms of factors that you see as contributing to and illustrative of secure and/or anxious attachments.

In situations where there appears to be secure attachment you may have observed caregivers:

- showing warmth and affection
- listening to children and answering questions
- playing with children and doing things together
- using reason, love and a calm, confident approach to discipline.

Separation

Separation is the other side of attachment. In Ainsworth's research in the 1970s she conducted an experiment known as the **'strange situation'** to examine how children dealt with separation. In this experiment children between 18 months and two years were initially in a room with their mother. The mother would then leave the room and a stranger enter the room. Later the mother returned in a stage called 'reunion', which was essential in the development of Ainsworth's thinking. There were variations on the experiment that included the mother being in the room when the stranger entered or returning while the stranger was still there. All observations were recorded and this led to a theory relating attachment and separation. Insecurely attached children experienced a disorganised attachment style with a disorganised, disoriented and frightened response to separation; children with a secure attachment style were able to cope with separation with little or no distress. They were secure in their relationship and secure in the knowledge that their mother would return as a safe and secure source of support. As stated above, we now know from later research by Bowlby and others that the attachment figure does not need to be the child's mother. We also now know that if attachment hasn't taken place in early childhood it is sometimes possible, with enough understanding and commitment, to compensate through the provision of opportunities for attachment later on.

One of the initial criticisms of Bowlby's work was his focus on the mother as the main attachment figure, though he remedied this in his later work. Research by Rutter (1979) and others emphasised the additional importance of 'resilience', considered below, and also that responses to neglect were the main source of difficulty for many people. 'Neglect', however, usually goes hand in hand with emotional deprivation and poor attachment so its effects are difficult to determine.

Activity *Attachment and separation*

Think about and discuss how you think ideas about attachment and separation are useful to care workers.

You may have thought of some of the following points:

- They provide insight into the stress and anxiety experienced by some service users when they encounter new or unfamiliar situations.
- They emphasise the need to provide a safe, secure and consistent environment in which service users can develop their potential.
- They provide a different way to look at and react to what may be regarded as difficult, defiant behaviour, and to see that this may be a reaction to anxious attachment.
- They enable you see the potential of the care relationship in helping to compensate for at least some of the gaps in attachment. You can use some of the positive features found in secure attachment situations: demonstrating warmth, using play and/or shared activities, listening and giving attention, and developing a consistent and agreed strategy for dealing with negative behaviours.

Judy Furnivall (2011) talks about 'attachment-informed practice' and says the following in relation to residential childcare:

> *Some residential settings have begun to reframe their interventions using a specific focus on attachment and recovery from trauma. Cameron and Maginn (2008) have developed the concept of the pillars of parenting, which emphasises the importance of authentic warmth between adults and children in residential child care. They describe seven essential dimensions of parenting, which include secure attachment, emotional competence and self-management. This model emphasises the crucial role of direct carers in healing severely hurt children through attuning to their needs, despite being exposed to extremely challenging behaviour. Edinburgh City Council has adopted an explicitly attachment-promoting model of residential child care …*

Resilience

The development of ideas about resilience provides useful insights into how some people, both children and adults, cope better than others in adverse circumstances. Sometimes a set of circumstances would lead you to expect adverse consequences, and indeed for many people this is the result. Yet some people seem to cope against the odds. This is largely due to their resilience. Resilience has many definitions; these include:

- favourable development in unfavourable circumstances (Gilligan, 2008, p.37)
- successful adaptation in spite of experiencing a high-risk trauma (Simpson, 2010, p.241)
- normal development under difficult conditions (Houston, 2010, p.357).

CASE STUDY

Quarriers homes

Tom Shaw was appointed by the Scottish Government to chair a pilot forum to listen and respond to former residents of Quarriers children's homes. Ninety-eight people took part, describing their childhood experiences of living at Quarriers residential homes from the 1930s to the 1980s. Participants who experienced abuse during their time in residential care reported a whole range of long-term effects. While some participants had difficulty coping with the after-effects of the abuse long into adulthood, it was also found that:

> *… many participants had managed to go on to lead very fruitful existences despite their very traumatic experiences in childhood.*
>
> (Scottish Government, 2011)

A possible explanation for this is resilience; a combination of personal, community and social elements that seems to contribute to an individual's ability to bounce back, even when the circumstances are very difficult or even traumatic.

Definitions of resilience describe positive personal responses in the face of adverse external events. Why are some individuals more resilient than others? Conway (Scottish Government, 2012) examined studies of resilience and summarised resilience factors. She indicates the following factors as important in resilience:

- Internal/personal factors:
  - **positive self-image**, with self-esteem and self-efficacy as personality traits
  - **control**, meaning the ability to act autonomously and make independent decisions. This includes self-determination and adaptability
  - **meaningfulness**, meaning being able to find positive meaning in life, for example valuing altruistic acts, or spirituality providing comfort and strength
  - **hope**, meaning being able to see a future that is achievable.
- External factors:
  - **relationships through the lifespan**, emphasising the importance of positive relationships throughout the lifespan
  - **early years relationships**, with the work of Bowlby and others on attachment seen as important. Brigid Daniel (2008), working with children who had experienced neglect, emphasised the value of building relationships as a way of building resilience
  - **structural factors**, such as the absence of poverty and discrimination. The effect of structural factors is affected by personal perception and the presence or absence of other internal and external factors. This dimension of resilience, however, draws attention to the possibility that structural change can have an impact on resilience.

Resilience factors can be summarised for the individual as:

- I have (e.g. … people I trust and love)
- I am (e.g. … a lovable person)
- I can (e.g. … find ways to solve problems).

Much of the work that care workers do can be seen as having the potential to promote resilience and to build on the resilience of the people with whom they are working. In Chapter 2 we examined the importance of the value base, communication and relationships, and in Chapter 6 we will look at many ways of helping individuals through the assessment, care planning and implementation process. All of this can be seen to play a part in building resilience.

Activity *Attachment and resilience*

Read the short account that follows and discuss or write about how you think ideas about attachment and resilience could help your understanding of the situation. You should also use the case study to think about links between attachment and resilience.

Refugee camp

A group of children have been separated from their parents in a war zone and are now in a refugee camp. Some of the children are very young, as young as three, and some are as old as 12. They have very little adult support but they come from the same village and know one another from nursery, school and from playing together. Most of the children cope remarkably well with the situation, demonstrating mutual support, and with older members of the group supporting younger members. A few children cope less well regardless of age, clinging to other members of the group and experiencing extreme distress, anger and frustration.

Transition and loss

Transitions

As individuals go through life they experience many changes. These changes affect an individual's development and behaviour and are known as transitions. Adams *et al.* (1977) described a transition as 'a discontinuity in a person's life space'. Some transitions are expected (we will all go through puberty; we will all age, if we live long enough), others are routine (starting school, starting a job, getting married) and others are non-routine (serious accident, redundancy). In this chapter, we consider some of the responses that people have to these events.

Adams *et al.* (1977) created a general model that attempts to explain the impact of transitions (see Figure 3.1). The seven-stage model shows how the experience of transition may affect an individual's self-esteem. An understanding of the model can help you to understand that people experience a range of feelings as they go through a transitional experience. The feelings are 'normal' and in time they will pass. There is also the idea that the person can have some control over what happens to them.

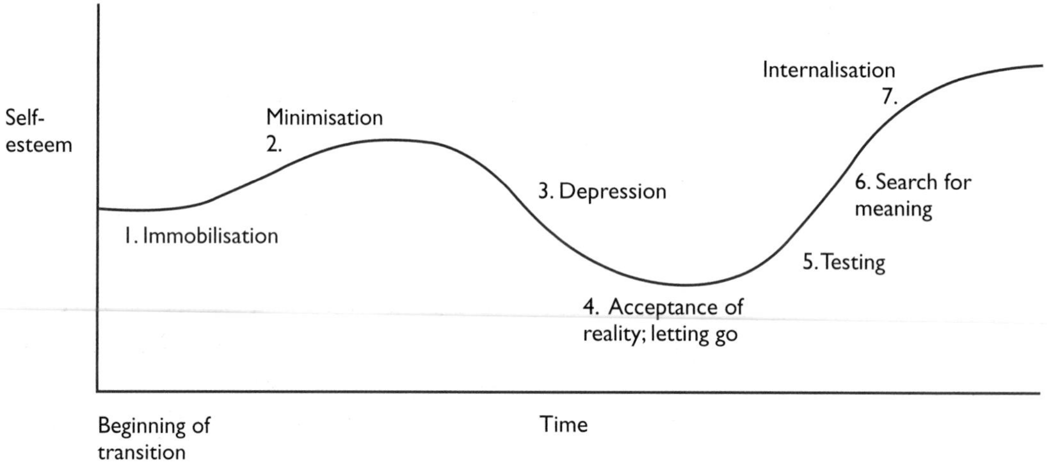

Figure 3.1 Self-esteem changes during transitions (Source: Adams *et al.*, 1977)

The stages of the model represent the cycle of experiencing a change. At first the individual may feel in a state of shock, or they may 'play down' what has happened, or they may feel depressed. As they move through the transition, they may begin to acknowledge the reality of the change, test out new ideas or behaviours, understand themselves and use the experience of the change to modify their behaviour. The level of the person's self-esteem varies across the stages and follows a predictable path. For a transition to be effectively managed, all seven stages have to be worked through. Individuals seldom move smoothly through all seven stages. Some may never move beyond the earlier stages, others may become 'stuck' in a state of depression. As life unfolds, an individual who has successfully reached the end of the stages after one transition may experience another major problem. Although he may be catapulted back to the beginning of the cycle, he is more likely to have laid the foundations for successful resolution.

Activity *Self-esteem changes*

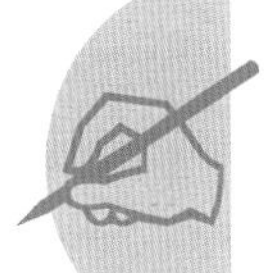

Read the story of Ken, who was diagnosed with Alzheimer's disease, a form of dementia. Ken gave permission for his story to be used. Look at how you can apply Adams *et al.*'s model of self-esteem changes. You may also come back and look at his story in terms of loss when you have read the next section.

Ken's story of transition and loss and gain

'I was diagnosed with Alzheimer's disease in my mid-fifties. Being diagnosed with dementia is brutal. It is horrendous. Only someone who has been through it can understand. You are given a mental death sentence. I felt the doctor left me in that frame of mind and left me to pick up the pieces of my life. Someone needs to give you hope, and tell you that you won't be a burden. You have to realise that this is not the end. You walk away from the diagnosis and nothing's changed but everything is different.

'Decay sets in at the moment of diagnosis. Medically nothing can be done. My wife is technically my carer but you need to continue to do things for yourself. There is a fine line between doing too much for someone and giving them the help they need.

'It is easy to look for reasons to not do things like going to the shops, and people offer to go so you don't have to, but I now make a point of doing everything. I like to push things, do things that are scary – it makes me feel how alive I am. I make sure I have a project ongoing at all times. I rebuilt a Harley Davison. My friends would come round and check that I had put the wheel nuts, etc., on.

'I used to earn a lot of money and I find it very frustrating not being able to work but I take great pleasure now in simple things like walking our dog in the woods and I do all the cooking and cleaning. We eat fresh vegetables and home-cooked food. I try to have a healthy lifestyle now. My life is pretty normal apart from the fact that I can't work.'

Loss

> *The mourner is in fact ill, but because this state of mind is common and seems so natural to us, we do not call mourning an illness.*
>
> (Melanie Klein, 1940)

One of the changes that happens in life is the experience of loss. It is part of everyone's life. Some losses may seem trifling, such as the loss of a book on the bus, but even this could have an effect on a person if the book was a gift from a loved one, or held some other special value for the person. Other losses can have a significant and long-term impact. For example, if your house is burgled and you lose a ring that your mother gave to you, or you lose all your family photographs in a house fire or flood. Loss can have a devastating effect on those who directly experience the loss and it may also have a powerful effect on friends, family and carers.

Activity *Types of loss*

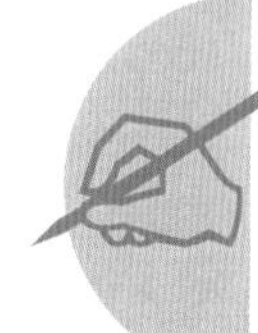

Can you think of other types of loss that may occur in people's lives and that may have a significant effect on them?

Some that might be on your list are:

- loss of a job – redundancy or dismissal
- loss of freedom – imprisonment
- loss of a pet
- loss of a limb – accident or illness
- loss of hearing/sight – accident or illness
- loss of a partner through divorce or death.

Death is the ultimate loss, and some would argue that in Britain the process of dying is being removed from everyday experience. Katz and Siddell (1994) describe this process as the 'unfamiliarity of death' and go on to say that Britain is a 'death-denying society'. Donnelly (2008) refers to a cultural resistance in Scotland to acknowledging the reality of death and dying as inevitable parts of life. In many cases, the whole process of death and dying has been removed from the family into the hands of the medical profession. The ever-increasing progress of public health and medical science has meant that people now live longer than they ever did in the past. In Scotland epidemics no longer kill thousands of people, children do not often die of childhood diseases such as diphtheria and smallpox, and mothers and babies rarely die in the process of birth. While this progress has no doubt had a positive effect on the health and welfare of the population, it has had a profound effect on how death is viewed. Nowadays death is often seen as a failure of the medical profession to keep someone alive. It is not seen as an integral part of everyday life. Even the language that is used offers some insight into how death is viewed.

Activity Phrases used to describe death

Make a list of some of the phrases you have heard that either try to be humorous about death, or that use a euphemism to try to 'soften' the idea of death.

Some you might have heard are:

- She's passed away.
- He's pushing up the daisies.
- He's kicked the bucket.
- She's fallen asleep.
- He's popped his clogs.
- She's gone to her last resting place.

Why do people need to talk about death in this way? Do you think this is healthy or unhealthy?

The death of a loved one represents a profound change in people's lives. If there is some agreement that society today has more and more come to ignore the reality and inevitability of death and to a large extent sanitises the whole subject, what implications does this have for individuals who are facing their own death or who experience the death of others? Much work has been carried out into the process of death and dying, and it is widely acknowledged that grieving or mourning is an essential part of coming to terms with the associated loss. Grief involves emotional feelings (of sadness, anger, perhaps guilt) but also includes physical aspects (e.g. upset stomach, difficulty breathing), cognitive elements (e.g. lack of concentration, forgetfulness) and behaviours (e.g. poor sleep patterns). It is not a kind of mental illness, but sometimes people feel they are 'ill' because it has disrupted their normal functioning in a number of ways. Grieving is an essential adaptive process, involving experiencing a number of phases after a loss.

Mourning is another word for how people express their grief. In all cultures mourning has two main parts:

- **how people show the feelings associated with grief**
- **the behaviour that is expected or accepted within a particular culture or society, such as wearing black or reciting prayers.**

Different religions and cultures have their own rituals. Hindus have a period of 13 days of mourning, when friends will visit and offer condolence. Muslims have an official mourning period of three days (longer for a remaining spouse), and this may include a special meal to remember the deceased. In the Jewish religion, the close family remains at home for a week and prays three times a day. Mourning ends after 30 days, except for the children of the deceased who mourn for a year.

When a loss occurs it is inevitable that transitions or changes will occur in a person's life. Transition can be very challenging because people gain a feeling of security from the present pattern of their life. Murray Parkes (2010) describes this as a person's 'assumptive world', the ideas about their world based on how it has always been. It is assumed that this is how it will always be; to think otherwise would cause feelings of insecurity. When loss happens, ideas have to be changed about what is normally taken for granted in order to cope with a world that has changed. The individual has to understand the feelings they are experiencing and face the practical aspects of life after loss. Murray Parkes uses the language of attachment theory, and indeed he worked alongside Bowlby at one time.

Colin Murray Parkes and Holly Prigerson

Murray Parkes and Prigerson (2010) propose a model of the process of grieving. Some models of loss are sequential, which means that it is expected that a person is likely to go through them in a certain order. Human experience is generally more complex than this, however, and Murray Parkes and Prigerson believe instead that people go through a process of grieving in order to resolve their grief. This process used to be referred to by Murray Parkes (1996) as 'the phases of grief'. In his work with Holly Prigerson, however, they refer instead to 'states of grief', seeing phases as presenting too rigid a framework. The states of grief that they identify are:

1. **Numbness:**
   - feelings of detachment and numbness
   - these feelings form a psychological barrier to block the pain of loss
   - this allows a person to apparently carry on with normal living
   - it is a way of staying temporarily 'beyond' the pain of grief.
2. **Pining:**
   - concentration levels fall
   - the individual adopts searching behaviours to try to locate that which has been lost
   - the individual pines for the lost person and develops 'pangs of grief'.
3. **Disorganisation and despair:**
   - realisation that the lost person/object will not return
   - searching becomes pointless
   - anger abates to be replaced by feelings of apathy and despair.
4. **Acceptance and recovery:**
   - former attachments are put behind the individual
   - the individual releases themselves from the lost attachment
   - the person can now adopt new thinking, relationships and attachments, and normal living.

Murray Parkes and Prigerson suggest there are a number of factors, **determinants of grief**, that affect the extent and depth to which an individual may experience the grieving process.

> *Those who are concerned with the effects of bereavement have to take into consideration many possible factors when trying to explain the differences between individuals in their response to this event. It is not enough to say that the loss of a love object causes grief, and leave it at that. Grief may be strong or weak, brief or prolonged, immediate or delayed; particular aspects of it may be distorted and symptoms that usually cause little trouble may become major sources of distress.*

(Murray Parkes and Prigerson, 2010, p.137)

Some of the factors that Murray Parkes and Prigerson suggest may affect a person's grief response include:

- **Attachment**: the intensity of the grief is affected by the intensity of love and attachment.
- **Gender**: it is very difficult to make generalisations based on gender, but studies reported in Murray Parkes and Prigerson (2010, pp.146–47), indicate that in general women show more immediate distress and symptoms than men, whereas in men the level of distress, while not demonstrably as intense initially, is slower to decline.
- **Age**: 'there is a great difference between the quiet slipping away of an old person and the tragic cutting off of a young one in his or her prime' (Murray Parkes and Prigerson, 2010, p.148).
- **Mode of death**: was it unexpected, violent, a suicide, an accident, part of a public incident such as a train or air crash?
- **Multiple losses**: multiple losses have a greater impact than a single loss and are especially prevalent in disaster areas.
- **Other stressful events**: other stressful events preceding a loss can affect the response to the loss.
- **Personal vulnerability**: you may associate this with attachment and resilience, which you read about earlier in the chapter. Personal vulnerability is also affected by cognitive ability.
- **Social and cultural influences**: these include the way society in general deals with death, family influences, social networks and the influence of poverty and deprivation. For example, does a family give space for individual expressions of grief or does it insist that everyone keep a stiff upper lip?

Activity *Applying Murray Parkes and Prigerson's model*

What particular aspects of the situation in the following case study might make it more difficult for Tony to recover from his grief, according to Murray Parkes and Prigerson?

Tony

Tony is 35 years old with a successful career in the computer industry near Edinburgh. Two years ago his wife, Angela, died of breast cancer. Tony was devastated by his wife's death. Everyone was very supportive of Tony and offered both emotional and practical help for quite a long time after Angela's death.

After two years this support began to scale down as both friends and family felt his period of mourning had 'elapsed' and he should now 'get on with his life'. His married friends began to invite him to parties and barbecues. Tony was initially quite happy to go as it got him out of the house, but he soon realised that there always seemed to be 'an available woman' at these events and it was expected that they would get together. Similarly, his male friends wanted him to 'get back on the scene' again and come out to pubs and clubs. When Tony refused, his friends accused him (behind his back) of wallowing in his grief. Their attitude was that he had no children to look after, he was still young and had enough money to enjoy himself. So he should put Angela's death behind him and start to enjoy life again.

But grief and mourning do not adhere to rigid timescales and Tony was not yet ready to adjust to life without his wife. It may be that Tony needs some help to come to terms with his wife's death in order that he can come through the grieving process.

As you read the following account of Worden's tasks of the grieving process, keep Tony in mind and think about what may be helpful to him.

William Worden

Worden (2010) looks at the process of grieving with a focus on what a person *has to do* in order to cope with the loss. Murray Parkes and Prigerson also examine 'helping the bereaved' but their strength lies in analysing grief, whereas Worden's lies in his slightly more active model of loss. This is useful in care work as it suggests things the person, or those around them, might be involved in doing to enable them to work through their process of grief. People use the mourning process to say 'goodbye' to their loved one, and everyone does this in a different way. People develop different thoughts and behaviours and then perhaps these need to change again if they are to move on. Worden talks about 'tasks' that a person needs to complete before they are likely to move on, rather than states of grief. This implies a more active engagement with the grieving process.

Before looking at Worden's model in more detail, he raises a point that relates to the question 'are psychological processes universal?' He states:

> *There is evidence that all humans grieve a loss to one degree or other. Anthropologists who have studied other societies, their cultures and their reactions to the loss of loved ones report that whatever the society studied, in whatever part of the world, there is an almost universal attempt to regain the lost loved object, and/or there is the belief in an afterlife where one can rejoin the loved one. In preliterate societies, however, bereavement pathology seems to be less common.*
>
> (Worden, 2010, p.16)

Worden identifies four 'tasks of mourning'. He was keen to point out that, although there is some ordering suggested in his definitions, these are not 'stages' that a person *has* to follow in a particular order. It is possible for someone to accomplish some of the tasks and not others. This would mean they would have an incomplete adaptation to the loss, which is similar to having incomplete healing from a physical injury.

Task 1: To accept the reality of the loss

The first task of grieving is to come to terms with the reality that the person is dead, that they are gone and that they are not going to return. Even if the person had been very ill for some time and the family knew that they were dying, it may still be difficult to accept that the loved one is actually dead.

Some people refuse to believe that the loss is real and therefore get stuck in their grieving at this first task. It is very normal after a death to hope for a reunion or to assume that the deceased is not gone. For most people, however, this illusion is short-lived and this acceptance allows them to move on to Task 2. Sometimes they will engage in 'mummification', where they retain the possessions of the deceased person, or keep their bedroom exactly as it was when they died. This is not unusual in the short term but becomes denial if it goes on for a longer time.

Activity *Task 1*

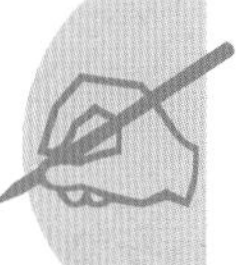

Read the case study below and discuss how this illustrates Task 1 in Worden's model. You may also look at it in terms of Murray Parkes and Prigerson's factors that affect grief.

Queen Victoria

When Queen Victoria's husband, Prince Albert, died within a short time of contracting typhoid fever in 1861 he was only 42 years old. The Queen mourned his death intensely, but this mourning was stuck for a very long time at the first task of grief, to the extent that she was unable to fulfil her role as Queen. This was understandable in the short term but her inability to accept that he had died meant that she was unable to move on from the first task in the grieving process. She had his shaving gear laid out every day for him and often went around speaking to him. His room was left as it had been when he died. She wore black for the remaining 40 years of her life. In a letter to her daughter Victoria, she wrote:

> *How am I, who leant on him for all and everything, without whom I did nothing, moved not a finger, arranged not a print or a photograph, didn't put on a gown or a bonnet if he didn't approve it shall go on, to live, to move, to help myself in difficult moments?*

It wasn't until 1866 that her mourning began to show signs of diminishing, five years after his death. You can see some of this in fictionalised form in the film *Mrs Brown*, which relates the story of Queen Victoria's friendship with John Brown, a servant in her household.

Task 2: To experience the pain of grief

It is necessary to acknowledge and work through this pain or it will manifest itself through some symptom or other form of unusual behaviour. Suppressing pain may prolong the process of grieving. Not everyone experiences the same intensity of pain or feels it in the same way, but it is impossible to lose someone you have been deeply attached to without experiencing some level of pain. Society may be uncomfortable with the mourner's feelings and this might make it difficult to express them honestly. People can deny that they feel pain by having 'thought-stopping' procedures or keeping very busy so there is no time to think.

CASE STUDY

George

When George's mother died he was able to accept that she had died but felt that it was unmanly to show his grief. He had been very close to his mother and held her in very high regard, seeing her on an almost daily basis. But when she died he went straight back to work and wouldn't express his grief, even to himself. Later in the year a distant relative died and George experienced unaccountable grief after the funeral. All of his suppressed emotions over the loss of his mother came to the fore and he was unable to do anything much for three weeks. Fortunately his GP realised what was happening and gave him the permission and paperwork to take time off work to deal with the delayed pain of losing his mother.

Task 3: To adjust to a world without the deceased

Worden indicates that there are three areas of adjustment after a loss:

- external adjustments
- internal adjustments
- spiritual adjustments.

External adjustment

Adapting to the external environment is different for every individual and depends to a large extent on the nature of the relationship before bereavement and the roles played by the bereaved person. For example, in some partnerships roles have been very clearly delineated. This means that when one partner dies the other is left to undertake tasks that they have never taken on before. Adjusting to this has different consequences for different people. A partner who has never dealt with family finance may resent taking on this task and continue to be angry at being left with this role or, after a period of adjustment, he or she may find a sense of achievement and satisfaction in acquiring new skills.

Internal adjustment

It is possible to make external adjustments and appear to be coping well with loss, while internally the individual is still in emotional turmoil. The internal, emotional tasks of this stage mean finding an identity and self-esteem independent of the deceased person. Where a relationship has been very close and individuals have seen themselves as half of a whole, this task may prove especially difficult. For example, Jane would ask herself for a very long time after her partner Chris died, 'What would Chris have done in this situation?' Eventually she realised that she could make decisions for herself and create a new, independent identity. It didn't mean that she rejected what Chris had contributed to her life, but that she now had an identity independent of her and was able to optimise the opportunities in a life without her.

Spiritual adjustment

This adjustment is about very fundamental values and beliefs. A loss may or may not challenge an individual's philosophical and belief system.

Rose felt a spiritual sense of peace after the death of her 92-year-old father, who died peacefully in his sleep at home, where he wanted to be. They had enjoyed a wonderful relationship for all of Rose's 65 years. Her father had been supportive of her career choice to work as a florist when she could have gone to university, and of her decision not to marry a man who her father regarded as his friend but instead to marry someone else with whom he didn't get on quite so well. He had provided warmth and love and accepted her and her choices, and in turn she had great respect and love for him.

In contrast, Jim felt that all his beliefs and faith were severely tested when his 18-year-son was stabbed to death. He needed counselling support to come to terms with his death at a spiritual level.

Task 4: To find an enduring connection with the deceased in the midst of embarking on a new life

Worden changed his thinking about this task between the various editions of his book. In the third edition (2003) this task was 'to withdraw emotional energy and reinvest it in another relationship'. Worden realised, however, that individuals don't actually 'withdraw emotional energy', but in a healthy adjustment to loss they find ways to have an enduring connection with the lost person while also being able to embark on a new life. He gives the example of the Harvard Bereavement Study (Silverman, Nickman and Worden, 1992), where young people who had adjusted well to the loss of a parent continued to feel protected by their lost parent. He quotes Volkan (1985, p.326), who suggested:

> *A mourner never altogether forgets the dead person who was so highly valued in life and never totally withdraws his investment in his representation. We can never purge those who have been close to us from our own history except by psychic acts damaging to our own identity.*

Managing to achieve the four tasks, in Worden's view, ensures that the person will be able to grieve and mourn for the person they have lost in a way that allows them to move on from the pain of the loss towards a positive readjustment of their own lives. Worden's tasks do offer some help in understanding the grieving process, but care must be taken in applying this model to everyone. All experiences of death are individual and not everyone will 'achieve' Worden's four tasks. There is no time limit to mourning nor to the feelings of grief. Each person will determine this process for themselves. The model indicates *dimensions* or *aspects* of the grieving process, and this enables you to understand why the person might be experiencing a range of sometimes apparently contradictory feelings.

CASE STUDY

Jin-ming

Jin-ming is a 78-year-old woman who lives in Glasgow on her own in the house she has lived in for more than 50 years. Nine years ago when she was 69 her husband Han-chen died suddenly of a stroke. Jin-ming was completely broken-hearted. They had recently celebrated their golden wedding anniversary (50 years) and had a good and happy marriage.

As the breadwinner, Han-chen had always been the one to deal with the money matters in the home. He had paid the mortgage, council tax and household bills. He had dealt with all the details of his pension and insurance policies. Han-chen had also taken responsibility for all the DIY tasks in the home. Jin-ming, meanwhile, did all the cooking, cleaning and shopping. Theirs was a traditional type of relationship.

When Han-chen died, Jin-ming found she could not cope with either the emotional or the practical aspects of life without him. She stopped going to her church groups and instead never ventured out of the house. She became quite depressed, and her family became worried about her. At first, she refused to go and live with any of them and would not accept a place in supported accommodation in the street next to her eldest daughter. Her daughter realised that her mother might take a while to accept that change was needed, so she didn't insist. Every time her mother came for a visit, she would take her on a walk past the supported accommodation and admire the garden. One day they stopped and spoke to some people who were sitting outside and they were invited to stay for a cup of tea. Although Jin-ming never got over the death of her husband, and continued to think about him every day, she decided she wanted to live in the accommodation near her daughter. She was now able to enjoy the new direction her life was taking.

Socialisation

Socialisation is relevant to a discussion of development from both a psychological and a sociological perspective, from the viewpoint of both the individual's development in society and the influence of society on the individual. It has, therefore, a place both in this chapter and in Chapter 5. Rather than discuss it twice, the main examination takes place here, with further reference to it in Chapter 5 (see page 210). Socialisation, defined as the process or way in which people learn the culture of their society, begins at birth and continues throughout life. It can be seen as preparation for taking adult roles, for taking a responsible and acceptable role in society. Socialisation takes place at both a formal level (e.g. in school) and at an informal level (e.g. through play). What is learned through socialisation in early life is critical to what happens later on. For care workers, an understanding of socialisation is essential. John Bowlby (1953) argued that children deprived of emotional stability failed in all sorts of ways and were often unable to form lasting, meaningful relationships later in life. Although this failure was to a very great degree one of emotional deprivation leading to poor attachment, it was often compounded by a lack of positive socialisation. Socialisation is influenced by and influences the other topics discussed in this chapter, and is itself determined by what are known as the main **agents of socialisation**: family, education, work, religion and the mass media, each of which is examined in turn below.

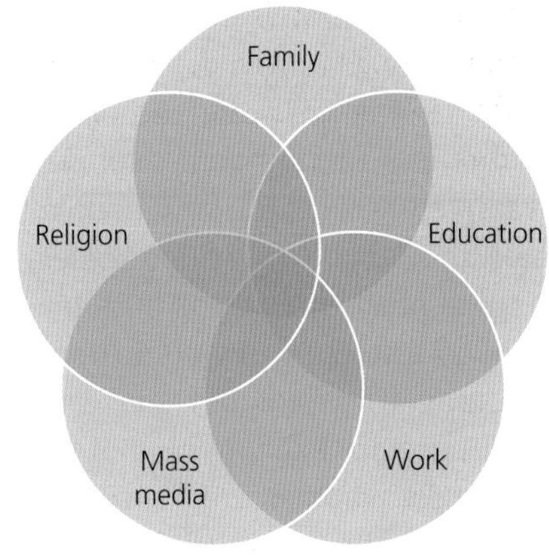

Figure 3.2 The main agents of socialisation

The family

The first agent of socialisation is the family and it is here that most, but not all, children learn how to behave appropriately, how to relate to other people, how to eat, drink and so on in ways that are socially and culturally acceptable. This initial socialisation is called **primary socialisation**. Its impact becomes evident through contrast with situations in which no primary socialisation has taken place. The following account demonstrates what is likely to occur in the absence of socialisation:

> *Police who entered a house in The Hague found a scrawny girl in the attic unable to walk or talk. She had not been let outside by her mother since her birth nearly four years ago. A police spokeswoman said the girl, who was surrounded by rubbish, flies and mosquitoes, was now being treated for malnutrition.*

(*Guardian*, 2 July 1998)

Activity *Socialisation at four years old*

When you have read the above account, write down what you would expect a four-year-old to have acquired through the socialisation process.

Not all children in the same culture gain the same things about that culture during primary socialisation. Rayner (1986) makes this point as follows:

> *Since each child is exposed to and has to adapt to a different environment from all other children, he must structure his mental life differently from the child next door or in the next continent. He is being socialised in ways particular to him.*

Thus socialisation is both a general cultural concept and a particular individual concept. Your family will provide you with some aspects of culture common to others of your culture but it will be served up in a particular way, with some things emphasised more than others, so that your experience of socialisation is different from everyone else's. An example of this is the way people are socialised within the family into the gender roles of male and female. In British society it is still common for some families to encourage girls to think of themselves as budding housewives and mothers. This kind of socialisation is called **anticipatory socialisation** because it anticipates adult roles. Other girls are encouraged to think of themselves as equal to boys in their career prospects, but even here there are likely to be cultural influences at work. Ann Oakley (1997), a feminist sociologist who has done research into the gender division of housework, says that even her father, the sociologist Richard Titmuss, relied on her mother to do most of the housework and childcare while he wrote his books. Although she was socialised to think of herself as equal to boys, her parents modelled very differentiated roles, with her father's career taking precedence over that of his wife. This relates to the discussion in Chapter 5 of a feminist perspective and also the examination in that chapter of inequality.

For some children it should be remembered that the role of the family is played in varying degrees by people other than their parents, including residential care workers and foster carers. Although in these circumstances the links with parents and other family members are maintained whenever this is possible and safe, the role of care workers in the socialisation process of these children should not be underestimated.

Education

As a child grows up he or she comes into contact with aspects of society outside the family, and these are responsible for **secondary socialisation**. Education provided through the school system is the second main socialising influence upon the developing child. Schools and other agents of secondary socialisation promote learning in relation to appropriate conduct in society and in behaviour towards people with different degrees of **status** and authority. The sociologist Emile Durkheim (1938) emphasised the importance of education in the development of the individual as a social being. The social being comprises the beliefs and behaviours that express a person's awareness of being a member of society. The culture transmitted by the education system has been the subject of much debate, some of which has resulted in the Curriculum for Excellence in Scotland. This curriculum aims to enable each child to be:

- a successful learner
- a confident individual
- a responsible citizen
- an effective contributor.

The notion of citizenship is emphasised and there is emphasis upon cultural awareness and a consideration of cultural diversity and tolerance. This indicates the potential of schools to change cultures and thinking through the secondary socialisation process.

Activity School

Think of your attendance at school. Suggest five attitudes or behaviours that your school promoted, and three ways in which you think that secondary socialisation in school took place.

Work

Work is also an agent of secondary socialisation. People do exercise some choice about the kind of work they do, but once they are in a work role they need to learn the appropriate behaviours and attitudes of this role. In this way they are socialised into the world of work. In order to maintain their place within it they must conform, at least to some extent, to the beliefs, aims and regulations of the workplace and its culture. Many sociologists argue that work is gendered, that 'society' has views about what is women's work and what is men's work. There is evidence to suggest that this continues to be the case. For example, more than 80 per cent of care workers are women. Even within the care sector, however, there are gender differences in the roles of care workers, with the numbers of men rising to 30 per cent in criminal justice and residential child care (SSSC, 2014b).

Activity Work

Consider three occupations that you think are usually regarded as 'men's work' and three regarded as 'women's work'. What part has socialisation played in this view?

Religion

Whatever your views about religion it has been a powerful source of socialisation throughout history. Even in a country like Scotland where a large percentage of the population does not participate in religious activity on a regular basis, religion still exerts a considerable influence, especially in terms of values and at critical points in life: birth, marriage, death. Different religions promote different values and cultures with regard to teachings about morality, the place of men and women in society, marriage and the family. Religion can be regarded as a belief in some form of supernatural power, and every known society has some form of religion. What religions can you identify in the area in which you live? You may have identified Protestants, Catholics, other Christian denominations, Jews, Hindus, Sikhs, Muslims and perhaps others. All of these include a set of beliefs and practices into which followers are socialised. For Christians the Ten Commandments set out principles that include instructions to believers to honour their parents, not to steal, not to kill, not to commit adultery. For Muslims the Qur'an sets out the rights and functions of men and women, expounding a philosophy of 'equal but different', with women playing a major role in family affairs and men in social affairs.

Activity *Religion*

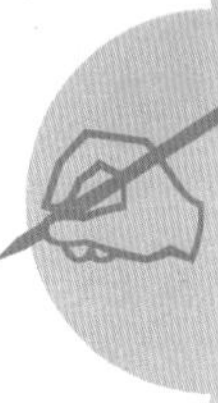

Research a religion that is unfamiliar to you. Describe five behaviours or rituals that a person following that religion is expected to demonstrate.

The mass media

The mass media are the final agent of socialisation to be considered here. They consist of television, radio, newspapers, books, advertisements, films, recorded music, the internet – anything that reaches a very large audience. Most people are exposed to some of these agents. They fill in where the rest of experience stops. It is impossible to experience directly more than a small portion of culture, life and the world. It is the media that form the link, mediating between the real world and what we come to think of as the real world. The media are responsible to some degree for what people share in common. What happened on TV or the latest music streamed online is often the first topic to be discussed at school or work. Influence, however, is a two-way process. People process information from the media alongside the other influences upon them, and the media are created by people based upon their own culture and creativity.

The six strands of development (SPECCS)

The changes and skills noted above have formed part of your development and can be grouped into six main strands, known as **social, physical, emotional, cognitive, cultural and spiritual**. These strands can conveniently be remembered as making the word SPECCS. They are not entirely separate from one another, and their separation here is only because it is a convenient way to discuss them. In fact development is holistic, with all of the strands interacting with one another and inseparable from the others.

- **Social development** is about how we interact with others, develop relationships and take on social roles. Socialisation underpins social development and is about enabling people to develop the knowledge, skills, attitudes and qualities not only for successful relationships but also to function effectively in our multi-ethnic and multicultural society.
- **Physical development** refers to how our bodies change, increase in skill and develop the ability to perform more complex activities. It includes sensory development, the development of the processes of vision, hearing, touch, smell, taste and proprioception (the sense that lets us know where the mobile parts of our body, e.g. arms and legs, are in relation to the rest of our body).
- **Emotional development** concerns the development of feelings, coping with feelings, developing self-esteem and gaining a sense of our own identity.

- **Cognitive development** refers to our thought processes and how we make sense of the world, especially through the development of language and learning. It concerns the development of the mind in terms of recognising, reasoning, knowing, understanding, decision making and making sense of what is perceived through the senses.
- **Cultural development** concerns how we acquire thoughts, beliefs and behaviours particular to the groups and institutions in society to which we belong. It concerns developing an understanding of our own culture, and developing respect for the values and assumptions of other cultures. Culture is closely linked with all other aspects of development. Like emotional development it contributes to the sense of self. It requires the cognitive skills associated with language development in order to communicate, receive and modify shared cultural values. Rogoff (2003) sees an understanding of cultural development as absolutely fundamental to understanding other aspects of development. She focuses on people's participation in their communities.
- **Spiritual development** concerns developing a sense of what matters, what is of genuine value, what is believed in and gives meaning to life. It may involve reflection, thought and special activities, such as praying or meditation. For some people, religion plays a large part in spiritual development. Others have very positive spiritual development without holding any religious beliefs. Like other aspects of development, it contributes to the development of a sense of self and self-esteem. It has aspects of other strands of development in varying degrees, especially cultural and social, but also to some extent cognitive and emotional.

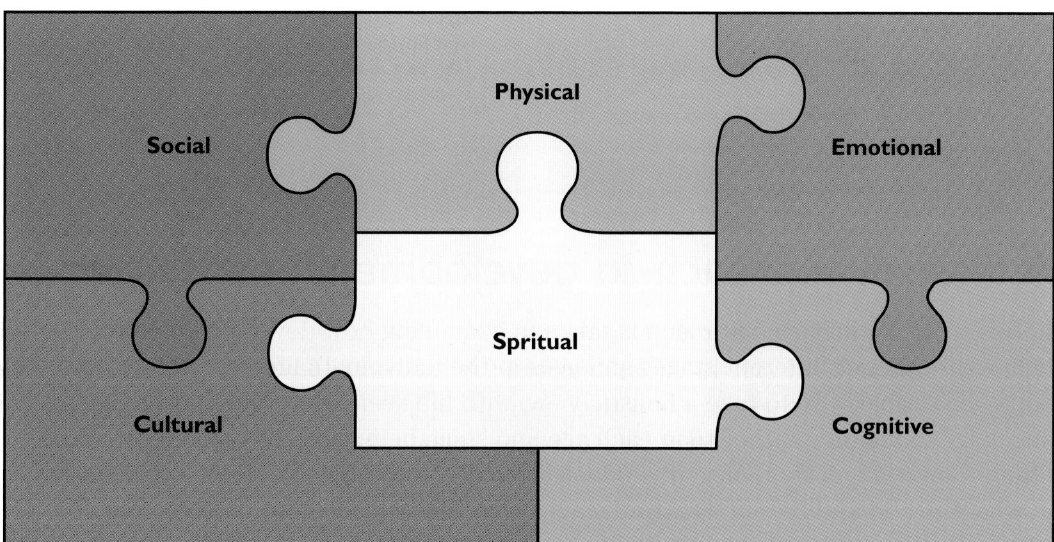

Figure 3.3 The six strands of development: SPECCS

These six strands of development will form the basis of discussion about development and behaviour throughout the lifespan.

Activity *SPECCS*

Draw an image of yourself surrounded by six boxes, as in the example below. Label the six boxes – social, physical, emotional, cognitive, cultural, spiritual – and place the changes and skills that you are aware of taking place during the past five years in the appropriate boxes. You will probably find that some things fit into several boxes, for example a relationship with a partner can have social, physical, emotional, cognitive, cultural and spiritual aspects.

Social
Able to have conversations
Made a lot of friends
Plays basketball
First boyfriend/girlfriend

Physical
Learnt to swim/play basketball
First boyfriend/girlfriend
Can do things for myself

Spiritual
Time by myself
Day dreaming
Interest in music
First boyfriend/girlfriend
Take part in discussions

Emotional
Made a lot of friends
Interest in music
First boyfriend/girlfriend

Cultural
Ability to have conversations
Take part in discussions
Interest in music
First boyfriend/girlfriend

Cognitive
Learned a lot
Able to have conversations
First boyfriend/girlfriend
Take part in discussions
Think to make decisions

Figure 3.4 Aspects of development

A lifespan approach to development and behaviour

In this section a lifespan approach is taken in examining how development and behaviour differ at different stages and ages in the individual's lifespan. A lifespan approach enables you to take a holistic view, with life seen as a process from one age and stage to another, rather than each age and stage being seen as discrete from the others. You will quickly realise if you look around you that people differ enormously in what they do at different ages and stages, and that any account here can only be about what can generally be expected. Joe at 12 months is already saying a few words and can walk, for instance, while Ryan at the same age is still crawling everywhere and makes a few incomprehensible sounds. By five Ryan might have overtaken Joe and be able to catch a ball and give a good account of his day to his mum, whereas Joe may not yet have mastered these skills. Sandy at 60 may be tired, overweight and unfit. Sheila is 60 too, but she is active, optimistic and thinking about taking a college course and changing her job. All of these people fall within the range of what is generally termed 'normal' development.

Various aspects of development considered earlier in this chapter, and influences considered in Chapters 4 and 5, may lead to what is known as 'atypical' development. Atypical development occurs when there are factors that limit development to such an extent that a person's development and behaviour fall outside the 'normal' range and may require help or intervention in some aspects of life. Sometimes there are social influences like poverty or prejudice that lead to or aggravate such development; sometimes there is a physical or psychological illness or impairment. Often atypical development can be alleviated if impeding social or psychological factors can be resolved. Studies of resilience, for example, have demonstrated that adverse circumstances do not always lead to atypical development.

We are all different and affected to differing degrees by all of the strands of development considered in the previous section. Below is an account of what generally happens from infancy to older adulthood, considered in separate sections: infancy (0–2 years); early childhood (2–5); middle childhood (5–12); **adolescence** (12–20 years); adulthood (20–65); and older adulthood (over 65). Social, physical, emotional, cognitive, cultural and spiritual development will be examined at each stage. When you read Chapters 4 and 5 you should be able to apply theoretical thinking to these ages and stages. The theory of Erikson (1968) is especially relevant to a consideration of the lifespan, and each stage that is considered is related to his lifespan theory.

Infancy: birth to two years

At birth a baby undertakes a phenomenal journey from being totally connected to the mother to being outside her body. Although the baby is still completely dependent upon others for the fulfilment of its needs, this transition has enormous implications. One day 'ventilation, nutrition and excretion take place through the placenta and umbilical cord' (Rayner, 1986); the next day the baby breathes independently; feeding by sucking starts in the next couple of days, and so does excretion. Other people have to reorganise their lives around this new, dependent person.

Activity *Observing babies and very young children*

Obtaining permission from their parents or carers first, try to watch babies and children in the first two years of their lives. Look at and make notes on their social, physical, emotional, cognitive, cultural and spiritual development, noting the age at which observations are made. You could record your results in a chart like Table 3.1 on page 131, adding other stages as you progress through your course. Remember that the divisions are in many ways artificial and that many observations may apply to several forms of development.

Social development

Most people who have been with small babies a lot will be convinced that they are sociable from a very early age. Whether or not they have any sense of a separate identity, a small baby's smiles and cries elicit responses from others to play, to comfort or just to smile back. From these beginnings the child between two and eight months usually begins to bond with and show attachment to one or more adults who are close. This early sociability is thus very much linked with the emotional development discussed below. A baby has little interest in other children in the first six months of life, but familiar children, such as brothers and sisters, are recognised and often elicit a response such as a smile of pleasure. From about eight months on the young child begins to spread his or her sociability to other people, though will often seek the reassurance and closeness of the most meaningful person if threatened, unsure, hungry, uncomfortable or tired.

Life becomes a series of advances into new situations and retreats for comfort. There is an increasing interest in other children. Most children aged one year will happily be with other children, but their actions are not yet an exchange between them. For example, at one year old a child who goes to playgroup may happily play alongside other children for up to an hour, but then may retreat to her mother for comfort. By two she may become much more independent and sociable but still her play will be what is known as **parallel play**. Play does not yet rest upon ideas of sharing and exchange. That has to wait for the next stage of development.

Physical development

Here are some of the physical developments you may have noticed in a child aged 0–2. There is increasing control over the body, beginning with control of the head and upper body. This progresses to the ability to sit independently, then to crawl, then to pull themselves up on to two feet and stand, then to walk with help, perhaps in a walker or pushing a toy trolley. Hand movements become more dexterous, with the ability to grasp things and then to hold objects in a pincer grip occurring at around nine months old. Then that remarkable day arrives, usually at between ten and eighteen months, when the child takes those first independent steps.

CASE STUDY

Physical development: Rachel, 0–2 years

As an example of one child's physical development, let's look at Rachel. At seven months she has learned to turn over from front to back. She can sit momentarily without support but soon flops forwards or backwards; she can hold a cloth book but can't yet turn the pages. By 14 months Rachel is walking and can sit in a small chair at a small table holding crayons or small objects and can transfer them from one container to another. She can turn the pages of a book, usually several pages at a time.

By 18 months she is running, though not very confidently and with rather a lot of falls. She can walk upstairs one at a time holding someone's hand but comes down on hands and knees backwards. She pushes a small trolley full of toy bricks everywhere. By two years she runs confidently and has learned to turn handles to open and close doors. Climbing is one of her new discoveries and she can 'escape' from her cot. She has a little tricycle and moves it by walking her feet along the ground. She now turns book pages one at a time. She uses her left hand more than her right hand and appears to be left-handed. She likes to build a tower with bricks, picking them up very carefully with her thumb and forefinger; then she loves to knock the whole thing down again – with great hilarity.

Emotional development

Critical to understanding a child's emotional development is the concept of attachment. A child's early experiences are crucial to emotional development. The presence of at least one consistent, caring and loving individual has been shown to be invaluable to the child's ability to thrive and to develop emotional stability, an integrated sense of self and relationships with others. Babies deprived of a close relationship may lose vitality, become apathetic and show many symptoms of depression. Sometimes they die. This is why there is so much emphasis on preventing the separation of young children from their families. When separation cannot be prevented, or is in the child's best interests, as in abusive situations, it is important to provide a situation that is as close as possible to a loving and warm parent–child relationship. Fortunately, the days of routinely separating children with disabilities from their parents have passed. Whenever possible the emphasis is on support within, rather than outside, the family. Parents are now encouraged to stay with their children in hospital to nurture their babies as soon as possible after birth and to respond to a baby's need for warmth, love and physical closeness.

At first a baby is not able to distinguish between him/herself and other people, or to distinguish the breast or the bottle as something separate. At this stage begins what Rayner (2005) calls the synchrony between a close parent or parent substitute and a baby. They fit themselves around each other, are in tune, and a baby establishes communication with at least one close 'significant other' within the first few weeks of life. Parents and babies vary in the nature of the synchrony that is established, but without it a baby is likely to be distressed. This synchrony is the basis for bonding and attachment between parent and child, on which depends the baby's later ability to gain a separate sense of self. It is also the basis of love, trust, empathy and a feeling of security.

Slowly but surely the baby begins to gain a sense of him/herself as separate from other people and things, so that somewhere between six months and a year a distinct identity begins to emerge. Crying changes in nature and becomes a call for someone else. Smiling, which has probably been present as a sign of pleasure from the first month of life, becomes increasingly a response to other people. Crying and smiling are the baby's main ways of communicating pain and pleasure, and require a response in order that the child can begin to gain a knowledge of communication as an exchange. At this stage too the child begins to test the world, to throw things away that are then put back, to get anxious if the closest person to her goes out, and to be reassured when she or he returns. As long as the person does come back the child learns to trust other people and to form a close bond with at least one significant other. Initial synchrony helps in this bonding process, though bonding at this stage is still entirely possible for children who have had early health difficulties and/or have been separated from their parents. Continued separation, however, increases the difficulties of bonding once a child reaches the stage of seeing him/herself as separate, as you have seen in the discussion about attachment and separation.

Although children thrive and survive in all kinds of different parenting situations, and can and do recover from short periods of separation, those deprived of love, closeness and the opportunity to bond and form a consequent attachment to an adult are unlikely to trust others or to develop a satisfactory **self-concept**. This can lead to difficulties in their relationships with others. Such emotional deprivation has also been shown to be associated with slow intellectual development and poor physical health. Spitz (1965), for example, observed children in large institutions where they were well fed and clean but had little personal attention or stimulation. These children had extreme difficulties with learning and responding emotionally to others, and were prone to infections. Their illness and death rates were much higher than those for children in less clean but emotionally warmer and more friendly places. In Chapter 4 you will see that Erikson (1968) refers to this stage as 'trust versus mistrust'.

Cognitive development

Cognitive development includes the child's thinking, language development, some aspects of play and the whole process of learning and understanding about the world. The five senses of sight, smell, touch, taste and hearing are used to learn about and explore surroundings. Memory is used to store up information that can be adapted initially to the same situations and subsequently to different ones. At first there is memory of the same face(s) meaning the same things: usually food and love. Recognition of one meaningful person, usually but not necessarily the child's mother, is among the first cognitive steps the child takes. For example, at a few weeks old a baby will stop crying at the sight of his or her mother's face, or the face of whoever happens to be the most significant person to that baby.

One way in which babies seem to learn is through imitation of those in their surrounding world. Even though adults and older children may not realise it, they are having an effect on a baby. What they do is very important from the earliest days of the child's life, not only in terms of the child's emotional security but also in terms of intellectual growth. There is evidence that babies imitate their mother's mouth movements from the age of about a month, even though they can't speak; similarly, body movements are imitated and learned. This topic is covered in more detail in Chapter 4 in the consideration of Bandura's work.

Exploration develops to the stage where by eighteen months a child remembers where objects belong, explores new environments with great interest and can manipulate building blocks so that they become towers. The development of language is perhaps one of the most fascinating aspects of cognitive development. From crying and cooing at three months of age, the child develops to babbling a whole mixture of sounds by six months. By nine or ten months the language of a child's culture can be recognised and by twelve months the first words are usually spoken. By two years there is usually a vocabulary of a hundred words or so. Andrew was saying Da, Ma, do (dog), ca (cat) and something that resembled 'hello' by his first birthday, whereas his friend Sam called everything 'ducker'. As the second year progressed both boys grasped the meaning of 'me' and 'mine' and parts of the body: nose, face, feet. By two they could also recognise most colours. They pretended to 'phone' one another on their toy telephones and had 'conversations'.

Cultural development

You may think that birth to two years is rather early to be talking about cultural development. An infant is surrounded, however, by cultural influences that have a major impact on how she develops culturally: the institution of the family, rituals such as baptism, the use of language, the beliefs of the family and society. All of these begin to permeate the infant's progress so that the development of a cultural identity is well under way by the time a child reaches the age of two. At this stage infants are becoming habituated to their culture, usually and predominantly through their family, but they are not yet at a stage where they question it or try to change it. They accept that what is there is there; they have no ability or reason to question things … yet. Cultural development can be illustrated by comparing its differences in infants from different societies and groups.

Activity Cultural development

Below are three descriptions of infants. Can you identify contrasting aspects of cultural development from these accounts?

James, Ellie, and Aka children

James, aged 9 months, was born into a moderately wealthy family in a northern Scottish town. His parents are articulate and introduce him at an early age to the groups to which they belong. He goes to the crèche when his parents attend their local church, and he was baptised there. His parents are his main carers, although he is also looked after by his grandmother while his mother works part-time. He sleeps in a cot in a separate room from his parents. Great emphasis is placed on the importance of developing intellectual and cognitive skills to the extent that, even as a baby, James is surrounded by books and encouraged to look at them. He is told stories at bedtime and his mother reads poems to him. Life could have been very different for James, however. As a student his mother became a regular drug user and abandoned her studies for several years.

Ellie is 18 months old. Her parents are both drug users. Their friends are predominantly drug users too and there is no contact with grandparents or other extended family members. Her parents expect Ellie to spend long periods of time entertaining herself. She cannot rely on them for regular meals. They do not introduce her to many influences outside the immediate nuclear family circle and there are few indications of any wider societal culture, except that surrounding drugs and their acquisition, and the television, which is continuously switched on. Ellie often shares her parents' bed at night.

The following is a quote from Hewlett in Rogoff (2003, p.34) in relation to **Aka children** in Central Africa:

> *Training for autonomy begins in infancy. Infants are allowed to crawl or walk to wherever they want in camp and allowed to use knives, machetes, digging sticks, and clay pots around camp. Only if an infant begins to crawl into a fire or hits another child do parents or others interfere … It was not unusual, for instance, to see an eight-month-old with a six-inch knife chopping the branch frame of its family's house.*

Aka infants are held most of the time for the first four months of their lives, and although their primary carer is their mother, they are transferred to other caregivers about seven times an hour and have seven different caregivers on an average day. Fathers also play a major role in caregiving, spending about 20 per cent of every day holding their infants.

In each of the above examples, what can be identified as cultural development? Consider:

- expectations about autonomy and responsibility, e.g. sleeping alone or with parents
- who the people are in the child's life and what they do, e.g. the part played by parents, grandparents
- the importance given to different activities, e.g. reading, work
- the nature of the family, e.g. extended or nuclear
- religious and ethnic practices, e.g. importance of baptism, use of sharp knives
- the emergence of a sense of self within a cultural context
- experience of physical contact – one person or many.

All of these aspects are part of cultural development. The child begins to move towards a greater understanding of what is required and expected by the wider society, and this is culturally specific. Building an identity is part of many aspects of development, but without cultural development this identity is incomplete.

Spiritual development

Building an identity is also part of spiritual development. There may not be much outward evidence for this aspect of development in such young children, but the foundations are already being laid. Through love and early attachments the infant can begin to feel secure so that a positive, happy sense of self can begin to emerge. Infants can begin to feel at ease with themselves, which is the beginning of spiritual development. There will probably be cultural dimensions to this aspect of development, influenced by family beliefs and/or religious practices. The nature of the environment also plays a part. Opportunities for peace, quiet times, imaginative use of colour, music and lighting can all contribute to balance and spiritual development.

Figure 3.5 Infant – new to walking

Table 3.1 Summary of general pattern of development: infancy

Social	Physical	Emotional	Cognitive	Cultural	Spiritual
Interacting/getting on with others • Bonding and attachment – importance of early close relationship(s) • Increasing interest in other children • Parallel play • Communication with others • Move from total dependence to more autonomy	How the body changes • Increasing control over body • All senses developing from birth • Sitting, crawling, walking, running • Co-ordination, finer hand movements • Brain growing in complexity – sensitive to environmental influences	Beginning to gain a sense of identity • Need for warmth, love and closeness • Secure or insecure base • Distinguishing self from others • Emotional responses to others; smiling, crying • Erikson: Trust vs mistrust (0–1yr); Autonomy vs shame and doubt (1–3 yrs)	How sense is made of the world • Recognition of meaningful people • Development of memory • Developing concept of objects, numbers and problem solving • Communication and language • Exploration	Beginning to acquire behaviours associated with culture • Affected by how the family behaves and is structured • Begins to take part in cultural practices • Learning the language reflects in culture • Cultural influences permeate development • Beginning of cultural participation and identity	Beginning to develop sense of wholeness • Importance of love and attachment • Influenced by all other aspects of development • Emerging sense of self and self-awareness • Cultural influences, e.g. religion • Need for periods of quietness and peace

Early childhood: two to five years

Social development

At this stage the child is moving outwards not only emotionally but also socially: from parents to siblings to other children and other adults. The child's social world is usually expanding beyond the family to nursery, playgroup and public places (shopping, swimming, holidays) and is a mixture of child and adult relationships.

Play is an area that combines all facets of development – social, physical, emotional, cognitive, cultural and spiritual. It is useful to examine here not only how play is part of social development at this stage, but also how it acts to integrate the various facets of development in the process of the growth of a well-balanced person.

At two a child generally participates in **parallel play**: children play *alongside* each other rather than *with* each other. If you watch children at this age, they can be very absorbed by a toy car – or by the toy car with which another child is playing, which they will then proceed to try to obtain. Obtaining the toy is more important than any kind of relationship with the other child. Play here is a learning process; it serves to develop physical and cognitive skills and is preparation for a much more social and emotional experience – but it isn't quite there yet. This process continues slowly until, by the age of five, children begin to co-operate, to divide roles and to share, though play is by no means always a harmonious experience. What the child does in terms of play activity will to some extent be culturally influenced; toy cars will not be present in every culture. The opportunities for quiet periods of play can set the scene for spiritual development.

Physical development

Parents may be preoccupied with 'toilet training' around the second birthday. Some time from eighteen months to three or four years magical things seem to happen: the child becomes increasingly able to control both bladder and bowel and can now communicate so well that he or she can begin to predict the need to use a potty and to say what is required. This new-found control is very important, for it further frees the child from dependence on adults for physical care. By age two, most children are fully weaned and can eat and drink independently. Development is very much tied up with growth at this stage. As the body grows stronger it also gains in co-ordination. Walking, running, climbing and balancing are increasingly skilled.

CASE STUDY

Physical development: Matty, 2½ years

Matty loves to visit the swings and slides. Tentatively he'll climb the ladder and slide down the slide. After ten minutes he's running from the end of the slide to the ladder, up one step at a time and whizzing down with great glee ... time after time after time. He loves to go to the swimming baths and flap around with armbands on, but needs to know that there's someone close by to help him. By age five or even three or four, he may go up the really big slide, co-ordinating climbing steps with alternate legs and being confident enough to go head first as well as feet first. Also, by age five, a lot of children learn to swim without the support of armbands. Some children do these things at an earlier stage, some later. Remember, this is a very generalised account.

This period from age two to five is one of consolidating skills, of increasing co-ordination of lots of movements, of running around and climbing. Gradually a child can learn to throw a ball and then to catch it, to pedal a tricycle and then to begin to balance on a bicycle. There is increasing skill gained in holding and manipulating toys so that, by age five, children can usually thread beads, create buildings with building blocks and draw by holding crayons quite skilfully.

Emotional development

Emotional development usually, though not always, goes hand in hand with intellectual development. As a child learns communication skills these facilitate interaction with others and the development of relationships. During the period of age two to five years children become considerably less dependent on their parents and strive towards greater autonomy. This is sometimes exhibited through temper tantrums when there is frustration that autonomy, wishes or wants are threatened or thwarted. Children of this age can usually be separated from parents for short periods without becoming too distressed. They begin to enjoy the company of others, especially siblings (brothers and sisters), spending as much time with them as with their parents. Siblings often begin to form strong bonds with one another at this stage, talking, playing, imitating, arguing, experiencing difficulties and attempting to sort them out. Sibling relationships are certainly not all plain sailing and some siblings never gain fulfilling, integrated relationships with one another for reasons of both nature and nurture. But there is the potential in sibling relationships for strong bonds to develop that are different from and additional to those with parents and friends. Parents still play a prominent part at this stage, being an emotional retreat when the child needs love, stability or reassurance.

It is at this stage that gender identity emerges, and girls and boys become more fully aware of the differences between them. Even before the age of two there are signs that boys and girls are aware that they are different from one another. Physical differences have emotional implications since these differences become part of identity, and children begin to pay attention to the different roles of boys and girls, men and women. The gaining of gender identity can be seen as progressing in four stages:

- **Awareness**: the child begins to notice gender differences (12–14 months).
- **Labelling**: the child correctly identifies gender in self and others (2–3 years).
- **Stability**: the child understands that gender remains over time, that a boy becomes a man and a girl becomes a woman (3–5 years).
- **Constancy**: the child understands that gender doesn't change when outward appearance changes (5 years).

When you refer to Erikson in Chapter 4 you will see that he labels the positive outcome of this stage as 'initiative', with the converse being 'guilt'.

Cognitive development

Language is one of the main avenues through which cognitive/intellectual development can be gauged at this age. Not only is vocabulary increasing but children are also very creative with their language. They do not completely mimic adults but often, once they have learned a few rules of language, they come up with entirely original constructions. Here are some sentences of children in this age range:

- I was tired. My eyes did lie down a little while.
- I not naughty. I just a little terror.
- I knowed Andrew at nursery school.
- I done some drawing.

Here is a conversation between a three-year-old and a six-year-old, quoted in Bee and Mitchell (1984), about the relative dangers of forgetting to feed the goldfish versus overfeeding them:

> ***Six-year-old***: *It's worse to forget to feed them.*
>
> ***Three-year-old***: *No, it's badder to feed them too much.*
>
> ***Six-year-old***: *You don't say badder, you say worser.*
>
> ***Three-year-old***: *But it's baddest to give them too much food.*
>
> ***Six-year-old***: *No, it's not. It's worsest to forget to feed them.*

These examples show really creative use of language which, although perhaps not grammatically correct, is inventive. One of the delights of this age is this remarkable grasp of some basic rules of grammar, combined with experimenting with them in original ways. By age three, children are constructing quite long, complex sentences. They have often replaced their own names with 'I' in their conversations as they gain confidence in themselves and their self-concept becomes more fully developed. For some children the acquisition of language may be affected by an impairment such as deafness. Having a rich linguistic environment is especially important for these children in order that the impact of their impairment is minimised in their development. The NDCS (National Deaf Children's Society) (2011) has produced some excellent guidance.

Children of this age are also learning about colours and shapes, numbers and time, what things in their environment are like and what they do. They will play shapes games, putting different shapes through appropriately shaped holes in boxes. They will investigate things to see what they do and what they feel like, and they will be trying to work out things like distances. One favourite word is often 'why'. 'Why?' is sometimes asked out of sheer habit, but it can also indicate a real desire to know why something is the way it is. 'How far' is also a favourite, especially on a long journey. 'How far is it? Are we nearly there?' a small voice asks ten minutes into a three-hour journey, and at five-minute intervals thereafter, unless there's a distraction and/or fun going on. It's certainly not far to age five now, but there's still a lot of life's journey to pursue.

Cultural development

From age two to five, the major determinant of cultural development in Western society continues to be the family. Other institutions are also beginning to impinge upon the child's life, however: nursery school, possibly a religious or other spiritual or faith institution, other families, friends and, for some children, a care situation such as foster care. Some children live within contrasting cultures that affect the way they develop culturally. For example, children in ethnically mixed families may have two cultures, or a mixed culture that takes some aspects of one culture, some of another. The child is still likely to accept unquestioningly the culture offered by family and the wider social groups with which she is in contact, but is now able to begin to make comparisons between the ways things are for her and the way they are for others. This comparison is not well developed at this stage, but this is already a stage at which cultural tolerance or intolerance modelled by those in the child's environment can influence early choices about with whom to spend time, and who is liked or not liked. These choices are likely not only to be culturally influenced but also to influence cultural development. Again, short examples may serve to illustrate this better than any amount of theorising.

CASE STUDY

Cultural development

Rogoff (2003) tells us that Aka children by the age of three or four can cook a meal for themselves on the fire. They participate in family work from a very early age and see their parents working. By contrast, most children in Scotland see their parents and their parents' activities in the home but rarely also see them at work, unless they work at home. As a consequence they do not get a sense of the full range of their parents' economic and social activities. The opportunity for Aka children to see their parents working means that they are more likely to participate in work activities at a very early age. Work is part of their culture and their identity, whereas Western children are expected to have activities completely separate from their parents and very often of a play or educational nature. Indeed, efforts to protect children from exploitation and to remove them from the world of work mean that cultural emphasis is placed on children being educated and well-rounded socially, but not on children being major economic contributors. The differing values that different cultures place on different experiences thus influence the child's cultural development.

Activity: *Observing cultural development in early childhood*

Through observing two children in the age range 2–5 years in social situations with their families or carers, identify five cultural aspects of development that are presented to them and that they adopt. Try to find contrasting children from different cultural backgrounds.

You may have looked at:

- how children relate to adults
- the values of influential adults in relation to education, play and work, and how these are conveyed to children
- the extent to which children are included in the institutions to which their family and/or carers belong
- how the developing sense of self reflects cultural development.

Activity: *Teegie*

Read the passage below from Rogoff (2003, p.325) and answer the questions that follow.

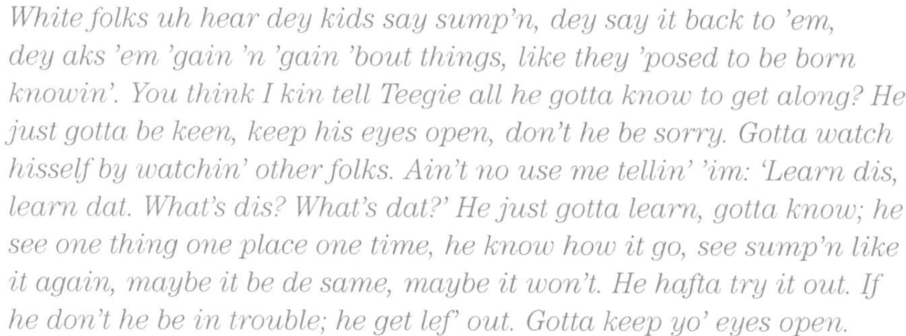

White folks uh hear dey kids say sump'n, dey say it back to 'em, dey aks 'em 'gain 'n 'gain 'bout things, like they 'posed to be born knowin'. You think I kin tell Teegie all he gotta know to get along? He just gotta be keen, keep his eyes open, don't he be sorry. Gotta watch hisself by watchin' other folks. Ain't no use me tellin' 'im: 'Learn dis, learn dat. What's dis? What's dat?' He just gotta learn, gotta know; he see one thing one place one time, he know how it go, see sump'n like it again, maybe it be de same, maybe it won't. He hafta try it out. If he don't he be in trouble; he get lef' out. Gotta keep yo' eyes open.

1 What things in the description above are important for Teegie in learning his culture?
2 Is this how children you have observed learn about their culture and develop culturally?
3 What other aspects of development are illustrated in this account?

Spiritual development

At age two to five, spiritual development is still in its very early stages. Love, attachment and the child's environment continue to set the scene for later development. A curiosity is already emerging about some of the mysteries of life, however: a need for explanations about why things are as they are. The young child may participate in some spiritual activities; for example, they may ask and seek to answer ultimate questions such as 'Why was I born?' This may occur through religion or other belief systems. Opportunities for contemplation or creative activities away from excessive noise and in a secure happy environment, can contribute to developing the child's sense of self and to whether or not this self is happy.

Table 3.2 Summary of general pattern of development: early childhood

Social	Physical	Emotional	Cognitive	Cultural	Spiritual
Building upon relationships • Moving outwards; expanding social world • Play: parallel play to playing with other children • Taking on roles in play, including gender roles • Importance of relationships with siblings and other family members	How the body changes • Steady growth: bigger, stronger but more slender body; increasing skills in walking, running, balancing • Control of bladder and bowel • Eating and drinking independently • Increasing physical independence • Increasing skill in co-ordination	Developing sense of identity • Less dependence on parents • Greater autonomy if emotionally stable • Emergence of gender identity • Begins to verbalise emotional responses • Developing relationships • Erikson: Initiative vs guilt	How sense is made of the world • Talking and using words and symbols creatively • Learning about everything: colours, shapes, numbers • Curiosity: often asks 'why' • Language as a route to relationships and culture • From self-centred to appreciating other's perspective	Behaviour, thoughts and beliefs culturally influenced • Culturally learned from family • Influence of other social institutions reinforces culture • Contrasting cultures in ethnically mixed families • Child can begin to make comparisons • Emergence of cultural identity	Developing sense of wholeness and balance • Curiosity about mysteries of life • Participating in spiritual aspects of some cultural practices • Increasing sense of self • Development of beliefs • Potential to be at ease with self

Childhood: five years to twelve or thirteen years

Childhood has a different time span for different children and for different cultures. In the UK it generally spans the ages of five until about twelve or thirteen, when puberty and adolescence occur. It is the time of starting school, making friends and moving further out from the confines of the family and home to the wider society.

Social development

Friends would be an apt title for a TV series about childhood. The peer group, children of the same or similar age, gains in importance as children increasingly move away from social dependence on adults. Competitive play and co-operative play develop alongside one another. Children compete in sports activities, in classroom situations and in their attempts to gain the attention of adults and other children. They also learn co-operation, enhanced in play situations where they act out such roles as mothers, fathers, doctors, nurses, older brothers and sisters, shop assistants, school teachers and pupils.

Play enables children to learn roles and to empathise with those who perform other roles in their lives. The self-concept, seen as part of emotional development, is developed to some extent through the social situations the child experiences and through the increasing ability of the child to put him/herself in other roles, to stand outside and to look in. Ideas about self-concept are further developed in Chapters 4 and 5.

Group participation, whether through the family, school group, interest group or friendship group, provides avenues for not only co-operation with others but also for the expression of opinions and the development of relationships. Children of this age have an enormous need for acceptance, which leads to what many adults see as an annoying conformity; children have to dress in similar ways to their peers, develop language patterns that are similar, hair that must be 'just so', and things that are not 'in' are viewed as very 'uncool'. Conformity sometimes looks cripplingly stifling of creativity and achievement, but for many children acceptance by the peer group is of much greater importance. The peer group itself, though, can be a source of creativity, interaction and the opportunity for co-operation and leadership. By age eight or nine, boys and girls are beginning to drift apart into same-sex groups, only to come together again to some extent in adolescence.

Adult relationships continue to retain a great deal of relevance. The family is still an important social focal point but other adult attachments often develop. Hero worship of teachers, sports coaches, instructors, Guide and Scout leaders, youth club leaders, care workers and social workers can develop. These are usually healthy attachments if the role models are positive and the power that could be associated with their roles is not abused.

For most children this is a happy time socially, with some friendships lasting well into adult life. There are fallings in and out, but gradually as the child develops confidence in him/herself, so confidence develops in relationships. Social development is thus closely associated with emotional development.

Physical development

Of course, children get bigger and bigger, though at different rates. How else do they change and develop before they reach that notorious adolescence? **Skills** and **sex** are the two clues to physical development from age five to twelve or thirteen. Skills involve more meticulous dexterity in manipulating their hands and bodies. At age six, children can usually tie laces and cut meat at the table and skilfully manipulate small pieces of Lego or Duplo. At age seven, lo and behold, a small person can balance on a plank, leap down several stairs at a time, dress – and undress – themselves. By age eight the child is roller-skating or roller-blading on Saturday evenings at the sports centre, skipping in the playground and riding a bike at full speed downhill. Sexually, children are inexorably moving towards puberty, girls usually at a faster rate than boys. Girls begin to develop pubic hair and breasts, and some begin menstruation, before they are twelve. Boys do not usually reach puberty at this age nor undergo any major growth spurts. Both sexes make steady progress in their ability to perform complex physical tasks, with the effects of puberty dominating not this stage of development but the next.

Emotional development

Most children become more self-assured between the ages of five and twelve, developing a concept of self that is more confident about their abilities and shows more insight into their own identity. Children between these ages start to question family relationships and emotions, and quite frequently push their parents to the limit of their patience. They like to see how far they can go, though if limits are imposed they are usually adhered to – eventually. In Erikson's theory of development this is the stage of 'industry versus inferiority'. This emphasises the importance of encouragement and praise, which can have an impact on industry and positive self-image, rather than negativity and criticism, which can lead to feelings of inferiority and negative self-image.

Cognitive development

Play continues to have a vital role in cognitive development, though formal learning at school is increasingly important at this time. Thinking changes in a number of ways. The child usually develops numerical/mathematical ability. For example, by age five a child can count sweets if they are placed in a straight line (though not if they are placed in a circle). By age eight, most children can count sweets placed in a circle. By between ages ten and twelve, concepts of addition, subtraction, multiplication and division are being grasped. Measuring and recording can be practised in both formal and informal situations through seeing how long and wide things are, how much items weigh (e.g. when baking a cake), and so on.

Time becomes increasingly meaningful, and during this stage most children learn to tell the time, understand the calendar in some detail (weeks, months, years), know the date and grasp that it is the same date and time everywhere in the UK. Writing ability is often more developed than speech. The use of increasingly complex sentences indicates growing language competence.

Cultural development

At this stage school is a major influence not only on social and cognitive development but also presents the child with new opportunities for cultural development. Schools, through the Curriculum for Excellence, aim to develop responsible citizens and effective contributors, and they include in their curricula the closely linked aspects of spiritual, moral, social and cultural development. In this chapter moral development is considered to have its basis in cultural and spiritual development, and as such is not considered separately. As Eagleton (2000, p.131) states:

> *Culture is not only what we live by. It is, also, in great measure, what we live for: affection, relationship, memory, kinship, place, community, emotional fulfilment, intellectual enjoyment, a sense of ultimate meaning.*

Activity — Cultural development

Read the case study of John below. Which of the factors mentioned by Eagleton (2000) can be distinguished as part of John's cultural development?

John, 10 years

A developing sense of identity is closely related to cultural development. John, aged 10, comes from a family living in a Scottish sea port. Like his parents and school friends, he supports the town's football team, speaks with the local accent and has strong beliefs about what is right and wrong, especially in relation to being true to his friends. John likes to dress similarly to his school friends so that he is not identified as being different from them.

The answer is that all of them can. Culture presents ways of belonging and of excluding those who do not belong, though it can also be part of a culture to accept and not judge those who are culturally different.

Spiritual development

The links between spiritual development and cultural development can be seen clearly in the quotation from Eagleton (2000) above, where he talks about 'a sense of ultimate meaning'. In some senses this is contrary to culture because it seems to cross cultural boundaries to indicate a sense of developing common humanity. In other senses, the ways in which this is done are greatly influenced by culture. The spiritual dimension of development, however, can begin to ask questions for which culture may not have the answers. These questions begin in childhood but become much more important in adolescence. At age 5–12 most children are concerned with fairness ('It's not fair' being a rather common expression), which may not seem very spiritual but does begin the establishment of a moral basis for behaviour. An appreciation of different viewpoints emerges. Time and space to be quiet and peaceful, to read, daydream or take part in creative, religious and/or other spiritual activities, and the importance of loving and more especially being loved, continue to underpin this aspect of development.

Activity Seonaid

Seonaid wrote the following description of herself at age eleven:

> *My name is Seonaid. I live in Dundee. My home is a flat. I was born in Fort William and when I was six weeks old I moved to Glasgow and stayed there for seven years. My school in Glasgow was […] and my best friend was called Joanne. I have brown hair cut short and I wear earrings. My best friend in Dundee is Ellie. I have a younger sister in Primary 2 and an older sister in third year. My mum works in a shop and my dad is a taxi driver. I go dancing after school every Wednesday.*
>
> *I go swimming quite often too. I collect pictures of cats in a scrapbook and I also collect stamps. I have a one-year-old cat called Snowy. My ambition is to look after lots of animals that have been abandoned. I am average size. My home has three bedrooms, a living room, a kitchen and a bathroom.*
>
> *I like skateboards and bikes.*

What was important to Seonaid at this age? From this account, identify which parts refer to social, physical, emotional, cognitive, cultural and spiritual development.

Figure 3.6 Children playing

Table 3.3 Summary of general pattern of development: childhood

Social	Physical	Emotional	Cognitive	Cultural	Spiritual
Moving outwards from the family • Importance of peers and peer pressure • Competitive and co-operative play • Learning roles and social competence • Group participation • Family still a focal point but child gaining more control over choices	How the body changes • Increased body strength and co-ordination; rate of growth slows down • Developing skills and co-ordination • Beginnings of sexual development • Progress in doing complex tasks, e.g. games and sports • Body proportions more like adult	Developing sense of identity • Developing self-image, self-esteem, pride • Questioning about emotions • Increasing independence • Play and its role in identity • Growing sensitivity • Erikson: Industry vs inferiority	How sense is made of the world • Importance of play: learning by doing • Numerical, language and memory skills increase – importance of education • Grasp of the concept of time • Less self-centred • Some children show particular cognitive needs and/or strengths	Behaviour thoughts and beliefs of culture • School reinforcing culture • Awareness of other cultures • Education introduces literature, art, etc. • Development of cultural identity • Practising values of culture	Developing sense of wholeness and balance • Concern with fairness • Begin to appreciate different viewpoints • Need time and space to be alone • Importance of loving and being loved

Adolescence

> *Indeed, all the terms that we use for the age group have an awkward feel. There is no neutral way of describing it: 'youth' has an air of causing trouble and needing clubs, 'juveniles' are obviously delinquent, 'adolescents' are most likely to have problems, and 'teenagers' to have spots.*
>
> (Open University U205 Course Team, 'Birth to Old Age', 1985)

> *Adolescence can be described as a 'transition' from childhood to adulthood.*
>
> (Sudbery, 2010)

Think about being a teenager. You may still be one, you may have just passed that stage or you may be well past it (not that adolescence is ever entirely left behind). What do you think are its most significant aspects? Is it a time of calm, natural transition from childhood to adulthood or a rather stormy passage, or a mixture of the two? A lot has been written about this period, which in Western society is often associated with problems, storm and stress; but is adolescence necessarily problematical? Is turbulence in adolescence a biological necessity or are social and cultural factors of paramount importance? Writers and theorists vary enormously in their views. The sections below, combined with your experience and thinking, should enable you to come to a few of your own conclusions.

Social development

Social development is greatly influenced by all other aspects of development in adolescence and bears many resemblances to emotional development. Sexual maturity leads the individual towards sexual relationships. In Western society the search for self and for emotional independence from parents establishes a new and different kind of relationship with them and with the peer group. The end of formal school education leads to a transition into the worlds of work or of further or higher education, or into other experiences such as gap years of travel. For some there is the frustrating world of unemployment, uncertainty and lack of money. Whatever avenue is taken by the adolescent, new and often meaningful and long-lasting relationships develop, usually with members of both the same and the opposite sex. For some young people this is a time when they realise that they are not sexually attracted to the other sex but instead to their own, and this will impact on their social development.

Parents, including step-parents, are a source of support, annoyance and aggravation at this age. One observer (Montemayor, 1983) noted that adolescents and their parents are in conflict in all families some of the time and in some families all of the time. Sometimes serious conflicts can lead to serious problems, which can include running away, drug abuse, underage pregnancy, attempted and actual suicide, and illness including eating disorders such as anorexia nervosa. Not all conflicts have serious repercussions and not all serious problems are caused by conflict with parents or others. Rayner (2005) also points out that a young person's adolescence brings the opportunity for his parents to be rejuvenated in mind – if not in body.

The peer group or friendship group is of prime importance in adolescence. 'Do I look okay?' doesn't mean 'Do I look beautiful?' but 'Do I conform to the norms of the peer group?' 'Is my skirt short enough, are the heels high enough, is the hair spiky enough, is the nose-ring in the right place, do the eight earrings in one ear conform to the peer group norms but still mark me out as "different"?' Many sets of relationships are being balanced at this stage; those with parents/guardians, those with teachers and/ or employers, those with peers and those with whom the individual has a sexual, or potentially sexual, relationship. A fifth relationship, the relationship with oneself, is also vying for attention. The ways in which these relationships develop depend on all of the influences considered in Chapters 4 and 5 and other aspects of development discussed earlier. The person who emerges – the young adult – is the subject of subsequent sections of this chapter.

Physical development

Adolescence is a time of rapid physical growth and development, more so than at any other period except infancy. Evidently more so than infants, however, adolescents are very aware of the changes taking place.

The physical changes that an adolescent undergoes are not just ones of growth but ones of transformation associated with the eventual ability, for most people, to reproduce and/ or to work as an adult. The changes have many emotional implications. The physical development of adolescents can be viewed as falling into three types:

1. There are general changes in **body shape**, including changes in the way fat and muscle are distributed. In girls, fat is laid down around the hips and breasts, while boys generally lose fat and develop greater muscle mass. The strength and stamina of both sexes greatly increase and become more greatly differentiated as adolescence progresses.
2. A **growth spurt** occurs in adolescence between the ages of eleven and sixteen. There is usually a rapid increase in height.
3. There is continuing development of the **reproductive system**, with changes in the level of sex hormones in the bloodstream, giving rise to internal and external changes. For boys these changes include a deepening of the voice, enlargement of the penis, and growth of pubic and body hair. For girls the changes include enlargement of the breasts, growth of pubic hair and the onset of menstruation (periods). Menstruation can begin at any age from about ten to sixteen but usually occurs at around thirteen in the UK. This period of sexual development is known as **puberty**.

Emotional development

A lot of people would say that the word 'emotional' is quite an apt one to apply to adolescence but would question the relevance of the word 'development'. Is all that storm really development? Well, yes, it is all part of life's rich, wondrous and varied pattern. For many people it is not a period of great trauma and upheaval, although it is certainly a period of change and transition. Children enter and adults emerge (although usually continuing to be adolescent in some aspects of their lives), and a lot of emotional development goes on in between. What is the nature of this development?

The continuing development of a sense of self is one of the main issues of this stage. The adolescent is quite intensely focused on this self, and behaviour is often rather egocentric. The main question is 'Who am I?', a question that people often continue to ask themselves throughout their lives. If you look at Seonaid's description of herself, aged eleven, on page 141, she is not really thinking about who she is but is instead content to describe herself in terms of where she lives, her interests, her parents, her average size. By sixteen she's writing some quite powerful poetry:

I feel rejection

And search for my world

In a mild way which does not make

It obvious to them

Who I really am.

Maybe one day

I will be happy

Not in the way that they believe they are

But in a way purer than the water I drink

Where I'm doing what I want

And don't care what they think

Because then I'll be at ease with me

And maybe then they'll see

That it's not important to be smart and rich

Because satisfaction is what matters to me

I could be in the gutter

And have people mutter

'What a waste of a life'

As they wander by

But I'd smile to myself

And think secret thoughts

At least I am happy and true to my heart

I don't pretend to be something I'm not.

Activity Seonaid's poem

What aspects of adolescent emotional development are evident in the poem on the previous page?

In answering this question you may have mentioned: the focus on feelings (in this case feelings of rejection); searching for something; a separation from 'them', who are presumably adults; a focus on 'I' ('Where I'm doing what I want'); a rejection of what she considers to be adult ways; an attitude of 'I don't care what they think'. There's an emphasis on being honest to yourself and on not pretending to be something you're not. There is a lot of questioning, which is working towards resolution of what many theorists see as the identity crisis of adolescence. For Erikson, this stage represents 'identity versus role confusion'.

Connected with the developing sense of self are issues related to **sexuality**. Part of the 'who am I' questioning is also about being heterosexual, homosexual or of another sexual orientation. Some people find themselves intensely dissatisfied with the conventional options open to them. Many adolescents and young adults experiment with aspects of sexuality until they resolve the conflicts within them. Some adult problems are associated with a lack of resolution of the question of sexuality because it comes into conflict with other aspects of themselves or with the society in which they live.

Separation, both physical and emotional, is one of the aspects of growth and also an issue of anxiety for many adolescents. They desperately want to be independent but many, especially if they continue into further or higher education, are financially dependent on their parents. The nuclear family is less and less important, as partnerships, friendships and sexual relationships increase in importance, yet the family is still a source of financial support, and emotional support in times of crisis. The back and forth, away from and towards the family, away from and sometimes back to (and sometimes away from again) long-established relationships, the contradictions and a move towards their resolution, are all part of adolescence. The way in which separation is dealt with in adolescence has connections with attachment, resilience, transition and loss, discussed earlier in this chapter.

There are particular issues in relation to emotional development and establishing an identity in adolescence for those who belong to various ethnic and/or cultural groups, for children who are 'looked after' in children's homes or by foster parents, and for children who are adopted. Can you think of others for whom adolescence may present particular issues?

You may have thought of adolescents with a disability, those who are or have parents who are gay, lesbian or **transvestite**, those who come from abusive or unstable environments. Although a whole book could be devoted to the issues surrounding all of these groups there just isn't the space here to do the subject justice. Instead, two short case studies are presented here for you to consider and discuss.

Emotional development

Cathy

Cathy is fifteen. She is looked after in a small, homely children's home. She has had a very difficult emotional life. Her mother was a lone parent and a drug addict who died when Cathy was four years old. Even at the age of four, Cathy was showing signs of disruptive behaviour and an inability to make friends. At the age of six, she was adopted by a loving couple who had one daughter of their own, five years older than Cathy. The adoption was a disaster, with Cathy and her adoptive mother in constant conflict. Cathy had temper tantrums for no apparent reason, used abusive language and didn't seem able to respond to any kind of love or affection shown to her. The adoption completely broke down a year ago and Cathy came to the children's home at that time.

Nadia

Nadia Ahmed appears in the case study in Appendix 1 when she is 18 and again in Chapter 7 when she is 26. This account refers to her when she is 18. Her parents were born in Pakistan but she was born in Edinburgh. She is part of an extended Muslim family. She is expected to help out at home and with the family shop, and to speak Urdu with her grandmother. Her family hopes that when she marries she will marry within her own faith and community. Nadia attends Edinburgh University where there are many Asian students. She is doing well there but, while she wants to feel part of the social life of the university, she is expected to come home at the end of the working day to help with domestic tasks.

Activity *Cathy and Nadia*

Copy and complete the table below in relation to adolescent emotional development, stating in the first column the main features of adolescent emotional development in general. In the second and third columns, state the features that may be additional or different for the two case study adolescents, Cathy and Nadia. The activity can be repeated in terms of social, cognitive and other strands of development.

Most adolescents	Cathy	Nadia

Cognitive development

As adolescence progresses, each individual usually moves towards more abstract thought. Thought is not confined to things that can be seen and recognised, but can be applied to unseen things. Ideas and reasoning about one problem can be transferred to similar problems, and experiments in thinking can be performed not only with concrete objects but also with ideas. The individual is capable of envisaging many possible consequences and not just one or two.

CASE STUDY

Cognitive development: Linda

Sixteen-year-old Linda decides to get a part-time job. She thinks around the problem and initially says something like 'I'd like to work in Tesda.' She makes a phone call to Tesda; she is told that she has to get an application form from the Jobcentre. The Jobcentre tells her that no application forms are available since Tesda doesn't have any vacancies at present. Linda doesn't stop there but now starts to think more widely around the problem. She realises that she has to use a lot of different strategies and has to keep persisting until she gets a job. She has to telephone, visit, answer advertisements, ask her friends and, if she still wants to work in Tesda eventually, has to keep contacting the Jobcentre until they have application forms. This strategy works. She hears through a friend that people are needed to serve in a café. She takes on that job and works there until she eventually gains employment at Tesda. A pre-adolescent child would have been capable of thinking it would be good to get a job at Tesda, but it is unlikely that he or she would have had the ability to see alternative avenues, conduct the experiments needed to find out about how to arrive at an alternative solution or have the persistence to get to Tesda in the end.

Some other aspects of cognitive development in adolescence are the ability to understand the impact of the past on the present and of the present on the future, to begin questioning the views of adults that have previously been accepted (through arguments with parents, 'debates' with teachers), to look behind the obvious in books and paintings to appreciate that they often contain more than is explicitly stated about life or the world. Adolescents do not confine themselves to progression in logical thought, they also progress in creative thought. Some adolescents develop immense creative ability through making imaginative leaps. One famous example is Einstein who, at sixteen, imagined himself as a particle of light travelling away from a planet. This sparked off his thoughts towards what eventually became known as the Theory of Relativity. Many young people begin to see the world with new eyes at this age and to make creative and imaginative leaps in the production of masterpieces. If you look at work produced for Standard Grade and Higher Art, the combination of analytical thought and creative leaps of imagination is often quite staggering.

Not all adolescents progress at the same rate or in the same way in their cognitive development. Some reach a stage of analytical thought well before adolescence, some never really reach it, some don't reach it until well into adult life, and some are slow starters but suddenly have an intellectual growth spurt somewhere between age fifteen and twenty-two. This is one of the reasons why some people who do only moderately well in National Certificates and Highers end up gaining first-class honours degrees at university. Another reason for this is the age range among a group of children in the same class. The youngest children in a class may struggle for many years before they are able to achieve parity with their older classmates.

Cultural development

> *... adolescence begins in biology and ends in culture ...*
>
> (Herbert, 2002, p.355)

Whatever the turbulence and search for identity in adolescence, the family, the school and other social institutions continue to be of critical importance in the cultural development of young people:

> *It is exceptional for teenagers to feel torn between the two 'worlds' of parents and peers, certainly on the more important issues of life. There are most likely to be differences of opinion on minor issues such as hairstyle, fashion, social habits and privileges, where parental views are likely to be rejected in favour of the standards of friends. Where major issues are concerned, it seems that only a minority of adolescents radically depart from their parents' views.*
>
> (Herbert, 2002, p.357)

There is another viewpoint that many more than 'a minority of adolescents' depart quite radically from their parents' views and culture, and where this happens it can cause difficulties in many areas of development. Sometimes this is associated with failure to do well at school. If a young person sees school and education negatively, this deprives them of a major influence on cultural development. For vulnerable young people who lack stable family backgrounds, such failure may constitute a double deprivation and they may be led into 'cultures' that affect quite detrimentally other areas of development. The examination of social influences in Chapter 5 provides further insight into this.

Spiritual development

In adolescence young people often think about ultimate questions: the meaning of life; whether or not God exists; who they are and who they want to be. They are concerned with being true to themselves while still trying to find out whom that self is. They are challenging parental and cultural beliefs and testing rules. This is all part of spiritual development.

Activity *Spiritual development*

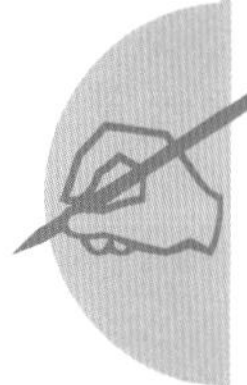

Look again at the poem written by Seonaid on page 145. What aspects of spiritual development can you identify in it?

Creative activities can provide opportunities for spiritual development. Poetry provides a medium for expressing feelings and thoughts; similarly art, drama, dance and other forms of expression can be used. Building on the giftedness of everyone, finding the things that interest them, what they enjoy doing, who they are, can also have a spiritual dimension through recognising these things as part of the essential self and as necessary for self-esteem.

Figure 3.7 Adolescence: young people participating in the Duke of Edinburgh's Award meet many aspects of development while enjoying themselves (see Chapter 6)
(Source: Duke of Edinburgh's Award Scotland)

Table 3.4 Summary of general pattern of development: adolescence

Social	Physical	Emotional	Cognitive	Cultural	Spiritual
Moving further away from the family • Influences of emotional factors • Sexual attraction • Changing relationship with parents • Importance of peer group • Changing roles	How the body changes • Rapid development/ growth spurt; profound physical changes • Development of reproductive system/ puberty – influence of hormones • Changes in body shape • Growth towards adult body shape • Health risks can arise from behavioural issues, e.g. anorexia, drug use, etc.	Developing sense of self • Change and transition • Focus upon self/ identity/ feelings/who am I? • Issues related to difference, e.g. ethnicity, sexuality • Separation • Extreme emotions; often feel misunderstood • Erikson: Identity vs role confusion	How sense is made of the world • More abstract and creative thought; understanding impact of past on present, present on future • Presenting arguments • Questioning views of adults • Thinking beyond conventional limits; use of reasoning • Importance of education	Questioning cultural assumptions • Increasing awareness of other cultures • Questioning and making choices • Increasing influence of friends • Culture reflected in behaviour, dress and activities • Dealing with conflicting cultures	Developing own beliefs; spiritual searching for self • Understanding other perspectives • Challenging parental beliefs • Testing rules • Need for personal space • Search for identity

Adulthood

Read the case studies of the MacDonald and Ahmed families in Chapter 7, where several adults make an appearance: Linda and Joe MacDonald, Aisha Bibi and Tanveer Ahmed, among others. Below are another two short case studies.

CASE STUDY

John and Linda

John and Linda are in their mid-thirties. They are married and have three daughters. At the time of the arrival of their third daughter John had left a stable but to him unsatisfactory career in finance to establish a property development business on a self-employed basis. Linda had a successful career as a scientist in a research laboratory. The couple agreed that after Linda's maternity leave she would return to work on a full-time basis and that John would take on the responsibilities of full-time carer of their children. This has been the most satisfactory option for everyone.

Alex

Alex is a journalist in his mid-forties. He lives alone and has never married but plays an active role as uncle to his four nieces and nephews. His career is very, very important to him and he loves his work, the unpredictability of it and the fact that he is frequently sent on assignments abroad. He is writing a book about motorbikes in his spare time. He has a boyfriend who is a doctor and with whom he has a long-standing sexual relationship. They have considered living together but decided to maintain independent households, especially as they lead such different lives. They do, however, spend holidays together every year.

All of these people are adults but their differing experiences reflect the enormous range of factors to be considered in this section. The period of adulthood examined here is from about 20 to 65, though some people much younger than 20 are functioning as adults, some people of 26 still appear to be experiencing adolescence, and some people over 65 are performing as adults in their middle years. Rayner (2005) emphasises that features of adolescence recur throughout adulthood:

> *However, if 'adolescing', with its regression, romance and madness, is not kept alive throughout our lives then we neither have the means to change ourselves nor can we provide the environment for others to change. We become either very dull, shrunken people unable to face crisis, or arthritic martinets, self-satisfied with power and unable to be either humble or flexible.*

Social development

Forming and maintaining intimate relationships including friendships, the changing roles brought about by parenthood, work and partnership, and the social networks that individuals form as a result of these roles and relationships, are all part of the pattern of social development. These major factors involved in social development are also those that influence emotional development (see page 155 for more detail on this). The subject of **work** is discussed as a link among all aspects of development in adulthood.

> *It is a great matter for a man to find his own line, and keep to it. You get along faster on your own rail …*
>
> (Janet Aitken in the Glasgow School of Art's magazine (1893) – 'man' here is an all-encompassing term for 'person'; quoted in Jones, 1990)

The case study below demonstrates some of the links among various aspects of development.

CASE STUDY

Stuart and Eileen

Stuart and Eileen are senior care workers in a residence for people with sensory and learning disability. They both enjoy their work and, in their desire to further their knowledge and career prospects, have signed up for an evening class in social sciences. They don't know that they have both signed up for the same course until they meet at the first class. They get into the habit of going for a drink after the class and often discuss their course homework while at work if they are on the same shift. Before long they are seeing each other for social events at the weekend, discover that they share similar ways of looking at life and the world, and eventually decide that they would like to live together and start a family.

This case study shows how work can link social, physical, emotional, cognitive, cultural and spiritual development. Through mutual interests, empathetic relationships can develop that are physical, cognitive, social, emotional, cultural and spiritual in nature. Work is one of the key sources of self-esteem for the individual and one way in which individuals identify themselves. If someone is asked to describe him/herself, the kind of work done is usually one of the ways in which the individual wishes to be known. In the short case studies at the beginning of this chapter and the longer ones at the end of the book you will see that: Alex's role as a journalist is very important to him; Linda is a scientist; John is a property developer and the main carer of his and Linda's children; Senga is a care manager; Tanveer is an engineer; and Aisha is a social worker. All of these work roles are bound up with other aspects of the individual's emotional life to promote self-esteem and develop identity. Self-esteem and identity are part of emotional development. Work, though, is also a social role and can be a source of friendship and partnership. In this sense it is also part of social development. Since work has the potential to contribute so much to development it is understandable that the loss of it may cause more problems than just the lack of a wage. It can have an impact on an individual's emotional and social life, as well as on other aspects of development.

Work is usually a term used to refer to paid employment, but many people do work for which they receive neither pay nor recognition. Unlike unemployment, this can provide a clear role and a strong sense of purpose and worth. Roy McGivney, who was interviewed for this book, volunteers as a Children's Panel member, an advocate and a drug and alcohol counsellor. He gains great work satisfaction from these roles, seeing them as his contribution to society (see quotation page 21). Anne Redpath, a Scottish artist born in Galashiels, makes the point that for many years she devoted herself to her family and her home, rather than to painting, and that this was just as relevant to her as any other kind of work. She says:

> *I put everything I had into house and furniture and dresses and good food and people. All that's the same as painting really, and the experience went back into art when I began painting again.*
>
> (Long, 1996)

This passage shows that there can be links between paid work and the work of being at home, and that the one has great relevance for the other. The experience of running a household and bringing up children does go back into and enrich later work experience, yet it is so often undervalued by employers, and often by people themselves.

Like work, **parenthood** also illustrates the links among all aspects of development. In terms of social development it provides the social roles of mother and father and it creates social as well as emotional bonds between parents and their children. Parenthood also provides networks with other parents through meeting at such places as playgroups, health centres and schools. It is often a source of change in social relationships and roles. As you read the following sections, examine parenthood in terms of each aspect of development.

Physical development

Until adulthood, physical development is a prime force influencing social and cognitive development. In adults cognitive, emotional and social forces influence physical change, development and health to a much greater degree than in earlier life. There are some physical changes, however, that are characteristic of adult life, some associated with younger adult life and others associated with middle adult life. By adulthood physical development, including sexual development, is virtually complete, though sexual identity in terms of heterosexuality, homosexuality or other sexual orientation may not be. Young adulthood is usually the healthiest period of life, when people are at peak fitness. Footballers, for example, usually play at their best in their twenties; athletes are also at their peak then. Serious illness in young adulthood is quite unusual, with the greatest threat to health being accidents, especially road traffic accidents. While the number of people killed or seriously injured in car accidents is steadily decreasing, the number of adults killed on bicycles is increasing. Young men in cars continue to be a high-risk group.

> *Deaths from road traffic accidents are much more prevalent among the under-25s than other causes of death often reported by the media such as hangings, shootings, stabbings, alcohol or drug abuse. Between the ages of 15 and 24 a young person is twice as likely to die from a road traffic accident than he is to be fatally assaulted by firearms, a sharp/blunt object or intentional self-harm via hanging combined. Those in the 15–24 age category are also four times more likely to die from a road traffic accident than from drug, alcohol or other substance poisoning.*
>
> (**www.racfoundation.org**, accessed 12 January 2015)

Activity *Age of peak fitness*

Find out the ages of ten key players in the Scottish Premier Football League or another very active sport of your choice. Calculate the average age by adding all the ages together and dividing by ten. This should give you some indication of the age of peak fitness.

Pregnancy and childbirth are among the major physical events for many young women. These have enormous implications for their emotional and social lives. The age at which women who have children give birth to their first child is on average much later than it was twenty years ago. There are now possibilities for women who would previously have been unable to have children to receive fertility treatment. Pregnancy and childbirth are still risky events in terms of health, though both maternal and infant mortality are at very low levels in Scotland compared with other countries and the rest of the UK. Between 2003 and 2009 there were 34 maternal deaths in Scotland, averaging 4.8 per year (*Herald Scotland*, 2013, based on NHS figures). A slight rise in maternal deaths in recent years is attributed to the increasing age at which women have their first child and to issues related to obesity.

As adulthood progresses, the individual's way of life determines to some extent the physical changes that take place. Many people from their thirties, forties or fifties onwards gain weight and lose physical fitness, but these gains and losses are neither universal nor inevitable. Lifestyle is a major influence, and a combination of diet, exercise and low stress levels can combine to promote good physical health throughout the adult years. Low alcohol consumption and not smoking also contribute to the maintenance of good health. There is some inevitable loss of speed of reaction and of muscularity as adulthood proceeds. This is why winners of the Tour de France, for example, are not usually over 30 years of age. On the other hand, stamina often increases with age and compensates for some of the physical losses. Mountaineers such as Chris Bonnington continued to conquer high peaks well into their fifties, and Beryl Burton, a cyclist, continued to compete in 100-mile races into her forties.

One major physical life event affecting women in middle adulthood is the **menopause**. This is caused by a decrease in levels of the hormone oestrogen, which leads to a cessation of menstruation and the ability to produce children. It does not lead to a cessation of sexual activity, though levels of sexual desire do usually decrease considerably for both men and women as young adulthood gives way to middle age. Like adolescence, menopause can be a time of great emotional upheaval, and a time when women reassess their lives, their relationships and their sense of self and purpose, particularly if they no longer have dependent children to care for.

Emotional development

The self continues to emerge throughout the adult years, and it is presented with many life experiences and events that contribute to this process. Work, partnership (marriage and other sexual relationships), friendships, parenthood, sexuality, transitions, crises, achievements and interests all play a part. The emerging self is constantly faced with choices and questions that influence the course of this development and the resulting adult identity. Women and men in their thirties, for example, may be asking themselves 'Should we have children?' or 'Should we have more children?' or 'Should I change my career, change my partner, am I happy with him/her?' Some periods of adulthood can be very emotionally stressful. Even quite positive events such as marriage and holidays can create tension. A sufficient number of tense or stressful events, or one extremely stressful one, can lead to a crisis. Usually in a crisis the individual's normal coping mechanisms do not work very well, and support from others may be of vital importance.

Activity *Stress and life events*

It is quite interesting for you to look at your own level of stress. One indicator of this is the scale devised by Holmes and Rahe (1967) and adapted by Powell (1997).

Look at the list of the major life events below. Read through them and circle those that you have experienced in the last twelve months. Once you have done this, add up your score, which will give you an approximate measure of how vulnerable you may be to stress-related problems.

Do not become too concerned if you score very highly (i.e. in excess of 300). You may just thrive on change and/or be very well supported. You are not necessarily in crisis.

1	death of spouse or life partner	100
2	divorce or separation	75
3	major illness or injury	70
4	loss of a job	70
5	problems with the law/imprisonment	70
6	death of someone close	60
7	marital reconciliation	60
8	retirement	60
9	illness in immediate family	50
10	marriage or moving in with partner	50
11	moving house or major renovation	50
12	gaining a new family member through birth or adoption	50
13	pregnancy	45
14	increase in the number of arguments or disagreements with partner	45
15	large mortgage, loan or debt	45
16	changing jobs or starting a new job	45
17	unexpected accident or trauma	45
18	changes at work/increased demands	35
19	outstanding personal achievement or promotion	35
20	caring for an elderly or sick relative or friend	35
21	problems with relatives, family, friends or neighbours	35
22	financial worries	35
23	examinations, extra study or having to speak in public	30

24 changes in social activities 30
25 changes in recreational activities 30
26 children going or 'growing' away 30
27 premenstrual syndrome or menopause 30
28 starting a new relationship 30
29 going on holiday 20
30 family gatherings, e.g. Christmas 20

How to interpret your score:

- **Over 280 (high vulnerability)**: you have experienced an unusually high number of stressful events in the last year. Illness is not inevitable, however, as a result of such events. Your resilience, personality and ability to cope will determine how well you react.
- **130–280 (moderate vulnerability)**: you have experienced a number of stressful events in the last year, which could increase your risk of stress-related illnesses. The more you know about such events and the likely effects they will have on you, the better prepared you will be for similar events in the future.
- **Below 130 (low vulnerability)**: you have experienced few stressful events in the last year and your life seems fairly settled. If you are aware of how affected you may be by major events, however, you will be better prepared for future changes.

Most of the events on the Holmes and Rahe scale are either **transitions** or losses (discussed earlier in this chapter). Two factors that are important in coping with transition and loss are the degree of support that is available to the individual and the individual's coping mechanisms. Part of emotional development is to find positive ways to deal with the many transitions and losses that adult life presents. If this is not achieved – either because the individual has not found ways to cope, or because of lack of support, or because the level of stress or crisis is just too great, or a combination of these things – the consequences for psychological and physical health can be severe. Table 3.5 shows a comparison of two possible routes to adjustment in adulthood.

Table 3.5 Adjustment to transition and loss

Positive adjustment	Negative adjustment
Excited about life	Anxious
Keen to seize opportunities	Dissatisfied
At home with self	Feelings of inadequacy
Happy about the future	Feelings of guilt
Well supported by friends and family	Doesn't feel well supported
Able to take transition in stride	Very stressed by transition
Works through loss by facing it and grieving	Experiences prolonged depression as a result of loss

Activity *Emotional adjustment*

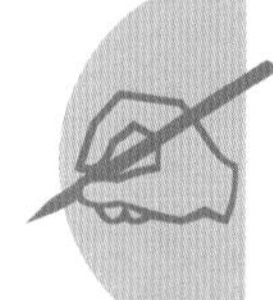

The emotional adjustment of adults to different events in their lives depends on many factors. From your reading in this chapter and your own experience, list at least six of these factors.

You may have thought of: past history including experience of attachment and loss, resilience, heredity, level of support, personality and attitude, state of physical health, stage of life.

Support has been mentioned several times as being important in adult emotional development. Where does this support come from? One important source is relationships of intimacy with partners/spouses, friends and relatives. These relationships of intimacy are, at their best, reciprocal, satisfying and a source of stability from which the individual can face the outside world and its challenges. They also contribute to the individual's identity. The roles of partner, husband, wife, friend, daughter, son, etc. all become ways in which the individual identifies him/herself in the outside world. Identity is also enhanced through the creative roles that the individual plays through parenthood, work and/or creative pursuits.

Parenthood is one major life transition that brings change in relationships, lifestyle, roles and responsibilities. Ideally for most people this experience is shared with someone they love and to whom they have made a meaningful, lasting and intimate commitment.

Sexuality influences many aspects of development in adulthood, including emotional development. We have seen statements from Seonaid as a twelve-year-old and during adolescence. Here she is again, aged 28 and embarking on a degree course, describing the impact of her sexuality.

CASE STUDY

Seonaid

'As a teenager I realised I was gay, which added to the confusion of who I was and where I belonged … I had a large group of friends at school but always felt different, never understanding the reasoning for this. Eventually I realised the root cause and kept it secret through fear of being discriminated against … Lack of awareness of homosexuality increased my discomfort with my own identity, and confused my expectations of those around me. Gradually I became more comfortable and began to tell people, which increased my confidence and self-acceptance. It was a long process, however, which was easier around strangers than people I knew.

'Whenever I began to feel settled in a place, I moved and re-invented myself somewhere new. This constant re-establishment provided insights into various other areas of life, which broadened my understanding of what makes different people act and react in certain ways. From these experiences my eyes were also opened to hardship and suffering, not only my own, but of those around me ... Being part of a minority group provides greater empathy and understanding of those in a similar position. The feelings of uncertainty and unsettlement that disadvantaged people experience, as well as knowledge of the damage discrimination can do, become a part of the personal value base. It also provides a genuine belief that everyone is equal and deserves the same chance in life.

'I was fortunate enough to meet a partner who encouraged me to recognise the lessons I had learned and put them to use ... I applied for several jobs in the care sector and was employed to work with disadvantaged adults ... Although the job was physically demanding and mentally draining, five minutes of positivity from a service user could overshadow an otherwise disastrous shift. Empowering a person to undertake tasks they were previously incapable of, and seeing the joy this could bring them, made it all worthwhile. It also allowed me to develop an understanding of people with severe learning disabilities, and realise that they are people the same as anyone else, with likes and dislikes, and opinions and ambitions ...'

Cognitive development

In adulthood cognitive/intellectual development is associated with knowledge and skills gained through further and higher education, work, hobbies and interests. The application and development of knowledge in relation to everyday life, for example, through parenthood, and the passing on of knowledge and skills to other people, are also of importance. Individuals make choices about cognitive development and also differ in the opportunities open to them. Some people see leaving school as the end of their need to develop intellectually, though many feel the frustration and stagnation of this in later years and return to some form of education and/or training. Others lack the opportunities to develop to their maximum potential. Cognitive development is, as a consequence, impaired or delayed. For some adults the intellectual demands of partnership and/or parenthood provide an additional or alternative route to cognitive development and they direct their thinking and learning towards making a success of home and/or family life.

Assuming that one or more of the above avenues of cognitive development is available, most adults show a fairly steady or improving level of ability throughout their young and middle adult years. For example, in a long-term study by Schaie (1994), mathematical ability and verbal comprehension began to decline only after the age of 67. Many adults show improving ability on tests of vocabulary, comprehension and general knowledge, especially if their everyday lives present opportunities for learning or they purposefully pursue intellectually stimulating interests, read a lot and/or travel.

If you look back at the case studies throughout this chapter you will see that the people discussed have developed cognitively in many different ways in adulthood; for example, Stuart and Eileen have undergone training for their respective careers. They have also decided to start a family, through which they can pass on their own learning and develop the skills of child care. Seonaid's cognitive development has been influenced by her sexuality, and she has used her experience of dislocation and discomfort to think about the needs of others and eventually to embark on a degree course.

Activity *Cognitive development*

Choose two of the adults mentioned in the case study at the beginning of this section (page 152). State how you think they may have developed cognitively during their adult lives, and consider the factors that have contributed to this.

Cultural development

By the time people reach adulthood they will have acquired many aspects of a cultural identity. They will speak in a language, and often a dialect, of others who share the way they do things; they will have customs that they follow, for example in relation to marriage or partnership, childbirth, celebrations such as Ramadan, Diwali and Chinese New Year; they may be established geographically in a particular place with an associated cultural identity; they may have tastes in music, art and literature that reflect their cultural heritage and their cultural preferences; there will be agreed norms and behaviours that they will expect of themselves and of others with whom they interact.

Activity *Cultural development*

Identify five aspects of your own life and identity that reflect your cultural development. Contrast these with those of someone with a very different cultural identity.

Spiritual development

> *Spirituality is increasingly of interest in both health and social care settings. We know that spiritual practices and attention to spiritual and/or religious needs help people to feel better and to cope with illness and distressful circumstances, as well as helping them to understand positive life experiences.*
>
> (Aberdeen City Council, 2011)

Adults who have had the opportunity to develop spiritually, to think and make decisions about what is important to them and what they believe in, to be fulfilled and to integrate this into the way they lead their lives, are likely to have a sense of spiritual well-being. It is unlikely that their lives are free from difficulty, but if they have established firm spiritual foundations they are more likely to have an optimistic outlook and ability to cope in times of stress. People continue to need personal space to think and reflect. Questioning is likely to continue throughout life but during adulthood beliefs are likely to become more firmly established and to be reinforced by the choice of friendships and partner and by the groups to which the individual belongs. Creative activities, and an appreciation of the creations of others, also provide opportunities for fulfilment and reflection and can play a part in spiritual development. All of this contributes to enabling people to become themselves, to become the person they want to be. This is of course a very optimistic view, but something for which spiritual development at least gives us the opportunity to strive.

Table 3.6 Summary of general pattern of development: adulthood

Social	Physical	Emotional	Cognitive	Cultural	Spiritual
Relationships • Intimate relationships/ partnerships • Roles and changes in role • Social networks – may experience stressful periods, e.g. mid-life transition • Effects of poverty and discrimination • Parenthood and responsibility	How the body changes • Importance of cognitive, emotional and social factors • Peak fitness in young adulthood; stamina increases • Pregnancy, childbirth and menopause • Relationship between lifestyle and health • Often loss of speed/ increase in bulk	Developing sense of identity • Influences of work, partnership, friends, parenthood • Transitions, crises and achievements • Importance of support • Roles and identity • Erikson: Intimacy vs isolation (20s); Generativity vs stagnation (late 20s to 50s)	How sense is made of the world • Different choices and opportunities • Often improving level of ability and creativity • Applying knowledge to work, parenthood and other life situations • Cognitive skills and ability to make moral judgements increase in complexity	Increasing confidence in cultural identity • Language and ethnicity as part of cultural identity • Passing culture to next generation • May accept other cultures • Belong to institutions that reflect cultural beliefs • Environment reflects culture	Sense of self, wholeness and balance • For well-being need to feel fulfilled and integrated • Gives direction and value • Beliefs more firmly established • Need for personal space to think • Sense of self

Older adulthood

> *The young photographer said he hoped that he would see his subject the following year. 'I don't see why not – you look in pretty good health to me,' replied Jeanne Calment on the occasion of her 120th birthday.*
>
> (Anon, 2007)

In this section a conscious effort is made to get away from the 'all doom and gloom' view of old age. Although old age is rather a mixed bag of advantages and disadvantages, many older people, even those with illnesses and disabilities, lead rich and fruitful lives. A class of care students was asked whom they thought are or were good examples of famous older adults. Here are their suggestions: Sean Connery, the Queen, Nelson Mandela, Bruce Forsyth, Omar Sharif, and Clint Eastwood. Their teachers added Paul Newman, Judi Dench, Meryl Streep, Billy Connelly, and Jeanne Calment, quoted above, who rode a bike until she was 100 and appeared in a film at the age of 114, the same year that she stopped smoking. You can probably think of other examples of older people who are or were active and content in old age. More opportunities than ever are available for older people to learn, to participate in exercise, to live in better health. Relative poverty is, unfortunately, still a problem for many, and efforts need to be made to maximise benefit uptake, for example, and to ensure that those who are young adults now make adequate financial provision for when they are old.

Social development

The influences and events of earlier life are important in the social development of older adults, but are not necessarily determining factors. For some this is a time of rejuvenation, increased social contacts, more friends and time to pursue social activities. Friendship can play a major part in the lives of many older adults. The functions of friendship in later life can be summed up through the 'three As': aid, affect and affirmation. Friends give and receive help, provide love and affirm people's self-concepts. This demonstrates a link between emotional and social well-being.

The initial average increase in social contacts tends to diminish in older adulthood as contact with friends can be lost through death and ill health. Unless an older adult, or others such as care workers and family members, makes a conscious effort to maintain outside links, isolation can result, which for many is a very depressing experience. Some isolation is aggravated by the restrictions placed on elderly people by low income, which makes facilitating claims for appropriate benefit entitlements particularly important. Empowerment can sometimes be gained only through access to cash.

Here are two examples from Slater (1995), which relate to the social lives of some older adults:

> *Police had to be called to Highwood Court old people's social club … after neighbours complained about the noise coming from a karaoke session.*

> *Mrs Harman now prefers the company of people her own age, who can talk about the same things …*

Other older adults may enjoy spending time with grandchildren, continuing to work in some capacity, attending the community centre, going line dancing or to step-and-tone classes, going to university or college, or joining the University of the Third Age, working in an allotment or going to the library. Heim's (1990) research indicated that, although physical confidence decreases with age, social confidence often increases. Here is an example of one couple who met later in life. As you can see, their social life also had an impact on their emotional life.

> *Lovebirds Fred and Mary Collingwood became one of Britain's oldest newlyweds when they married last Thursday – with a combined age of 178. War hero Fred, who was blinded at Normandy during the Second World War, met bride Mary at a social club for blind and partially sighted people in May. The pair formed a close friendship, and said that turned to romance after a 'quick kiss and a cuddle' on a sofa at the club … Mary said: 'It has been a whirlwind and now I couldn't do without him. I've said to him that if he dies we are going together. I've been happier than I've been in years. Freddie is a wonderful man and a great companion and makes me laugh a lot. I've had a wonderful day and I'm looking forward to many more years of fun and friendship with Freddie. I always talk to him as if he can see. I just can't get it into my head that he's blind.'*
>
> (**www.bbc.co.uk/news**, 20 October 2014)

Bee and Mitchell (1984) sum up social development as follows. From ages 65 to 75 there is:

> *Usually a maintenance of social contacts, particularly with family. Friends are important here especially for maintaining life satisfaction. There is little evidence of any withdrawal or disengagement. Retirement, which occurs during this time for most adults, appears to cause relatively little trauma for most.*

From age 75 on:

> *There appears to be some social disengagement, at least for some older adults, during this period, although most elderly adults continue to see their children and other family members with some regularity and to spend time with friends.*

Physical development

> *The really cool thing is that even nonagenarians who have lost muscle strength can get it back … we're reaching old age in better and better shape …*
>
> (Anon, 2007)

When you first look at old age the evidence does seem somewhat negative: hearing, vision and balance tend to deteriorate, speed of movement decreases, skin loses elasticity and is more likely to wrinkle, there is usually some hair loss and hair pigment loss so that most 'old people' have grey or white hair. The major organs of the body deteriorate, but much more slowly than you probably think. This is all balanced to some extent by fewer physical demands. The physical effects of ageing can be ameliorated by exercise, attitude and nutrition, as well as by inherited genetic characteristics and other environmental influences. When you actually look at older adults the variation is enormous. One person of 80 may be confined to a wheelchair or able to walk only very short distances with a Zimmer, he may have a multitude of minor ailments; another will be cycling to play cards with her friends and ploughing up and down the lanes at the swimming pool three times a week. She may have several minor ailments but when asked about her health will say 'I'm fine' ... and mean it. There are those who still have an active sex life into their seventies and eighties.

On the positive side, then, improvements in health, nutrition and hygiene in recent years mean that fewer people are dying prematurely and that those who do survive into their eighties are generally healthier than they would have been ten years ago. People are living longer in general. In 2013 there were an estimated 850 centenarians (people aged 100 or over) in Scotland. This is a 60 per cent increase from 2003, when there were an estimated 530 centenarians (General Register Office for Scotland, 2014a). In 2011, 18 per cent of the residents of Scotland were over 65 (General Register Office for Scotland, 2014b). A large majority of these people are able to live rich, full lives with health that is at least moderately good. The negative view of old age results not from the effects of primary ageing, which is slow and gradual, but from the results of secondary ageing resulting from disease, lack of exercise and such pursuits as excessive drinking and smoking. People who continue to be fit and active can usually expect to reap the benefits in a healthier old age.

Emotional development

There is an emotional rollercoaster in older age: down for bereavement and loss, up for becoming a grandparent; down for retirement for some, up for retirement for others; down when a child gets divorced, up for a sense of contentment; down when ill health occurs, up if health is maintained; down when a family member or friend moves away, up when new friends and activities are gained; down for dependence, up for independence. Some of the losses of old age can have profound effects of either a short- or long-term nature. Loss and bereavement were discussed earlier in the chapter and are therefore not discussed here. One major transition of old age that has both emotional and social consequences is that of **retirement**. For many people a part of self-image and identity is their paid or unpaid work. Paid work usually ceases any time from 55 to 75 and this, for some people, results in a loss of both status and self-esteem. This is to some extent a reflection of negative attitudes of society to retired people, but there can be compensations. Some people see retirement not as a loss but as an opportunity and a release from stress.

CASE STUDY

Alan

Alan has been employed all of his working life in a brewery but what he had always really wanted to do was have a beautiful garden. He had always kept his fairly large garden neat and tidy but had never been able to devote much time to it. When he retired he was able to pursue his lifelong passion for plants. He bought a greenhouse, grew some unusual varieties of plant from seed and entered horticultural competitions. He was so successful that within a year of retirement he exhibited some begonia plants in a competition, gaining first prize.

A less positive reaction to retirement is quoted in Rayner (1986):

> *Mrs F. went on working in a pub until she was over 70, when she slipped and bruised herself one day. She lost her job through being off sick. She recovered quite quickly but never went back to work ... She slowly became quiet and apathetic ... She usually shuffled about the house in boots and several layers of clothing.*

Activity ***Attitudes to retirement***

Research the reactions to retirement of four older people whom you know or to whom you are able to talk. Write a short account of their response in terms of consequences for their emotional lives, including self-esteem and self-concept. If you do not know anyone to talk to, look at relevant websites such as that of Age UK.

In care settings it is most important that the way in which care is provided maintains or enhances self-esteem as far as possible. This means promoting empowerment and independence and minimising possible effects of institutionalisation, which can lead to what Goffman (1968) called 'mortification of self' and a state of learned helplessness. Learned helplessness is a decline in the desire and ability to do things beyond what may be expected in relation to a person's state of health. It usually occurs among people who 'give up' because other people won't let them do things or allow them to exercise any control over their own lives.

The emotional situation of older people from **ethnic minorities** deserves some special attention. Most people of Asian and Caribbean ancestry place a very high value on the care of their older people. If they have few or no supports, however, this can result in shame, loss and depression; this was illustrated by Fenton (1987) in relation to research in Bristol. Emotional problems may be compounded by isolation, poverty, racism and discrimination. Building positive self-esteem among this population can be a vital part of the care task.

There are many **positive aspects** to growing older. For many older adults, grandchildren can be a source of great joy and emotional satisfaction. Grandchildren come without many of the financial and emotional stresses of parenthood. Grandparents can enjoy their company and care in time-limited amounts, though they still need to work to create positive and fulfilling relationships. Slater (1995) writes about Mrs Patel, who loves the noise and laughter her grandchildren bring.

Old age presents a sense of freedom for some older adults. Marjorie Dickens appears to have a great deal of emotional satisfaction in her present state:

> *I like it that I can do as I please, go where I want, and if I can afford it, buy what I want to, and eat what I want.*

(Slater, 1995)

Cognitive development

Slowing down is generally regarded as one of the features of the cognitive state of older adults. This is different from deterioration, for which there is scant evidence except in people experiencing specific illnesses such as Alzheimer's disease.

Here's an example quoted by Slater (1995):

> *I am a 73-year-old 'wrinkly' who, determined not to become a cabbage after retirement, took up the piano at the age of 70. So far I have obtained Grades 1 and 2 … Three days a week I work for an international trading company. My shorthand is still 120 plus and touch typing is second nature to me. I would like to take up other things but time is too demanding at present …*

Longitudinal studies (which study the same people over a period of time) show little, if any, drop in mental ability with age (Schaie, 1994). Although there is some slowing down in the rate at which people process information and some decline in tasks that require speed, 'there is no sizable decline in memory, knowledge or the ability to learn'. It is interesting that, in a test of 'obscure knowledge', older adults actually did better than younger ones. Do you know what 'deliticulate' means, or for what the Greek writer Antigorus was noted? Older people (over 65) scored higher on such items than younger persons (Slater, 1995).

Evidence from studies of older adults on adult learning courses (for example, those run by the Open University or the University of the Third Age, which, at the beginning of 2015, had 342,783 members in the UK) illustrates that, although older people may be slower, they have more time to grasp things, they persevere more than younger learners, and they bring to their learning wisdom and experience of life that compensate for a lack of speed (Slater, 1995). Birren and Fisher (1992) indicated a link between physical health, exercise and cognitive ability, concluding that exercise may help to ameliorate some of the age-related slowing down in responses. *Mastermind*, the long-lived test of knowledge on television, was the subject of a study by Maylor (1994), who found that ageing didn't seem to affect performance at all on the 'specialised subject' round and that older 'masterminds' did better than younger on general knowledge.

While there are many adults who do show a decline in cognitive functioning in later life, as with physical ageing there are enormous variations often related to such secondary causes as disease, lack of exercise and high alcohol consumption. In general, although there is a decline in the speed at which intellectual tasks can be performed, there is stability in solving the problems of everyday life and in knowledge and verbal comprehension.

Cultural development

Cultural development continues into old age and is usually a continuation of the developments experienced in earlier adulthood. As with all aspects of older adulthood, there are both losses and gains. The world and culture of work usually, though not always, becomes less important in old age, while other aspects of culture may become more important. Some older adults become grandparents and take on new roles, which themselves vary from culture to culture. Different cultures have different attitudes and practices in relation to old age. Erikson (see Chapter 4) saw old age as a conflict between integrity and despair. Cultural attitudes of negativity to older adults in many Western countries can lead to despair for some people, who can see their ageing process only in terms of loss; for others, new roles and opportunities for cultural development lead them towards integrity.

Spiritual development

The positive integration of all aspects of development can lead to the positive spiritual outcomes of feeling respected, valued and worthwhile. There continues to be development in this aspect of life, with older adults helped or hindered by their resolution of moral and spiritual dilemmas. They may be helped by their established beliefs towards a feeling of wholeness and balance. If they feel that they have achieved what they wanted to achieve they are likely to feel spiritual well-being, although cultural attitudes towards old age can affect aspects of spiritual development.

Whatever the older adult's circumstances, there continues to be a need for opportunities to gain or maintain spiritual well-being through shared and individual activities and periods of peacefulness, respect for their beliefs and opportunities to practise them, and the provision of resources for creative and imaginative activities. A poetry group was one of the highlights of a day centre for older adults in which I worked. Almost everyone participated either as a writer or as a listener and/or critic. For some people it was a major avenue for expressing feelings, the way they felt about life; they could say things in a poem that it was almost impossible to say through any other medium. In this way their spiritual development was enhanced.

Figure 3.8 Across the generations

Table 3.7 Summary of general pattern of development: older adulthood

Social	Physical	Emotional	Cognitive	Cultural	Spiritual
Relationships • Friends, family and social networks or isolation • Changing roles, e.g. due to retirement • Social confidence • Sometimes improvements in social life and networks – more time for these • Relationships across generations, e.g. grand-parenting	How the body changes • Usually healthy; slow but gradual loss of abilities • Importance of exercise/diet • Enormous variation • Dealing with health crises • Greatly influenced by other aspects of development	Sense of self • Identity issues often related to changing roles • Transition and loss, e.g. bereavement • Influence of isolation, discrimination, poverty and their opposites • Changing sense of self • Erikson: Integrity vs despair	How sense is made of the world • Wisdom and experience • May be slower to grasp new things but usually able to compensate • Continuing ability to learn • Linked with health • Most people mentally alert but may be short-term memory loss	Behaviour, thoughts and beliefs of culture • Attitudes to old age culturally influenced • Maintenance of cultural identity • Culture of work replaced with other activities • Grandparent roles culturally varied • Cultural interests may be developed, e.g. art, music	Sense of self, wholeness and balance • Search for meaning in life is of great significance • Continuing need for wholeness and balance • Need opportunities for peace and reflection • Need to feel respected, valued and worthwhile • Belief may help process of ageing and attitudes to death and dying

SUMMARY

This chapter has encouraged you to develop a lifespan approach to seeing development as a process that continues throughout life. We looked at some underpinning concepts in understanding development and behaviour, and the meaning of behaviour and development along the strands of social, physical, emotional, cognitive, cultural and spiritual. Throughout this chapter you have been encouraged to apply your learning to case study situations. The following areas have been covered in this chapter:

- the meaning of development and behaviour
- the nature/nurture debate
- developmental concepts: attachment and separation; resilience; transition and loss; socialisation
- the strands of development and behaviour (social, physical, emotional, cognitive, cultural, spiritual) and their characteristics at different life stages, from infancy to older adulthood
- activities and case studies, which encourage you to apply your thinking.

The following Activity, in common with all of the Activities in this chapter, covers content for the Higher and National 4 and 5 units Care: Human Development and Behaviour. It provides the foundation for the application of the psychological and sociological perspectives and theories outlined in Chapters 4 and 5.

Activity *A tale of two families*

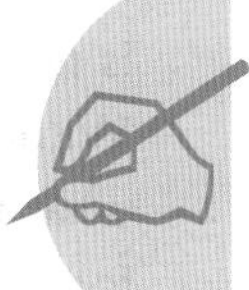

Read the accounts below of individuals in the MacDonald and Ahmed families at different life stages, and then answer the questions that follow. The people referred to are described in Chapter 7 and in Appendix 1.

The MacDonald and Ahmed families

Alisha Ahmed is 6 months old. Her great aunt, Aisha Bibi, is looking after her one weekend afternoon and gets out a book of nursery rhymes. Alisha tries to grab the book and put it in her mouth. When her aunt starts to sing some of the rhymes to her she becomes very excited and, although she can't say the words, she makes sounds as if she is joining in. She has heard most of these rhymes before and laughs when she can anticipate what will happen next. When it comes to 'Incy, wincy spider' she tries to do the hand movements of the spider climbing the water spout.

Billy McKay, aged 2, is on a family outing to the park with his parents. He seems to be enjoying himself as he is pushed backwards and forwards on the swing and goes down the small slide. He then has two biscuits and a drink for his snack. He says 'more' after the second biscuit; when his father says, 'No, come on, let's go back to the swings', Billy throws himself on the ground and screams for another biscuit. His father gets annoyed and tells him to be quiet and they all leave the park with Billy still crying for another biscuit. Billy falls asleep in his pushchair on the way home and when he wakes up an hour later he is smiling, gives his parents a hug and plays with his toys.

Kamran Ahmed is 6 years old. He is at a family birthday party for one of his cousins but he is not participating in any of the games. He sits surrounded by building blocks seemingly oblivious to all of the other children, intent on building a tower. He gets very upset when this is knocked down by one of the other children, going into a state of panic and breathing jerkily until he is almost blue in the face. His mother tries to comfort him. He doesn't respond to this but eventually calms down when he is distracted by another building toy. His grandmother calls his name from the other side of the room but he doesn't seem to recognise that she is calling him. He just carries on trying to fit together pieces of the second building toy.

Joey MacDonald is now 21. You should imagine Joey when he was 13, however, as in the case study in Appendix 1. Joey has arranged to go to an evening football match with Fred, his befriender. This is usually an event to which they both look forward. They arrange to meet at Joey's house at 5 p.m. But where is Joey? It is now 6 p.m., and kick-off isn't far off. At 6:15 Joey slouches into the house. Without saying anything he goes to his room and slams the door. When Fred asks what the matter is Joey tells him to go away, says that he hates Fred and hates football and wants to be left alone.

Farah Riaz, aged 29, trained as an accountant and is the mother of Kamran and Alisha. She is enjoying a weekend away with her sister, visiting their aunt and uncle in Lancashire. They spend a day visiting old haunts from their childhood and reminding one another of what they used to do when they were students together. For Farah this is a welcome interval in a rather difficult, though generally happy, life. She enjoys being a mother and feels guilty about being away from her children. On the other hand she knows she needs a rest and a break, especially as her son Kamran is a source of great anxiety. She talks a lot about her children and her concerns.

Jean Davies, aged 80, is spending the day at the Doward, where she has chosen to take a dance class in the morning, stay for her lunch and participate in an international development group in the afternoon run by a member of the centre, where she learns about the issues affecting different countries and uses her sewing skills to make clothes to send to families in need. She loves her day as it gives her contact with other people and a chance to make a contribution. She says she may be 80 but she isn't old yet. She experiences one or two health problems, with angina being the worst of these. She can remember quite well but says she has to write things down or she forgets to do them. She forgot to meet her daughter Maureen for lunch last week, but she says that was because the lunch hadn't been finalised so she hadn't written it down. She goes home after her day at the centre and cooks herself a meal, before settling down to do the daily crossword in the newspaper. Her daughter Senga phones in the evening to ask what sort of day she had.

Choose two of the above people and answer the following questions in relation to each one.

1 Copy and complete the table below for each person. Give two features of 'normal' development for a person of their age for each strand (SPECCS), and give two features of development for each strand for each of the two individuals you have chosen (which may be the same, or different from, the norm).

	Social	**Physical**	**Emotional**	**Cognitive**	**Cultural**	**Spiritual**
'Normal' development (1)						
'Normal' development (2)						
Person A (1)						
Person A (2)						
Person B (1)						
Person B (2)						

2 For each individual you have chosen, identify relevant features and consequences of two of the following: attachment, separation, loss, transition, resilience.
3 Once you have completed this activity for two people, go on to complete it for the other people described.

Suggested reading

Books

Crawford, K. and Walker, J. (2014) *Social Work and Human Development*, **4th edition. London: Sage.**

This book demonstrates how knowledge of human development helps in establishing effective partnerships with people who use social work services.

Meggitt, C. (2012) *Child Development: An illustrated guide*, **3rd edition. Harlow: Pearson Education.**

Covers the development of children and young people up to 19 years in a no-nonsense, descriptive and straightforward way, with lots of summaries and pictures. Gives research examples and new developments in neuroscience. Comes with a helpful accompanying DVD.

Murray Parkes, C. and Prigerson, H. (2010) *Bereavement: Studies of grief in adult life*, **4th edition. London: Penguin.**

An updated classic that incorporates new information about traumatic losses, disasters and complicated grief.

NDCS (2011) *Social Care for Deaf Children and Young People*. **National Deaf Children's Society.** www.ndcs.org.uk.

Contains useful and practical information about the development of deaf young people.

Papalia, D., Wendkos Olds, S. and Feldman, R.D. (2009) *Human Development*, **11th edition. New York: McGraw Hill.**

A comprehensive guidebook to human development, full of interesting international examples, which has relevance to both this chapter and Chapter 4.

Rayner, E. with Joyce, A., Ross, J., Twyman, M. and Clulow, C. (2005) *Human Development: An introduction to the psychodynamics of growth, maturity and ageing*. **Hove: Routledge.**

A detailed and fascinating new edition of a classic work, which takes you through each of the crucial stages in human development.

Rogoff, B. (2003) *The Cultural Nature of Human Development*. **Oxford: Oxford University Press.**

This book focuses on how culture matters in human development, and provides interesting examples from many diverse cultures.

Slater, R. (1995) *The Psychology of Growing Old.* **Buckingham: Open University Press.**

A very positive book about the challenge of later life.

Worden, J.W. (2010) *Grief Counselling and Grief Therapy: A handbook for the mental health practitioner*, **4th edition. Hove: Routledge.**

An interesting and clearly written book with lots of examples of how people deal with loss, grief and the future, and how they can be helped through the process of grieving. A real classic with some useful revisions in the 4th edition.

Films

Seven Up – classic UK Granada study of 7-year-old children, followed up at seven-year intervals into their forties and fifties.

Sunday's Child – a detailed film of one child's development over two years. Available from Lynn Barnett, Iddeleigh House Clinic, EX1 2ND, Tel: 01392 76348.

Facing Death: St Christopher's Hospice, London.

Many further films and resources that you may find useful are also listed in Rayner in the book above.

CHAPTER 4
Psychological approaches and theories

> *Psychology should be able to help document what kinds of families result in children who flourish, what work settings support the greatest satisfaction among workers, what policies result in the strongest civic engagement, and how people's lives can be most worth living.*
>
> (Seligman and Csikszentmihalyi, 2000, p.1)

Introduction

This chapter will look at how psychological approaches and theories can contribute to your understanding of human development and behaviour. You already have some considerable understanding of human development and behaviour from the previous chapter. It will now be useful to look at a range of explanations offered by three psychological approaches or perspectives, and two psychological theories within each of these approaches. The content of the chapter should enable you to understand more fully the process of human development and behaviour, which should enable you to work with service users more effectively.

The chapter covers content for the Higher and National 5 units Care: Human Development and Behaviour. It also provides important underpinning knowledge and understanding for Scottish Vocational Qualifications SVQ2 and SVQ3 in Social Services (Children and Young People) and Social Services and Healthcare, and for the HNC in Social Care and HNC in Health Care. It provides useful additional theoretical input to build on understanding gained for the National 4 unit Human Development and Behaviour.

By the end of this chapter you should be able to:

- ★ define psychology and explain how it can help you to understand human behaviour and development
- ★ explain behaviour and development using psychological approaches and theories
- ★ discuss key concepts from six psychological theories

- ★ evaluate psychological theories
- ★ explain how an understanding of psychology can help you as a care worker to understand behaviour and development.

What is psychology?

Psychology is defined by the British Psychological Society as 'the scientific study of people, the mind and behaviour'. It is concerned with attempting to explain individual behaviour and development. This chapter does not attempt to cover the whole of psychology but it does provide you with an introduction to approaches and theories that can help you to understand human development and behaviour. It is useful at this point to examine the concepts of approach, perspective and theory. In the context of this chapter the words **'approach'** and **'perspective'** are used to refer to the same thing and either concept could have been used. Both an approach and a perspective are ways of looking at something. Each approach may contain a number of different theories that are consistent with the fundamental ideas of the approach, but with each theory having a different focus or emphasis. A psychological **theory** is defined as a set of related statements or ideas that are intended to explain aspects of development and behaviour.

One of the issues that should be kept in mind throughout this chapter is whether the psychological approaches and theories discussed are universally applicable – do they apply to other cultures and countries? Do people develop and behave differently, in psychological terms, depending on the culture in which they are brought up? The field of cross-cultural psychology investigates this question in order to test the generality of existing psychological theories, and it explores other cultures in order to find psychological variations.

> *Cross-cultural psychology is the study of similarities and differences in individual psychological functioning in various cultural and ethno-cultural groups; of ongoing changes in variables reflecting such functioning; and of the relationships of psychological variables with sociocultural, ecological and biological variables.*
>
> (Berry *et al.*, 2011, p.5)

If you look at human biology, you can see that every human being needs to eat, sleep and drink, but the ways in which these needs are met vary enormously in different cultures. For example, in Spain it is usual to have a siesta after lunch. What about psychological factors such as perception, grieving, conformity, the development of a personality? Do these manifest themselves in different ways depending on the culture in which you are raised? An awareness of this issue is important to the discussion in this chapter, since Scotland, while having cultural features that are distinctly Scottish, is also a culturally and ethnically diverse country. If the psychological theories that care workers use are 'blind' to the experience of people from different cultures or ethnic backgrounds, then there is a likelihood of people being misunderstood and negatively labelled.

How can you use psychology to help explain human development and behaviour in a care context? It may be useful to consider psychological ways of explaining human development and behaviour as 'tools' in a toolbox. You will not use all the tools every time you want to understand or assess a service user. Rather, you will choose one, or perhaps several, of the tools to help your understanding. The previous chapter looked at the variety of changes that take place throughout our lives, using a lifespan perspective. Psychology seeks to understand this process and explain why people develop and behave in the way they do. After examining the different psychological approaches in this chapter, you will be able to apply this knowledge to help you more fully understand the people with whom you work. During the assessment process, the psychological approaches may help you to understand some of the reasons why service users have developed in the way they have. The different approaches will help to explain the behaviour of service users, staff and carers. This informed approach should encourage more effective planning and evaluation of the care process. Although psychology doesn't provide all the answers, it can help you to be clearer about the best ways of working with service users.

Psychological approaches

Three psychological approaches will be considered, each of which takes a different view of human development (see Table 4.1). Each approach has been developed over many years, and has been used by many people involved in the care sector, such as care workers, nurses, addiction workers, social workers, occupational therapists, psychiatrists, and counsellors. There is no one particular approach that is always the best for every situation. Each approach has strengths and weaknesses and the approaches you use will depend on the needs of the service user, the resources of the care organisation and your training and ability. In most cases, a combination of approaches will be used, depending on the situation.

This chapter does not provide a full discussion of each of these approaches. For that you will need to consult a psychology textbook or look at the website of the British Psychological Society: **www.bps.org.uk**. Instead, we will look at the aspects of each approach that are most relevant and useful for care settings.

Table 4.1 Psychological approaches

Approach	Originated	Main ideas
Psychodynamic	1890s	• People are born with drives and instincts. • Early childhood experiences influence us throughout our lives. • People's behaviour is influenced by unconscious forces.
Cognitive/behavioural	1910s	• People are born a 'blank slate'. • All behaviour is learned. • Thoughts are processed and can be changed.
Humanistic	1950s	• People are born with a drive for growth. • People are motivated to fulfil their potential. • The whole person has to be understood, not just one aspect.

Psychodynamic approach

The psychodynamic approach is based on the work of Sigmund Freud (1856–1939). Put simply, psychodynamic means 'energy' or 'forces' of the mind. The underlying assumption of this perspective is that the way a person thinks and behaves is determined by the experiences they have had in their early years. As such, emotional disturbance at any age is caused by unresolved conflicts stemming from childhood. The psychodynamic approach states that these experiences may be buried in our unconscious mind, and so it is difficult to acknowledge the importance they still play in our current life. Behaviour, therefore, is seen as being determined largely by past experiences, of which we often have no conscious memory. In order to understand why people act the way they do in a care setting, it may be necessary to help them explore their past for possible causes and to help them find ways of changing the negative patterns of relating to people and reacting to events that they have developed. This may or may not be part of your particular role, depending on the level of skill and knowledge you acquire.

Freud believed that there were three parts to personality: the **Id, Ego and Superego** (see Table 4.2). These three aspects develop and interact as we develop, and manifest themselves differently in each person, depending on childhood experiences. As adults, we have a combination of all three parts in our personality. For some people their Id is the most powerful force, which means they may be impulsive and spontaneous; for others the dominant force is their Superego, and they may be controlling of self and others and quite critical. A psychologically healthy person has a strong Ego and is able to balance the demands of both Id and Superego.

All of us encounter situations that make us anxious, and none of us likes being in that situation. Freud suggests that we have unconsciously developed ways to protect ourselves from feeling anxiety. These are called **defence mechanisms**. They are coping strategies that help us deflect the pain and distress we experience due to anxiety. These defence mechanisms include:

- **repression**: ignoring feelings of fear or hurt
- **regression**: displaying childlike behaviours, such as having a tantrum
- **sublimation**: venting your anger and frustration on an object or an activity, rather than the person who caused it.

When we don't want to face up to reality, because it is too painful to admit how we feel, we put up these barriers to protect ourselves from the bad feelings, until the feelings subside enough for us and we can face up to them. Of course, in some circumstances, people are never able to face up to some of their feelings, and this is when it becomes psychologically unhealthy. People develop these defence mechanisms as routine ways

Table 4.2 Parts of the personality

Id	The 'childlike' part of your personality; the part that demands things *now*, wanting instant gratification; the 'Pleasure Principle'
Ego	The 'adult' part of your personality; the part that knows it may have to wait for your needs to be met; the 'Reality Principle'
Superego	The 'parent' part of your personality; the part that tells you what is right and wrong; your conscience; the 'Morality Principle'

of coping with the pressures and hassles they experience, but there often comes a time (because of bereavement, divorce, illness, etc.) when they are unable to keep the defence 'shield' up any more and they have to face up to a lot of unresolved issues at one time.

The psychodynamic approach can be criticised for the fact that it is all based on ideas that no one can prove or disprove. No one can measure the size of your unconscious and, although it is likely that early experiences do influence us in later life, it is impossible to say exactly what degree of importance they have. We have so many different influences on us throughout our lives, who knows what has been most significant? A lot of Freud's ideas and his methodology have been heavily criticised, but when most people read about this approach in general, they see that a lot of their behaviour can be explained by the key concepts.

Cognitive/behavioural approach

This approach combines two strands: behavioural and cognitive. The **behavioural approach** explains human development in terms of what a person has learned. Behaviourists believed that the psychodynamic approach was unscientific because it was not based on facts or evidence. They wanted to research only the part of experience that was observable: behaviour. The initial ideas were developed by researchers, such as Pavlov and Skinner, working in laboratories with animals. They developed the idea that a certain stimulus will trigger a certain response, because an association is made between the two. So, for instance, a researcher walking into a laboratory with a plate of food will trigger the salivary glands in a dog, before it even sees the food, because over time it has developed an association between the door opening and 'mealtime'! Another important part of this process is the consequences of what happens when a person responds in a certain way. The behaviour is more likely to be repeated if it is reinforced, or rewarded. The association between the door opening and salivation would weaken after a while if the food stopped appearing.

Human beings, however, differ from animals in that we don't just act; we are capable of thinking first. We think about our feelings, we interpret the situation and we consider what has happened in the past. We don't just react, we respond. The ideas of the behaviourists were developed to make them more appropriate and relevant to human beings by including cognition or thinking processes. **Cognitive/behavioural approaches** look at the influence of our perception on behaviour. How we act depends on how we see the situation. If we can change our view of the situation, we will act differently. A lot of work in care settings is based on this cognitive/behavioural model as the work is both focused on producing change that is very clear to see and can be carried out in a relatively short period of time.

People criticise the cognitive/behavioural approach by saying that it deals with only the symptoms of a person's problem, not the causes. The approach provides a lot of useful tools to examine and understand *aspects* of behaviour, but it does not look at the whole person, in the context of their whole life. If you were a doctor, for instance, and someone came to you with a bad cough, you would want to know if they had TB, lung cancer or just a bad cold before you decided on the most appropriate treatment. So, if someone in a care setting is getting angry, it can be 'treated' by attending anger management sessions.

This may treat the symptoms of this behaviour. If they never find out the cause of their anger, however, then it may always be there, ready to cause problems in the future. This medical analogy doesn't quite explain the whole picture, because the situation is often more complex when talking about psychology than biology. One key difference is that a doctor could carry out tests to find out fairly conclusively if someone has cancer or TB, but in psychology there is no simple 'test' to determine the cause of a person's problem. Sometimes it is easier, quicker and more effective to treat just the symptoms.

Humanistic approach

The humanistic approach is based on a positive view of human development and is associated with the work of Carl Rogers (1902–87). Rogers' work has already been considered in Chapter 2 in relation to communication. Rogers had trained as a psychodynamic therapist, but felt that the people he saw didn't seem to gain the benefits from analysis that he had expected. People could talk in therapy for months and not see any difference in their day-to-day lives. Rogers concluded that this was because the approach concentrated on the past and not on the whole picture of the person's life: their feelings, beliefs and spirituality. He also believed that cognitive/behaviourists took a rather narrow view of human beings, only looking at what they did and what they could say about their thought processes. After counselling many clients, Rogers came to see that he wasn't the expert in the person's life, they were. There was no sense in him analysing the person or motivating his clients to change. It had to come from the clients themselves. The humanistic approach regards both past and present as having equal importance. It assumes that all human beings are unique, rational and self-determining, that they have free will and that they continuously strive to grow and develop. It sees human beings as having an inherent need to develop their potential to the full. Emotional disturbance happens because individuals are not allowed to 'be themselves'. In an attempt to be accepted by others, individuals suppress their own true nature and make choices to please not themselves but others.

Activity *Queuing*

Josh

Josh is a 34-year-old man with learning disabilities who attends a day centre near his home in Motherwell. At 10:30 a.m. the tea bar is opened for the morning break. The centre is a very busy place and the queue is very long. Every morning as he stands in the queue Josh becomes very agitated. He begins to shout and swear and becomes abusive to anyone who is standing beside him. His care workers are concerned that he will hurt someone so they take him to the front of the queue. Having chosen his cake and drink, Josh sits quietly at his table with his friends until it is time to return to the activity room. His care workers have tried to stand beside Josh in the queue but have decided that he does not like queues and it is easier to get him served first.

Using information from the three approaches above, what do you think his care workers might have done differently?

Should the care workers ignore Josh's behaviour? What about restraining or punishing him? The care workers could make him stay in the activity room until all the people in the queue have been served. Or they could tell him that if he 'misbehaves' again he will not be allowed to go on the trip to the bowling alley. Do you think this will help?

Behaviourists are clear about this and state that, while unpleasant experiences might stop a particular behaviour at the time, it does not mean that future behaviour will be affected. Josh might experiment with different behaviour – screaming, kicking, lying down on the floor – the list is endless! So what is the answer? The answer, according to behaviourists, lies in understanding how reinforcement is working in the present situation, to examine that reinforcement and look for alternatives.

Using the psychodynamic approach might help you to understand that Josh may be experiencing some anxiety in the queue, and is demonstrating this by regressing to 'childlike' behaviour.

If staff can use the humanistic approach to try to see the world from Josh's point of view, they might be able to understand more clearly why he is feeling such anxiety. Is he worried he won't get back to his group in time if he doesn't get served first? Did he not have anything to eat before he left home in the morning?

Perhaps Josh's carers could start by placing him near the very front of the queue, spend time with him, talk to him and use a humanistic approach to help understand how he sees the changing situation. Gradually, they could encourage him to stand further back in the queue. They could tell him how good his behaviour is, praise him for his patience while standing in the queue and make him feel good about achieving this new behaviour. Josh will have learned a new piece of behaviour, which has been reinforced, and this behaviour will be repeated in the future.

Psychological theories

As you have seen, each psychological approach was originally based on the ideas and work of certain theorists, but there are many writers who have developed the ideas of the original theorists. They have the benefit of having listened to discussions about the ideas, and of seeing how the approach works in practice. The original theorists sometimes emphasise an aspect of their theory that later turns out to be weak, and only time tells which are the most enduring and useful aspects of the theory. Within each approach, one writer who has developed the original ideas will be considered at National 5 level, and one writer at Higher level. The aspects of each theory that are most relevant for care settings will be highlighted. Table 4.3 summarises the writers who will be discussed.

Table 4.3 Psychological approaches and theorists

Approach	Writer	Theory	Key concepts
		Psychodynamic	
National 5	Eric Berne	Transactional analysis	Ego states
Higher	Erik Erikson	Lifespan theory	8 stages; ego conflicts
		Cognitive/behavioural	
National 5	Albert Bandura	Social learning theory	Observational learning; **modelling**
Higher	Albert Ellis	Rational emotive behaviour therapy	ABCDE; irrational beliefs
		Humanistic	
National 5	Abraham Maslow	Hierarchy of needs	5 stages; self-actualisation
Higher	Carl Rogers	Person-centred theory	Self-concept; conditions of worth

Psychodynamic

Eric Berne: transactional analysis (National 5 level)

Writing more than 50 years after Freud, Berne (1910–70) would have known all about the ideas of the psychoanalytic and the behaviourist schools of thought. He was developing his ideas roughly at the same time as the cognitive and humanistic writers. He suggested that people were actors in their own life and 'played games' according to certain 'scripts'. He didn't mean by this that people were false. What he, like Freud, meant was that people were not always consciously aware of why they acted in the way they did, but that they had developed certain patterns of behaviour ('scripts'), which they were likely to repeat unless they became aware of the games they were playing.

Berne was interested in the transactions (his word for interactions) between people, and came up with some ideas that are useful in care settings, whether looking at staff or at service users. He was the person who coined the phrase 'I'm OK, you're OK'. By this he meant that, in the most successful interactions, both people would be content and feel that they had achieved what they wanted. On the other hand, you can get interactions where the dynamic is 'I'm OK, you're *not* OK'. This would be when one person thinks they are superior to the other and perhaps bullies or undermines them. Equally, some people play the 'I'm not OK, you're OK' game. This situation might occur in a care setting where the service user looks at the worker as the expert, the one who can 'make them better'. This is not a healthy professional working relationship, because it is unequal and based on a power imbalance. The worker would want to encourage the service user to become more actively involved in decision making. The final transaction is 'I'm not OK, you're not OK'. This is where both people interact on the basis of their perceived victim status. They both feel worthless, or are people who define themselves by their problems. If an interaction gets stuck in this script, it can stop both people moving on. Remember that we are talking about a psychodynamic approach, however, which suggests there may be unconscious reasons why people want to stay in a relationship that from the outside appears negative. For instance, there may be a sense of safety or familiarity in their position, no matter how painful it is.

Berne suggests that when we interact with others, we do so from one of three **'ego states'**: Child, Adult or Parent. These three states link to Feud's three parts of the personality: Id, Ego and Superego. A person's ego is just their sense of self: their picture of whom they are when they say 'I'. Berne believes that every person has a mixture of these three ego states in their personality and that, depending on the situation and the person with whom they are interacting, they will play out one role more than the others.

- The **Child** ego state is one where we are spontaneous and playful, but also prone to moods and tantrums.
- The **Adult** ego state is where we are balanced, can see our own and other people's strengths and weaknesses, and can accept these.
- The **Parent** ego state is either controlling and punitive or nurturing and caring.

When one person acts in a situation based on an ego state, the other person has a choice about to which ego state they respond. Since these transactions are happening unconsciously, however, people often find themselves reacting to the role. Thus if someone is in the Parent ego state and criticises you, you may find yourself reacting in Child mode, perhaps by stomping off in a mood, getting angry with them, or bursting into tears. Berne would say that a psychologically healthy person would see what was going on and choose to respond in their Adult ego state. By doing this, it might change the 'game' into an 'I'm OK, you're OK' situation where the person responds in Adult mode, apologises for their tone, and manages to discuss their point without hostility.

Erik Erikson: lifespan theory (Higher level)

Erikson (1902–94) suggested that psychological development is a lifelong process and is not fixed when you reach adolescence, as Freud had believed. He also differed from Freud because he believed that the conflicts people encounter are linked to their relationships with other people rather than with their own psychosexual development. This is why his theory is known as a **psycho-social theory** of development. Sociocultural factors such as the person's **social class** and the political regime in which they live, as well as the cultural expectations of their society, will affect the way people develop. Erikson thought that an individual would develop a healthy personality if they were able to resolve the basic psychological conflicts they meet at different stages of their lives. If they were able to resolve the conflicts, they would develop a particular ego strength, and this would help them to face up to challenges later in life. He identified eight stages of psychological development: four in childhood, one in adolescence and three in adulthood. Table 4.4 outlines the main stages and the conflict that has to be resolved at each stage. This table also contains a column on care tasks so that you can see the relationship between Erikson's theory and the task of the care worker in resolving the conflicts. This was not part of Erikson's theory.

Table 4.4 Erikson: eight stages of development (adapted from Erikson (1968) and Becket and Taylor (2010))

Life crisis	Favourable outcome Ego strength of	Unfavourable outcome	Care task
First year ***Trust** vs **mistrust***	**Hope** Trust in people and the environment	**Mistrust** Suspicion, insecurity and fear	To provide consistent, stable and loving care
Second and third years ***Autonomy** vs **shame and doubt***	**Will** A sense of self-esteem and autonomy	**Shame and doubt** Doubt of own ability to control behaviour and actions, leading to shame	Continuation of consistent, stable and loving environment that allows child to explore and develop autonomy; importance of praise and boundaries
Fourth and fifth years ***Initiative** vs **guilt***	**Purpose** Developing an increasing sense of purpose and ability to initiate activities	**Guilt** Fear of punishment, and guilt about own feelings	Provide opportunities to explore surroundings and try new things in secure, loving environment
Ages six to eleven ***Industry** vs **inferiority***	**Competence** Learning to overcome challenges and gain a sense of competence	**Inferiority** Unfavourable reactions from others leading to acceptance of sense of failure	Importance of positive socialisation, praise, love and encouragement
Adolescence 12–20 years ***Identity** vs **role confusion***	**Fidelity** Developing a consistent sense of personal identity	**Role confusion** Confusion about whom you are and your role in life	Support for individual's evolving identity and vocational choices; importance of positive peer group and role models
Young adulthood 20–40 years ***Intimacy** vs **isolation***	**Love** Developing intimate and trusting relationships with others	**Isolation** Avoidance of relationships as threatening and painful	Support in developing and maintaining deep and lasting relationships
Adulthood 40–65 years ***Generativity** vs **stagnation***	**Care** To develop a productive and positive life	**Stagnation** Failure to grow emotionally	Support to be productive and creative and to make a contribution to society
Maturity 65 years onwards ***Integrity** vs **despair***	**Wisdom** Satisfaction with life and ability to look back positively	**Despair** Feeling that life has been meaningless and futile	Respect as an individual with a relevant past and present life. Making up for lost time through new interests and relationships

In order to resolve the conflicts and develop the ego strengths, we need to have the right people around us at the relevant time. Our parents' care and attention is crucial in our childhood, whereas our friends become more important in our teenage years. If these social conditions and relationships are not positive, then we may fail to resolve the conflict, and this will weaken us psychologically. Equally, positive early experiences of, for example, trust can still be shattered later by negative experiences, but at least we have spent our formative years seeing ourselves and the world from a psychologically healthy perspective. Erikson believed that it was possible to make up for unsatisfactory experiences at a later stage, although this was harder to do. This is why this model is useful for care workers. If a service user had problems during adolescence, for example, they may never have developed a strong sense of identity. This might explain why as an adult they find it difficult to find a place for themselves in society: they just don't know where they fit in. As a care worker, you can't help them rewind to their adolescence and change things, but you could work with the service user to create tasks that give them a sense of identity now. Erikson's theory helps to remind you that the service users with whom you work are people who, although they have been through a process of development, are still continuing to develop, no matter what age they are.

Does Erikson's model apply to everyone? There are at least two arguments that question the universality of his model: one on the basis of **gender-blindness** (Erikson doesn't address any differences there may be in boys and girls, men and women in relation to the relative importance of different aspects of his theory) and one on the basis of its **cultural limitations** (do people in all cultures and societies go through these stages?). For example, there is a long-standing debate in psychology about whether adolescence is a biologically or socially determined life stage.

> *The anthropological evidence from all over the world clearly shows that, while adolescence is everywhere a time for learning new social roles, with attendant psychological tensions, it is not universally the period of storm and stress claimed by Western psychologists ... In some cases, such as rural India where children have to fulfil adult tasks from a very early age, not as much time and attention can be spent on adolescence as the Western world, and more affluent urban Indians, define it.*
>
> (Berry *et al.*, 2011)

O'Brien (2011) points out that it is hard to prove or disprove Erikson's theory because it is so full of generalisations, and he does not explain in any detail how people move from one stage to another. What Erikson does provide, however, is an emphasis on emotional states and the possible outcomes if things go wrong. In recognising differing consequences for differing stages of life the care worker can begin to see the kind of emotional help that may be useful.

Conclusion: psychodynamic approaches

Psychodynamic approaches in general have often been associated with the image of a bearded psychiatrist interpreting dreams while the client lies on a couch! You can see, however, that they are about looking at the unconscious influences on development and the way people interact with one another. It is often difficult to pinpoint the exact reasons from our past that influence our actions, but we can recognise patterns of behaviour and aspects of our current behaviour that are causing problems with our relationships, at work or at home. Knowing about defence mechanisms, psychological conflicts, ego states, life scripts and ego strengths may help you to understand where changes might be made.

Behaviourist

Bandura: social learning theory (National 5 level)

Bandura agreed with the original behaviourist writers that reinforcement plays an important role in determining behaviour, but his research indicated that the process of learning is much more complex than they had detailed. He believed that thought processes allow the individual to interpret the consequences of their behaviour. The interpretation of these consequences exerts its influence on future behaviour by giving the individual information about what effects can be expected if they behave that way again in a similar situation.

In particular, Bandura and other social learning theorists believe that a person's development and behaviour are the result of social interaction with others. **Social interaction starts** when a baby is born and continues throughout a person's life. It involves the process of socialisation, which is discussed in Chapter 3. It is the process whereby a person learns to conform to the norms of society and to act in ways that are considered acceptable. It is therefore a helpful tool in understanding the different social expectations and practices of different cultures and the effects these can have on the development and behaviour of individuals. Social learning theory in general highlights three main ways in which socialisation occurs: imitation and identification; punishments and rewards; and social expectations.

Imitation and identification

From children's earliest stages they will observe the behaviour of others and copy or imitate it. This allows children to learn a range of physical skills very quickly and efficiently, and they will often incorporate this learning into their play activities. Small children love to 'play' at being a grown up. They will play at being mummies and daddies, doctors and teachers, soldiers and firefighters. Imitation can be a powerful influence on behaviour. In the experiments he carried out with school-age children, Bandura found that they did not imitate all adult models equally. They were much more likely to imitate models who were similar to themselves, such as those of the same sex. His findings seemed to show that there can be a difference in what children learn and what shows immediately in their behaviour.

Identification is the second part of the process. Not only do children imitate behaviour but, as time goes by, they begin to model themselves on another person; the learning becomes internalised and they come to identify with that person or that role. Role models act as a blueprint of behaviour, attitudes and values that the child may adopt in later adult life. It is believed that identification is responsible for individuals learning social roles such as gender roles.

Punishments and rewards

Another important way in which a child learns to behave is through direct reaction from adults. Behaviour may be rewarded or punished, and through these means the child learns to act in ways that are appropriate and acceptable. Rewards teach the child the types of behaviour likely to bring about a pleasant outcome. Rewards will vary from culture to culture. They may take the form of paying attention to the child, playing with them or giving them sweets, treats or hugs and praise. These rewards act as reinforcers of appropriate behaviour. Research indicates, however, that they are only effective if there is a strong affectionate bond between the child and the adult (Eysenck, 2000).

Punishment can take many forms – smacking, hitting, beating, withdrawal of privileges, stopping pocket money or grounding (not letting the child go out of the house). Many social learning theorists believe that punishment often produces hostility and resentment, as well as fear and avoidance of the punisher. The child also quickly learns to suppress the punishable behaviour in the presence of the punisher but tends to be more likely to carry out this behaviour out of sight of the adult who has punished them. Punishment only teaches the child what they should *not* do, not what they *should* or might do. It may also teach children that behaviour can be controlled by another person by virtue of their age, gender, strength or status. The child may learn to follow this model and could in later years themselves use punishing strategies to control the behaviour of others (e.g. their own children, their partner, their friends, their work colleagues or members of the opposite sex).

Why are there sometimes inconsistencies in a person's aggressive behaviour – why are they aggressive in some situations but not in others? It may be because their behaviour is reinforced differently in each situation. They have learned to behave differently in the two situations because aggressiveness brings 'rewards' (feelings of power, dominance) in one situation, but not in the other.

Activity *Social learning theory and parenting styles*

O'Brien (2011) reports that, in Bandura's study of hyper-aggressive boys, parental modelling of aggressive behaviours was found to play a significant role in the transmission of aggression.

Using Bandura's theory, what role do you think other adults with whom such children come into contact could play in breaking the cycle of aggression?

Social expectations

Social expectations (the type of behaviour that is regarded as appropriate in particular situations) can vary dramatically from one culture to another. The way in which a society's culture is constructed can play a large part in determining the kinds of expected behaviour; this is discussed more fully in Chapters 3 and 5.

Cognitive/behaviourist

Albert Ellis: rational emotive behaviour therapy (Higher level)

Albert Ellis (1913–2007) is one of the many psychological theorists, like Carl Rogers, who started their professional life as a therapist working within the psychodynamic model. Ellis, however, came to believe that this was too limited. He believed that it wasn't what had actually happened to people that influenced their psychological development, but rather their **perceptions** of what had happened to them, the story they told themselves about their past. By 1961 he had developed the basis of rational emotive therapy, and in 1993 he renamed it rational emotive behaviour therapy (REBT) to show that, although cognition and emotions were crucial, behaviour was also central. In 2007 (the year he died, aged 93) Ellis, a colourful and iconoclastic character, was still writing books and developing his ideas. As with all the theorists included in the syllabus, we will focus on particular aspects of his theory that are relevant in a care context.

The main ideas of REBT are that our cognition, the way we think about things, is the key element in determining how we respond to an event, and that there is an interaction between our cognition, emotion and behaviour. These are not separate systems that can be examined and 'treated' independently. If we learn to accept ourselves, and do not impose unrealistic conditions on ourselves and others, then we are more likely to achieve a healthy psychological balance in our lives.

Ellis's theory follows an 'ABC' model: An **Activating** event (the stimulus) results in a **Belief** (rational or irrational) about the event, which has a **Consequence** for how the person feels, thinks and behaves. Ellis adds two other steps, D and E, to this basic cognitive model. If the irrational belief is **Disputed** or debated (either by the person, or by someone else), then there will be a different **Effect** for the person: they will feel different, because they will develop more effective rational beliefs, their emotional response will be more appropriate and their behaviour will be more in line with their goals. Ellis developed his theory over the decades and it has been presented in a number of different ways. Beware of this if you carry out any background research!

Ellis considers that the beliefs or thoughts we have about an event can be rational or irrational. Rational thoughts are logical and flexible. They view the world as it is and not through a distorted lens.

> *[In REBT] humans are seen as having two basic goals: to stay alive and to be happy. While there are shared methods of pursuing the former goal (e.g. seeking adequate shelter from the elements, maintaining a proper diet) there are myriad different ways of pursuing the latter. Humans are remarkably idiosyncratic in what they find personally meaningful or fulfilling. Given the above considerations, the term 'rational' means that* ***which helps people to achieve their basic goals and purposes.***
>
> (Dryden *et al.*, 1999, p.6, original emphasis)

Irrational beliefs, on the other hand, are illogical, rigid, stated in 'absolute' terms, and often self-defeating because they impede us from attaining our goals and are disruptive to our relationships. We develop these irrational beliefs throughout our lives and through repetition they become part of a patterned way of thinking and behaving.

Irrational beliefs fall into four categories:

1 **Rigid demands**: 'I must be approved of'

2 **Awfulising beliefs**: 'If I'm disapproved of, it's the end of the world'

3 **Low frustration tolerance beliefs**: 'I can't tolerate being disapproved of'

4 **Depreciation beliefs**:

   a) **Self-depreciation**: 'I am worthless if I am disapproved of'
   b) **Other-depreciation**: 'You are horrible if you disapprove of me'
   c) **Life-depreciation**: 'Life is all bad because this tragedy happened'.

(Dryden, 2006, p.276)

A rational belief, such as 'I would like to do well in my Higher Care course assessments' can easily transform into an irrational one when a person adds conditions, such as 'must', 'should', 'ought' or 'have to', to the statement. Ellis memorably calls these terms 'musterbations' because they are such clear indicators of the inflexible, absolutist stance that underlies an irrational belief. The statement 'I must do well in my Higher Care course assessments' tends to have a second part in which the person either explicitly or implicitly states '*or* I'll never get into university and move on to the career I want'. The thought processes associated with irrational beliefs are often 'catastrophising', imagining the worst case scenario.

If people can learn to identify and dispute their irrational beliefs, they can reframe their thoughts into more logical perceptions of reality. The irrational belief would be reformulated into 'I'd like to pass the Higher Care course assessments', perhaps with a mediating statement at the end such as '*but my future doesn't depend on it*'. This enables the person to give themselves permission to be less than perfect, that is human and fallible.

Reframing thoughts like this encourages the person to move away from repetitive, self-defeating thoughts and to stop procrastinating. How often have you put something off time and again, because you don't think you're quite ready to do it, or circumstances aren't quite right yet? When will they ever be perfect? The famous crime novelist P.D. James didn't write any books until she was in her forties. She then came to the conclusion that there would always be too much to do to write a book but she would do it anyway. REBT challenges a person to check their underlying beliefs about themselves and about the world, and to make changes.

This theory is useful in a care setting as it responds to some of the observable aspects of a person's situation. It helps clarify what their perception of a situation is, based on their behaviour and how they talk about it. It is a theory that can be used both to understand one-off situations and to facilitate change in longer-term therapeutic work with a service user. It encourages people to engage actively in self-healing by taking responsibility for their perceptions and behaviours.

Ellis can be **criticised**, however, for his lack of sympathy for people who do not actively work to change their perceptions, and this is an aspect of his approach, and indeed that of many cognitive/behavioural theorists, that care workers need to be careful not to reinforce. With the wrong emphasis, this could be turned into a criticism of the person for not doing enough to change their situation. Underpinned by a sound care value base, this model can provide a very useful way of working with service users on some issues. Compare it to Egan's three-stage model, which was discussed in Chapter 2. Do you see the similarities? Egan states that challenging is an appropriate skill to use *once a trusting relationship has been developed*, and Ellis's theory would also be relevant to use at this stage in working with a service user. The other main drawback of this approach is that, although it can lead to people examining and changing aspects of their perceptions and behaviour, it doesn't examine *where* the irrational beliefs came from in the first place.

Humanistic

Maslow: hierarchy of needs (National 5 level)

One of the main ways in which psychology can help you in your work with service users is in the process of assessment and care planning (see Chapter 6). The assessment of needs with the service user represents one of the key components in the care planning process. All human beings have a range of needs, but are any needs more important than the others? As early as 1954, Abraham Maslow put forward the idea that human beings have a number of complex needs and, coming from a humanistic perspective, he believed that all of us constantly strive towards fulfilling these needs. Maslow formulated the idea that needs are not always equally important: some are more important than others at any given time.

He believed that human beings are motivated by two systems of needs – **deficiency needs** and **growth needs**. The basic needs are termed deficiency, because when they are not satisfied individuals engage in behaviours designed to remedy this lack of satisfaction. For example, hunger represents a deficiency that can be satisfied by eating. The growth needs are so termed because activities that relate to them do not fulfil a lack but lead towards the ultimate end of growth: fulfilling your potential.

According to Maslow, needs are organised as a hierarchy – that is, each can only be satisfied if the one below has already been at least partially achieved. As you can see from Maslow's **hierarchy of needs** in Figure 4.1, the needs at the base are those necessary to sustain life itself – food, water, rest, shelter and security. It is towards these needs that a person's energy or motivation will be directed as a means of survival and security. Only when these basic needs are satisfied will a person become focused on the next level of needs – social/emotional. As these needs are met, the person can use their energy and attention to move up the pyramid towards the highest point, self-actualisation.

The concept of **self-actualisation** refers to the potential within all individuals for personal growth, to be the person you want to be, to make full use of your talents and capabilities. Maslow believed that all human beings are born with an innate tendency to strive towards self-actualisation, that is, that they are motivated towards reaching their full potential. The satisfaction associated with self-actualisation comes from within the person rather than from outside. In contrast, satisfaction of lower-order needs, such as self-esteem, is associated with external sources of reinforcement (approval and recognition). In an international study of workplaces, self-actualisation was rated as the most important need to meet, but also the least likely to be achieved (Berry *et al.*, 2002, p.403).

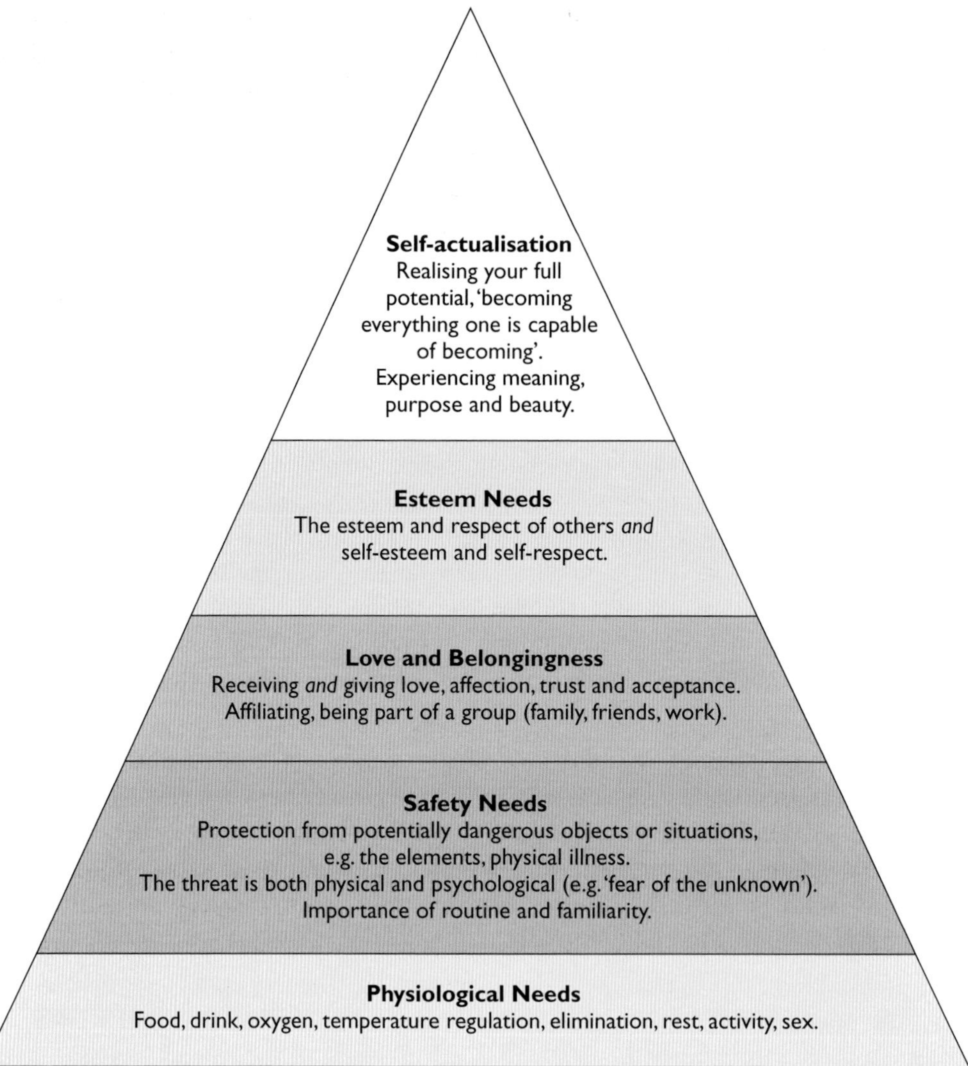

Figure 4.1 Maslow's hierarchy of needs

Those who fail to move towards self-actualisation do so because of circumstances in which they find themselves, for example, people living in poverty and other circumstances where all available time and energy are spent meeting the basic needs and coping with struggles at those levels. Other circumstances may also prevent an individual progressing towards self-actualisation, such as being in the middle of a separation or divorce, losing a job, experiencing violence and abuse, or being unable to take part in activities that would be fulfilling. These circumstances and many others will act against the individual being able to move up the hierarchy towards self-actualisation.

Even people who are highly successful don't stay at the peak of self-actualisation forever. No matter what you have achieved in your life, there is always something else to strive for, and there are always setbacks that you will encounter, as well as all the day-to-day issues of poor health and relationship problems that we all face. It is probably more useful therefore to consider self-actualisation as a process that guides a person towards growth rather than as a state that is attained once and for all. It is also important to remember that self-actualisation is relative: we are not all striving for the same thing. Many people have a lifetime ambition to play the piano well or to get a university degree, whereas other people have achieved these things and don't particularly value them: they have other things for which they are striving. Someone who has had a stroke may view being able to walk unaided as fulfilling their potential, even though they used to jog when they were younger. Someone who has had mental health problems may consider that they have fulfilled their potential by getting out of the house on a regular basis and managing to hold down a job. Someone who has had an addiction in the past may feel a sense of self-actualisation when they are there to see their child winning a race at the first sports day that they have been organised enough and lucid enough to be able to attend. The smile on their child's face is a peak experience that demonstrates to them how far they are into their recovery.

Activity *Maslow*

How does Maslow's theory help you to understand the needs of Ampin in the case study below?

Ampin

Ampin is an 84-year-old woman who has been in residential care since her husband died a year ago. Her health is relatively good and she eats and sleeps well. She has her own room, which has many items from her previous house – her chair, photographs, clothes, ornaments and TV. Ampin's only daughter moved away six months ago when her husband's job was relocated to Canada. She writes to her mother once a month and plans to visit her at Christmas time. The staff in the home are very caring towards Ampin. They are concerned, however, that she has not made any friends in the home and tends to sit in her room or on her own in the lounge.

You may have noted that it would appear that Ampin's physiological needs are being met. She has food, warmth, shelter and rest. It would also appear that her safety needs are being met. She feels safe, secure and out of danger. Her room contains mementos and familiar objects from her own home. There are things she knows, things that evoke fond memories and which in themselves make her feel secure.

It is very likely, however, that Ampin's need for love and belonging are not being met. She has lost her husband, her daughter has moved away and Ampin has not made any friends in the home. Since the fulfilment of some needs is lacking, Ampin is finding it difficult to progress towards self-actualisation. It is towards the love and belongingness part of Maslow's hierarchy of needs that Ampin, with the help of the staff, may now want to focus. If Ampin wishes, this will become part of her assessment, and the helping process should work towards meeting these needs, dealing with her loss and the transition to new surroundings, and helping her progress towards the peak of the pyramid: self-actualisation.

Maslow's hierarchy of needs is a useful 'tool' to develop an understanding of the needs of service users. The humanistic perspective from which it is derived encourages a view of service users as individuals who are all striving to meet their basic and developmental needs. Effective assessment and care planning should be designed to help them to achieve these. Care services are often good at meeting the basic physical and safety needs of service users, by providing warm and comfortable surroundings. But, bearing in mind the positive care practice approach in Chapter 6, they sometimes struggle to provide meaningful and challenging lives and activities for service users. There may be all kinds of reasons for this: lack of staff, poor resources, inadequate training. But it is a real missed opportunity for the workers and organisations to help people make a real difference to their lives. There are some models in Chapter 6 that you may recognise as having built on the ideas of Maslow, for example the SHANARRI model included in GIRFEC (Getting it Right for Every Child, Scottish Executive, 2006). SHANARRI stands for **safe, healthy, achieving, nurtured, active, respected, responsible** and **included**. Personalisation and a person-centred approach are also compatible with Maslow's emphasis on striving towards self-actualisation.

Can you identify any **weaknesses** in Maslow's theory? Probably the major flaw in the theory is the idea that lower needs have to be at least partially satisfied first before higher needs become important. Some people, for example workaholics, will often neglect their personal needs such as for food and sleep in their pursuit to complete a work or college project. Students often hand a piece of work in with the words 'I was up until 3 this morning doing this.' The motivation to complete the work was stronger than their increasingly desperate need for sleep!

Carl Rogers: person-centred theory (Higher level)

One of the major differences between human beings and animals is the ability of human beings to be aware of themselves. This is called self-consciousness or self-awareness. Animals may have consciousness and feel hunger or pain, but only human beings have self-consciousness. This does not mean that people feel shy or embarrassed. Rather, it means that when you think about yourself you are the person doing the thinking but you are also the person being thought about. Cooley (1902) described this as the 'looking glass self'. What he meant by this was that human beings are aware of what kind of person they are, what they think about themselves and what kind of personality they have. They are able to do this because they have self-consciousness: they have an awareness about what others think about them and this is how they develop an impression of what they are like. Robert Burns, the national poet of Scotland, obviously understood this idea. In his poem 'To a Louse' he notes:

O wad some Power the giftie gie us

To see oursels as ithers see us!

Rogers was interested in the ability of people to fulfil their potential and, through his work as a therapist, developed the idea of a **self-concept** that is made up of three aspects: **self-image**, **ideal self** and **self-esteem**. These three aspects interact with each other in order to create the person's identity.

Self-image

Activity *Self-image*

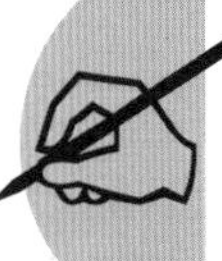

Try this activity either on your own or with a group of friends or family. Ask each person to write down a list of words or phrases that describe themselves. Ask them to list about twenty things. Remember they can write down some negative aspects about themselves as well as positive.

Self-image is how individuals describe themselves. An individual's list will probably comprise three main categories that make up the person's self-image: social roles, personality traits and body image.

- **Social roles**: the person has probably described themselves in terms of their social roles: as a student, sister, father, friend, son. These roles can be verified by others.
- **Personality traits**: the person might also have described themselves in terms of personality traits. These traits or characteristics will be formed from their own opinion about themselves: friendly, under-confident, generous, nervous, bad-tempered. These may be traits they consider themselves to have, but other people may not hold the same view.
- **Body image**: The last group on their list might be descriptions of how the person looks, their body image. They might have included descriptions such as tall, fat, thin, blue-eyed, attractive, brunette, etc. One of the important features of body image is biological identity, whether someone is male or female. The other important feature of body image is that, as individuals grow and develop, so too do their bodies and appearance. Changes in appearance may be something simple like getting their hair cut or their nose pierced, or something more significant, such as the changes in their body during puberty or their skin becoming wrinkled and their hair turning white when they get older. Some of these descriptions are factual, but others (e.g. 'attractive') are judgements or opinions, and other people may not agree with them. This is especially the case if the person suffers from an eating disorder such as anorexia. The crucial point is not what the external reality is, but what the person *believes* to be true.

Ideal self

Your ideal self is the kind of person you would like to be. Perhaps you would just like to be a little thinner, a bit wiser, more outgoing or better at sports. Or perhaps you would like to be a better friend, a more caring person or a better mother. At a more extreme level, you may even want to be like someone else! At times this can act as a motivation to improve yourself and make positive changes in your life, but at other times it can mean losing your individuality and becoming a weaker copy of someone else. Socialisation, particularly popular culture in magazines, films, TV, the internet, etc., plays a major part in defining what looks, lifestyle, house, car are desirable.

Self-esteem

Self-esteem is what an individual thinks about themselves, how they value themselves as a person, how much they like themselves. To a large extent this is influenced by the relationship between their self-image and their ideal self. If they are very unhappy with their self-image and want to be like someone else (ideal self) then most likely their self-esteem will be low. If they are happy with the person they are, however, then their self-esteem is more likely to be high. The wider the gap between self-image and ideal self, the lower a person's self-esteem is likely to be.

The type of culture in which people live has a large influence on how individuals view themselves. British culture today holds certain physical attributes in high regard. Women are deemed to be attractive if they are young, tall, slim, have beautiful faces, good skin and long shapely legs. Men are seen as attractive if they are young, tall and slim, have a 'six pack', good skin and look as if they 'work out'. In contrast, other cultures regard fuller-bodied people as attractive. Mma Ramotse in Alexander McCall Smith's (1998 onwards) *The No. 1 Ladies' Detective Agency* novels, for instance, is very proud of being 'traditionally built'. Other aspects of culture, status and orientation – ethnicity, gender, age, social background, education, marital status or sexual orientation – will also affect how people see themselves, and how they feel about themselves.

Carl Rogers believes our self-concept is influenced by many things, including the conditions of worth that people have placed on us throughout our lives. These are the sometimes spoken, but often unspoken, expectations about how we should behave and what opinions we should have if we are to be loved by those around us. We encounter these conditions – 'You are worthy of my love/approval, but only if you…' – from all kinds of people throughout our lives: from parents, friends, teachers, lovers, children. And remember, you are part of the process too: you will have imposed some conditions on other people throughout your life.

People often think they are being caring and 'looking after the best interests' of the person when they make these conditions, but they are seeing the world from their own point of view, and not the point of view of the other person. As a father or as a wife, you have a certain vested interest in the relationship and it is difficult for you to be completely neutral in your opinions. That is only to be expected. It becomes a problem, however, when it starts to constrain and limit the other person. This can lead to the point where they have an external locus of evaluation: they are unable to make up their own mind about things without reference to someone else's opinions. This is often the case in people who have been in care settings for a while, where people may have valued them for being quiet and compliant. The staff like them because they are not 'troublemakers'. The person, however, in the process of fitting in to these expectations, loses the last sense of self they had, and becomes dependent on staff to do things for them that they might be capable of doing for themselves. This was described in Chapter 1 in the discussion of institutionalisation and can also be seen in terms of symbolic interactionism discussed in Chapter 5.

CASE STUDY

Emma

Emma is 23 years old and is of dual ethnicity. She is a lone parent with two children under the age of five and lives in a high-rise block of flats in one of the large housing schemes in Glasgow. She left school at 16 with no qualifications. She used drugs for several years and her children were in foster care for quite a long time. With help from the local drug rehabilitation team and her social worker, Emma has stopped using drugs and her children have been returned to live with her.

Emma's self-esteem is very low and when her social worker suggested that she attend a college course for adult returners, Emma felt that she was not 'good enough' to go to college with 'a lot of brainy people' from the 'posh area'. After a year off drugs, however, Emma did attend a foundation computer course at her local community centre and showed a real aptitude for this subject. The out-reach tutor from the college who taught the course eventually persuaded her to attend a full-time computer course at the college the following year. Emma is now studying for an HNC in computer studies and sees herself as 'as good as anybody else'. Her self-esteem continues to grow.

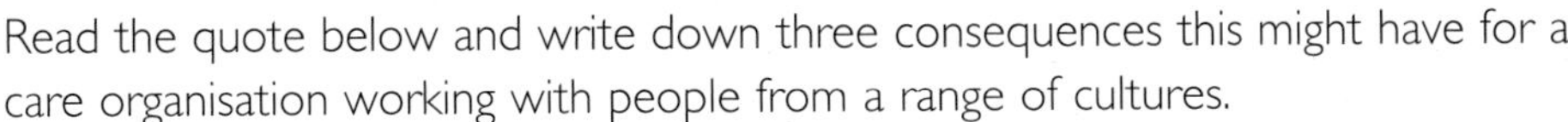

Activity *Independent or interdependent identity?*

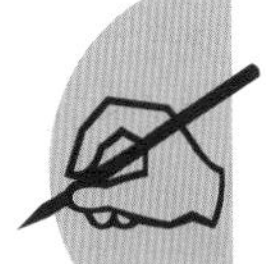

It is argued that self-concept is one of the psychological concepts that has a cultural dimension, and that this has consequences for how people experience themselves and how they relate to others.

Read the quote below and write down three consequences this might have for a care organisation working with people from a range of cultures.

> *Generally the Western conception of self is of an individual who is separate, autonomous, and atomised (made up of a set of discrete traits, abilities, values and motives), seeking separateness and independence from others. In contrast, in Eastern cultures relatedness, connectedness, and interdependence are sought, rooted in a concept of the self not as a discrete entity, but as inherently linked to others. The person is made 'whole' only when situated in his or her place in a social unit. The independent construal of the self further implies that persons see themselves as unique, promote their own goals, and seek self-expression. Persons with an interdependent construal of the self seek to belong and fit in, to promote others' goals, and to occupy their proper place.*
>
> (Berry *et al.*, 2011)

The contribution of psychological understanding to care practice

Activity *Psychological understanding*

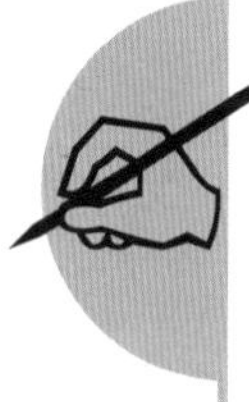

Before you read the following section, identify at least four ways in which you think that an understanding of psychological approaches and theories can contribute to positive care practice. Some of this information has been integrated into discussions throughout the chapter.

In undertaking the Activity above you may have thought of the points below or of different points from your own personal perspective.

Psychological understanding of human development and behaviour helps care workers in:

- **Assessment**: for example, understanding the needs of service users using Maslow's hierarchy of needs can help you to understand unmet need at several levels; understanding outcomes of service users' early experiences such as abuse and lack of attachment can help you to understand mistrust rather than trust (Erikson's theory of eight stages of development).
- **Explaining the behaviour of service users, staff and carers**: for example, if negative behaviours, such as temper tantrums, have been reinforced by giving a person additional attention, this could escalate the behaviour (Bandura's social learning theory).
- **More effective care planning**: for example, if an individual always sets unrealistic learning/educational goals this could result in discouragement. Their care plan could establish learning/educational outcomes that are realistic with consequences that are encouraging (Albert Ellis – rational emotive behaviour therapy).
- **Finding the best ways to work with service users and carers**: for example, using Carl Rogers' person-centred theory helped Emma, in the case study, to build self-esteem.

SUMMARY

In this chapter, which covers material at National 5 and Higher levels, you have been encouraged to look at how psychology can help you to understand the ways in which people develop and behave. A variety of 'tools' have been used in the form of approaches and theories that help to explain aspects of the development and behaviour of the people with whom you work. These 'tools' offer general guidelines and explanations. They cannot be used as precise answers or explanations because all people are individuals with unique life experiences, but they do at least go some way towards giving you a body of knowledge to help you be a more self-aware and knowledgeable worker.

The chapter has included discussion of both the strengths and the weaknesses of three different psychological approaches and the work of six psychological theorists, aspects of which can be applied in care services.

Activity

Applying psychological approaches and theories to the MacDonald and Ahmed families

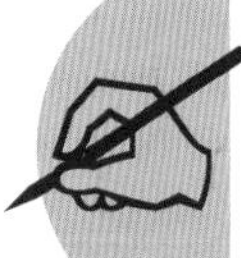

1. Using Erikson's eight stages of development, outline the stages of development and their outcomes for four members of the MacDonald and Ahmed families (see 'Case study: A tale of two families' in Chapter 7 and Appendix 1).
2. Choose one person from each family in the case study and, using a psychological theory, describe how far their needs are being met.
3. What is self-concept? Describe the self-esteem of one member of each family.

Suggested reading

Books

Berry, J., Poortinga, Y., Breugelmans, S., Chasiotis, A., Sam, D. (2011) *Cross-Cultural Psychology: Research and applications*, **3rd edition. Cambridge: Cambridge University Press.**

This book provides a detailed discussion about the rapidly growing field of cross-cultural psychology. It covers topics such as personality, cognition, emotion and language.

Cardwell, M., Clark, L. and Meldrum, C. (2008) *Psychology*, **4th edition. London: Collins.**

A comprehensive look at psychology, sometimes at a more detailed level than required here. It provides a good introduction to a number of the topics covered in this and the previous chapter, such as psychological approaches, attachment theory and cultural bias in psychology.

O'Brien, E. (2011) *Psychology for Social Care: An Irish perspective.* **Dublin: Gill and Macmillan.**

This book provides an excellent and up-to-date overview of psychology in relation to social care. The content extends well beyond the Irish perspective. It is clearly written and explains different psychological approaches.

Websites

British Psychological Society – www.bps.org.uk

CHAPTER 5 Social influences and sociology

A sociological approach ... complements anti-oppressive practice and supports and strengthens critical practice, as it sets out the theoretical basis for understanding oppression and disadvantage.

(Cunningham, 2014)

Introduction

A sociological approach to positive care practice presents you with a theoretical basis for understanding social influences. This chapter aims to enable you to acquire an understanding of sociological concepts, perspectives and theories, which will enable you to analyse how social influences affect individuals who use care services. The chapter begins with an examination of the meaning of sociology and some of the concepts and social influences that are fundamental to sociological understanding. Five contrasting sociological theories are considered: functionalist, conflict, symbolic interactionist, social constructionist and feminist. It is useful to examine different theories since no single theoretical framework can encompass all of the ways of examining aspects of society. Different theorists approach and see things from different angles and with different emphases. Some may be diametrically opposed, while others will differ in less radical ways. All, however, offer you the opportunity to see the social world from a different perspective.

The chapter proceeds to an examination of how the theories may be applied to a study of social influences. The social influences of and on the family, inequality and poverty, and discrimination are considered, as well as the ways in which social influences have an impact on people's development and life chances. At the end of the chapter there is an opportunity to reflect on how you can apply your knowledge of sociology and social influences in the care context.

The material in this chapter is relevant to Care: Social Influences (Higher). It also covers material that will be useful to learners studying Care: Social Influences at National 4 and 5 levels, Scottish Vocational Qualifications SVQ2 and SVQ3 in Social Services (Children and Young People) and Social Services and Healthcare, and the HNC Social Care and the HNC Health Care.

By the end of this chapter you should be able to:

- ★ define sociology and understand key sociological concepts
- ★ examine the meaning of social influences and their impact on development and life chances
- ★ identify and explain five different sociological theories
- ★ understand that different sociological perspectives and theories can help you to appreciate that there are different ways of perceiving and understanding the social world
- ★ examine the social influences of and on the family, inequality and poverty, and discrimination in terms of sociological theory
- ★ apply your knowledge of social influences and sociology to the care context.

Sociology: definitions and concepts

> *Sociology is surprising ... I don't think that I ever really thought hard about the world around me until I began to study sociology.*
>
> (Laurie Taylor, quoted in *Discover Sociology*, 2015, p.15)

Figure 5.1 Laurie Taylor

Sociology is a fascinating subject. It provides useful and sometimes unexpected insights into the way society works. It enables you to look at familiar things with different eyes. In common with psychology, it is an alternative to 'common sense' explanations of human behaviour, and it often turns 'common sense' on its head. It provides concepts to help you to understand things, rather than just to describe them. There is no one single definition of sociology, and the more you study it the more you will realise that the definition depends to some extent on the perspective or theory that you are using. Before reading further, imagine that you have said to a friend that you're going to study sociology and your friend asks 'What's sociology?' What ideas do you have in your mind about sociology and what it is that you will be studying?

To get you started in your thinking about sociology some definitions and statements are given below, but do not take these as the whole story. At the end of the chapter you will be asked again to try to define sociology, and hopefully you will be able to give a fuller answer then.

Some statements about sociology:

> *Sociology tries to capture an understanding of society in a systematic way and provide substantive explanations which nevertheless are understandable in terms of everyday life.*
>
> (British Sociological Association, 2014; this is a summary of a rather long statement about sociology)

> *Sociology: the science of the development and nature and laws of human (esp. civilised) society; study of social problems.*
>
> (Oxford English Dictionary)

> *Sociology is left-wing rubbish.*
>
> (Edwina Currie, former Conservative Minister of Health; quoted in Dominelli, 1997)

> *Sociology is a vast discipline characterised by a variety of theoretical approaches and perspectives.*
>
> (Dominelli, 1997)

Sociology, social influences and care practice

The aim of this chapter is not to make you a sociologist, but to offer you some sociological insights and ways of looking at the social influences that may affect people who use care services. You will then understand more clearly the influence of, for example, the family, poverty and discrimination on the lives of people and their life chances. You will also see that there are many influences *on* these influences. For example, class, age, gender and disability all influence the ways in which the family, poverty and discrimination are experienced. Sociology also has the potential to enable you to look critically at the institutions in which you live and work. 'Institution' in this sense has a sociological meaning, being one of the structures that constitute the building blocks of society, for example the family, schools and care organisations. You will consider more fully how to work within, at times alongside and at other times taking a reflective critical view of, these institutions.

Some people have seen the study of sociology as potentially damaging to care workers. They fear that too much insight and too much analysis may make workers unduly critical of the structures and ways in which they work, of the bureaucracies in which they are enmeshed and of the services that provide care to thousands of vulnerable people. Others, however, see sociology as empowering for care workers, as it provides some insights into society, culture, institutions and the impact of social influences, which can enable them to contribute to improvements in the quality of life of those with whom they work. It is this latter view that is promoted in this chapter.

Psychology helps us look at individual differences in behaviour, but it is only when people are also seen as part of the group and society within which they live that a more complete picture is possible. Something that is a personal problem affects just the individual and those closest to them. When a problem affects a number of people, however, it becomes a concern for society. Sociology looks at how these problems arise, how they get defined, and how society responds to them. There is a great deal of overlap between sociology and psychology, and some theories and concepts incorporate aspects of both. A single chapter devoted to sociology cannot hope to give you more than an introduction to such a wide-ranging subject. You are encouraged to refer to some of the recommended resources at the end of the chapter if you wish to take your thinking further.

Sociological concepts

Comte, or to give him his full name, Auguste Francois Marie Xavier Comte (1789–1857) was the first person to use the term 'sociology', in the late 1830s. For Comte, sociology could be seen as the scientific study of society, seeking to provide an understanding of it. He stated his belief in these words: '*Savoir pour prevoir et prevoir pour pouvoir*'. This can be roughly translated as: 'To know in order to predict, and to predict in order to be able or to empower'. Although the scientific status of sociology continues to be an area of debate and dispute, Comte's aim to understand society, and through this understanding to be able to promote change, continues to be relevant to this day.

In sociology there are some fundamental concepts (ideas) that it is as well to consider at the very beginning of your study so that in later discussion they can be used without further explanation. From the many sociological concepts, brief consideration will be given here to: **society**; **social influence**; **culture**, **norms and values**; **role**, **status and social class**; and **life chances**. **Socialisation** is also a sociological concept of prime importance but, since it was examined fully in Chapter 3 (see page 118), it is touched on only briefly in this chapter. These are not the only concepts that are relevant to your study, and others (family, inequality and poverty, and discrimination) receive consideration later in this chapter. Many of these are not only useful concepts but can also be seen as social influences. This will become clearer as the chapter progresses.

Society

Activity *What is meant by 'society'?*

Sociology leads to the careful and detailed examination of society and the way it works. But what is meant by 'society'? Before going further a useful activity (adapted from Brown, 1979) is to draw a simple picture or diagram that represents 'society' for you. You can use shapes and pictures but no words, and should spend no more than five minutes doing this.

The picture you drew will say something about your view of society, about where you see people fitting into it and about the assumptions you make about the world around you. If you were to compare your picture with one produced by someone else, there would almost certainly be differences. You might have included something that others have left out, and vice versa, and there may have been differences of emphasis.

Why do you think there might be significant differences between your diagram and that of someone else?

What might be the implications of these differences?

Now examine Figure 5.2 and answer the following questions.

1 What do you think each of these illustrations suggests about society?
2 What do you think the boxes in (c) stand for? Make a copy of the diagram and fill in the boxes.
3 Explain your own diagram and discuss what it says about your interpretation of society.

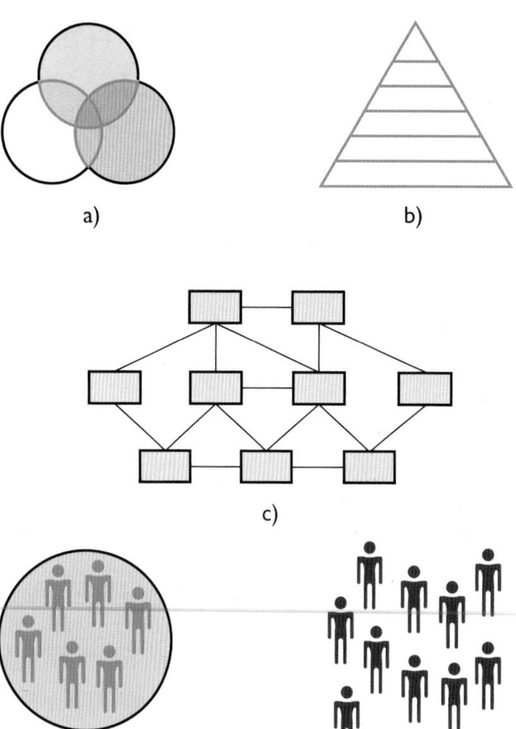

Figure 5.2 Diagrams that illustrate 'society'

Although some theorists argue that we are moving towards a global society, 'society' is still usually regarded as the country or nation state in which you live. The Scottish Referendum in 2014 gave rise to huge expressions of nationalism and both 'sides' voted for what they saw as best for Scotland's future. Scotland is increasingly seen as a society that is distinct from other parts of Britain in many ways, though having a great deal in common in others. Language often defines a society. Laws, education, religion and other aspects of culture are among the things that distinguish one 'society' from another. Although Scotland shares a language with the rest of Britain, there are distinct Scottish turns of phrase and dialects. Gaelic is still spoken in the Highlands and Islands and is increasingly being taught in other parts of Scotland. Scotland has its own parliament, legal system, education system and religious denominations. It is a multicultural society in its own right, but remains part of the United Kingdom in many social, economic, political and cultural ways.

Often 'society' is referred to as something distinct and independent, as a thing in itself rather than just the sum total of the members who are part of it. 'Society' is often blamed for things like the inability of people to change their circumstances or the problems that they face. Avril Taylor (1993), for example, in her study of women drug users in Glasgow, talks of 'the inability of society either to recognise or to cater for such women's needs'. Mark Macaskill (2014), in an article headed 'Blame society, not Buckfast', examines a controversial row about Buckfast, the alcoholic drink produced by monks in Devon and blamed in some quarters for fuelling social problems in the west of Scotland.

Social influences

A social influence may be defined as an effect on the individual or social group that is external and is part of the social environment. Social influences were touched upon briefly in Chapter 3 in the sections on strands of development (SPECCS), with the aspects of social, cultural and spiritual very much in the sociological domain. But all aspects of development, behaviour and life chances are subject to social influences, which is why it is so important to consider them.

'Social influence' covers a broad area and many of the concepts considered in this section can be viewed as social influences. Society, culture, norms, values, role, status, social class, agents of socialisation: all exert a social influence on the lives of individuals. The three main topics considered later this chapter (the family, inequality and poverty, and discrimination) are all influenced by these social influences, but they are all themselves social influences in their own right, influencing one another. Although the chapter is divided into neat, discrete sections you can see that all parts of it are interconnected and in reality much more difficult to separate out. Figure 5.3 illustrates the way in which the chapter is structured in terms of sociology, social influences and the selected topics of the family, inequality and poverty, and discrimination, and how these can be linked with aspects of behaviour and development discussed in Chapter 3.

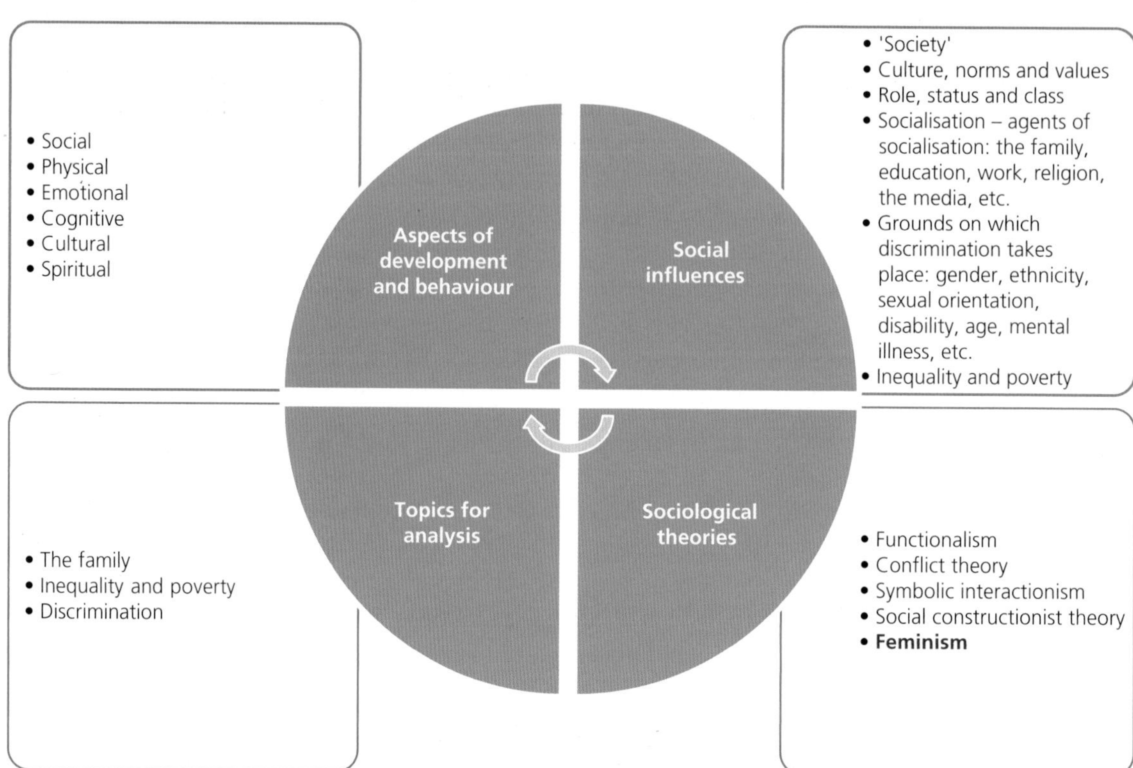

Figure 5.3 The context of social influences

Culture, norms and values

As a human being you learn a great deal of your behaviour. How much you believe you learn depends on your position in the nature/nurture debate. You do not just behave instinctively: you use your intelligence, observational skills and learning. You learn how to behave, and you share much of this behaviour with other members of the society to which you belong. This learned, shared behaviour is known as **culture**. Culture is the way of life of society's members. It includes the values, beliefs, customs, norms and rules that human beings learn as members of a society. Without culture, human society could not exist.

Activity *Music as an example of culture*

Write down ten things that come to mind when you think of the phrase 'Scottish music'.

Did you think of bagpipes and the massed bands of the Edinburgh Tattoo? Or maybe 'social dancing' at school or the 'Eightsome Reel' at a ceilidh? Maybe you thought of Emeli Sandé, AC/DC, or Travis. If you are of a certain age, you may have memories of Rod Stewart, the Bay City Rollers, Sydney Devine, or even Andy Stewart. Many people 'see the New Year in' to Aly Bain and Phil Cunningham playing the fiddle on TV, go to hear them at Celtic Connections in Glasgow in January, or visit the Amber Festival in Perthshire in October for the music of Dougie MacLean.

Most of the above artists are, or were, fairly mainstream Scottish musicians and singers, and they represent a wide enough range. But there are many other musical traditions in Scotland that show even greater diversity, even in this one aspect of culture. There is still a very lively tradition of Gaelic singing and the Mod is still held annually each October in a different venue in Scotland. A lot of Scottish bands, such as Salsa Celtica and the Afro-Celt Sound System, have developed fusion music where they mix Scottish instruments and arrangements with musical traditions from other countries. There is Eurydice, a socialist woman's choir who sing contemporary and traditional protest songs, and choirs of asylum seekers that sing songs from all the different countries represented.

Gaelic punk, Scottish-Asian, the list of musical combinations is endless, and that's the point: there is not just one type of 'Scottish music'. You may never pay money to hear the new opera by James MacMillan or Judith Weir, or you might happily avoid going within ten miles of the Loopallu or Wickerman festivals, but many people in Scotland would make one or the other their priority. That is the diversity of culture: it is never 'one size fits all'!

Figure 5.4 Scottish music. Harry MacFadyen plays Scottish music on an array of instruments for all kinds of events, including for the charity Music in Hospitals. The Taiko tradition also illustrated originates from the west coast of Japan. Each spring, Japanese Matsuri for Glasgow holds a festival in the Botanic Gardens. The aim is to advance education of Japanese culture and heritage, and to promote wide community involvement in the awareness of diverse cultures.

Culture can and does change. Sometimes it changes because attitudes change: things that have previously been accepted as 'right' or inevitable come to be seen as unnecessary, oppressive or disempowering. For instance, 100 years ago, women weren't able to vote and people with disabilities were placed in institutions, far away from their local community. Advances in technology have led to other cultural changes, such as the use of txt language and the ability of parents to know whether their unborn child has a specific disability. The impact of the media is much larger now, because people have much greater access to a wide range of images through the internet, Apps and numerous TV channels, and this influences greatly how we understand the world and our place it. Changes in demography, the way the population is structured, have led to other cultural changes, such as the increase in the number of older adults who have greater spending power ('the grey pound') but who may also need more care services as their health deteriorates.

Norms are unwritten rules that are generally agreed to be the right way to do things in any situation. You don't often know what they are until you have broken one – especially in a new situation. If you go to hear a Mozart symphony in a concert hall for the first time, you may wonder why people don't clap at the end of each section of music. It is the norm to wait until the very end to applaud (generally so that you don't interrupt the focus of the musicians). It doesn't say this on the ticket or in the programme – you are just expected to know it. You will certainly pick it up very quickly, if you are the only one clapping and other people turn round and glare! Can you remember back to the first few days of a school or college course, or the start of a new job? People tend to hold back and wait to see how things are (what the norms are) before they feel they have the true picture of what's going on. For instance, college tutors may say that you have 15 minutes for your break, but only some of them make a big deal about it if you are late back. For a service user or worker visiting a care setting for the first time, the norms are often more important, and more difficult to work out, than the officially stated rules and policies.

Values are your beliefs about what it is vital to uphold above all else. People have differing viewpoints about what is important or not in life, and this often leads to conflict. Many parents value education as the way for their children to do better in life than they did, but their children may see things differently. They often cannot see the benefit of remaining at school or college and maybe not even getting a job at the end, or of having to give up the things that they value at the moment: social contact, having a girlfriend/boyfriend, experimenting with drink, etc. In fact, a lot of the issues in the 'generation gap' come from this difference in values and priorities. Within care settings, one person in a care home may value peace and quiet while the person in the next room may like to chat and have the TV on, and this can cause conflict. Neither person is right, but it is difficult for both to meet their needs at the same time.

Activity *Religious attendance*

An example of how culture and values vary over time is religion. In the Scottish census in 2011, 56.3 per cent of the population answered that they had a religion, compared with 67 per cent in 2001; and 36.7 per cent of the population answered that they had no religion, compared with 28 per cent in 2001. Those with no religion tended to have a younger profile than those who had a religion. Look at Figure 5.5 and write about or discuss to what you attribute these changes. What do they say about 'society'?

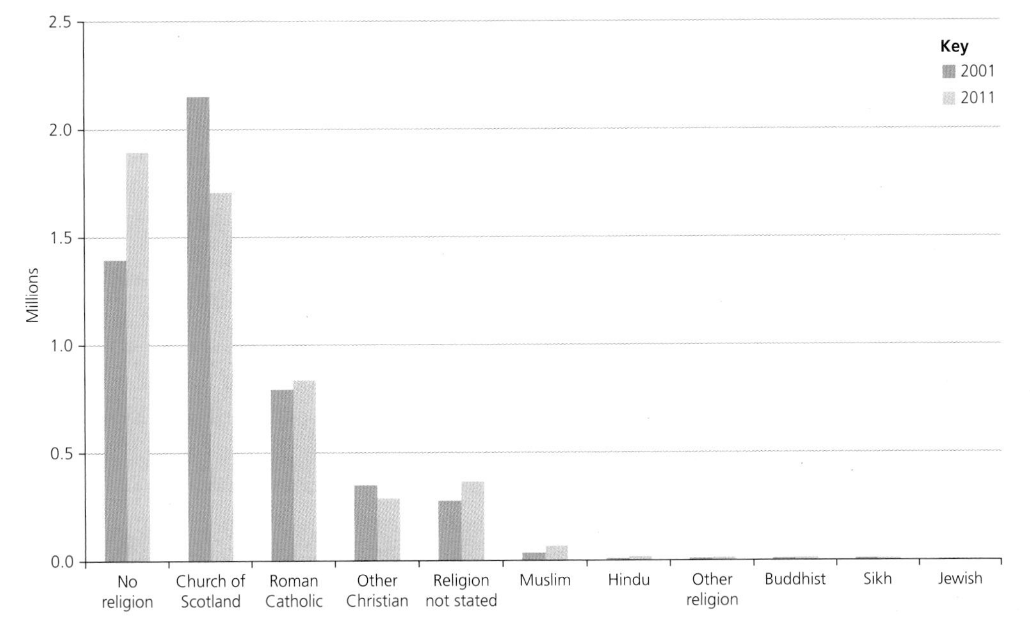

Figure 5.5 Religion in Scotland, 2001 and 2011
(Source: Scottish Government 2011 Census, www.scotland.gov.uk)

Role, status and social class

All the world's a stage,

And all the men and women merely players:

They have their exits and their entrances;

And one man in his time plays many parts …

(William Shakespeare, *As You Like It*, 1599)

In a sense, society provides individuals with scripts that enable them, like actors in a theatre, to play their roles.

(Heraud, 1970)

The above quotations refer to people's social roles. Role, status and social class are three further fundamental sociological concepts. A fairly straightforward definition of **role** is that it is the part that an individual appears to play in a group, and the behaviour that is expected from a person in that position. The predictability of behaviour associated with a role (mums are expected to …, teachers are generally …) enables us to interact more easily with each other. A role has three constituents: part, behaviour and social expectation. A role such as son or daughter is *ascribed* (given), but other roles can be *achieved*, or chosen, such as teacher or student. Most people have multiple roles. For example, the roles of wife, mother, teacher, daughter can all be held by the same person at the same time, sometimes in harmony, sometimes in conflict with one another.

The roles that a person has will, to a large extent, determine the status that person has in society. **Status** refers to the position a person has in society and the degree of respect that this position commands. As with role, some statuses are achieved and some are ascribed. One status that is largely ascribed is that of **social class**, though change in social class can be achieved, either up or down, through *social mobility*. Upward mobility is somewhat harder to achieve than downward mobility and can be hampered by earlier class, status and role positions. A lawyer has a fairly high status and can be defined as being a member of the middle class. But if she loses her job, can't pay the mortgage, and ends up in a hostel for homeless people, then there is a clear difference in her role, status and class position. Some of the people we work with in care settings have experienced a change in their role, status and/or class and are in the process of adapting to this difference.

There are many ways in which social class can be viewed. You can pretend it doesn't exist. Margaret Thatcher tried to convince us that the UK is a classless society. Or you can take an academic approach and view class as an aspect of society and a social influence. In official statistics, including the census, the term 'social grade' has replaced the term social class in the UK today. **Social grades** are socioeconomic groupings drawn up by the Office of National Statistics and are called NS-SEC (National Statistics Socio-Economic Classifications). Table 5.1 shows the structure of Scotland's 1.8 million households by social grade, based on 2011 census data.

Table 5.1 Social grades in Scotland, 2011

Social grade	Description	Percentage of Scotland's households
A B	Higher and intermediate managerial/administrative/professional	19%
C1	Supervisory, clerical, junior managerial/administrative/ professional	32%
C2	Skilled manual workers	22%
DE	Semi-skilled and unskilled manual workers Those on state benefit; unemployed; lowest grade workers	28%

Although the term 'social class' has been abandoned in favour of the socioeconomic 'social grades' in the census and much market research, it is still part of our language in relation to society. It continues to be used in sociology to distinguish among groups in society along much broader lines than by socioeconomic position based on paid occupation or lack of it. The BBC's Great British Class Survey 2011, devised and analysed by sociologists (Savage *et al.*, 2013), proposed seven social classes as representing British society today (see Table 5.2). These classes are based on a model using ideas about economic, social and cultural capital. Economic capital refers to wealth and income, social capital refers to contacts and connections that enable people to draw on their networks, and cultural capital refers to the ability to engage with cultural activities as well as the level of educational attainment. These factors combine to provide a measure of class position. You can measure your own position on this scale, using the 'Great British Class Calculator' at: **www.bbc.co.uk/news/magazine-22000973**. You shouldn't put too much store by this, especially if you are a young, not-very-wealthy student, care worker, health worker or even lecturer or writer, since it may not quite capture who you are, were or will be. But it gives a perspective on British society not provided by the rather limited socioeconomic grades.

Table 5.2 Social class in the Great British Class Survey 2011

Class position	Class name	Class description	Percentage of survey population	Average age
Class 1	Elite	The wealthiest and most privileged group, the UK's biggest earners; many went to private schools and elite universities; this group is exclusive and hard to join	6%	57
Class 2	Established middle class	Second wealthiest group; socialise with a wide range of people; often work in management or professional occupations; enjoy a diverse range of cultural activities; often from middle class backgrounds	25%	46
Class 3	Technical middle class	Small, prosperous and distinctive new class often working in science, research and technical occupations; tend to mix with their own occupational group; tend to prefer emerging culture; often from middle class backgrounds	6%	52
Class 4	New affluent workers	This class group is sociable; has lots of cultural interests; sits in the middle of all the groups in terms of wealth	15%	44
Class 5	Traditional working class	Low scores for economic, social and cultural factors, but they do have some financial security	14%	66
Class 6	Emergent service workers	Financially insecure with low scores for house value and savings, but high for social and cultural factors	19%	34
Class 7	Precariat	The poorest and most deprived group; low economic, social and cultural capital; 80 per cent rent their accommodation	15%	50

Life chances

Life chances refer to the differing possibilities people have to access opportunities in society, for example differences in access to health services, employment, housing, education and a safe environment. People's life chances are subject to both nature and nurture, to what they are born with and to the influences on them. Social influences play a crucial role in determining life chances and many of these are the subject of this chapter. People's life chances are especially influenced by their status and social class, by their family and all the agents of socialisation, by inequality and poverty, and by discrimination.

Socialisation

In Chapter 3 socialisation was defined as the process by which people learn the culture of their society. At this point you are advised to go back to Chapter 3 (see pages 118–22) to read the account of socialisation again, and to remind yourself of the relevant terms: **primary** and **secondary socialisation**, and **agents of socialisation**.

Table 5.3 Sociological concepts and influences

Society	Country or nation state; often distinguished from other societies by language, laws, education, religion, etc.
Social influence	An effect that is external to the individual and is part of his/her social environment
Culture	Learned, shared behaviours; the way of life of a society's members
Role	The part that an individual plays in a group and the behaviour that is expected of a person in that position
Status	Position in society and the degree of respect that this position commands
Social grade	Social grades based on socioeconomic position devised by the Office of National Statistics, and used by the government and for census and market research
Social class	Division in society, usually on the basis of wealth, occupation and education; the Great British Class Survey 2011 found seven social classes in the UK, based on economic, social and cultural capital
Norms	Unwritten rules that are generally accepted as the way to act in certain situations
Values	Beliefs about what is right and wrong, and what is important or not
Social inequality	An unequal distribution of the opportunities and rewards in society, because of the way in which society is structured
Life chances	The differing possibilities people have to access opportunities in society, e.g. differences in access to health, employment, housing, education and a safe environment
Socialisation	The process by which people acquire and learn the culture of their society

Sociological perspectives and theories

So far you have been introduced to a number of concepts and influences that will be woven through this chapter and the rest of the book. They present some of the fundamental building blocks upon which thinking about the behaviour of people in society can be built. In order to gain a fuller understanding of sociology and the way in which it sets out to explain the social world, it is necessary to look at the perspectives of different sociologists and the theories applied within these perspectives to explain the impact of social influences. In the context of this chapter the term '**perspective**' is used in the same way as '**approach**' was used in Chapter 4. Both an approach and a perspective are a way of looking at something. '**Theory**' here is used in a broad sense to mean a set of related statements that seeks to provide an explanation about an aspect or aspects of the social world.

There are two main perspectives in sociology. These are the macro-sociological and the micro-sociological perspectives.

- **Macro-sociological** perspectives regard individual behaviour as being predominantly influenced by the demands and constraints of the social systems in which the person lives. This includes **functionalist** and **conflict theories**.
- **Micro-sociological** perspectives regard the individual as capable of exerting influence on society, and not just conforming to the requirements of the society in which they live. This includes **symbolic interactionist theory**.

Feminism incorporates the whole range of sociological theories, with its emphasis on viewing the world from a female gender-specific macro- and/or micro-sociological perspective. **Social constructionist theory** also contains aspects of both a macro- and a micro-sociological perspective.

One way of seeing the macro/micro difference in explanation is that in the micro-sociological approach individuals are seen as constantly creating their reality, but in the macro-sociological approach they are seen as being largely subject to the external forces of the systems in which they live. A 'system', in the sense in which it is used here, reflects or incorporates any group of people bound by rules and norms. A family is a system, as is a care organisation, and of course society itself. In reality you need a combination of theoretical approaches to explain 'society'. To stick too rigidly to one set of explanations from one perspective is to limit your interpretation of the impact of social influences.

Table 5.4 Sociological perspectives and related theories

Macro-sociological perspective	Micro-sociological perspective	Combined sociological perspective
Functionalist theory	Symbolic interactionism	Social constructionism
Conflict theory		Feminism

Table 5.4 shows the perspectives of the main sociological theories. These are not the only sociological theories but they provide a useful introduction to the range of theories used to explain aspects of society.

These main theories will be discussed in the following sections:

- functionalist theory
- conflict theory
- symbolic interactionist theory
- social constructionist theory
- feminist theory.

Functionalist theory

Functionalism is one of the earliest sociological theories and still remains useful in its emphasis on looking at society as something more than the sum total of individuals who make it up. Its early emphasis on scientific method also retains some relevance in sociological thought, as long as this is balanced with other theories.

Emile Durkheim (1858–1917), a professor at the University of Bordeaux and then at the Sorbonne in Paris, was a great thinker and writer who developed ideas about society using the term 'functionalism' for the first time. In its earlier stages the essential ideas of functionalism were that social groups and institutions perform functions that are useful to society as a whole. Society is seen as being made up of interrelated parts that form a system, the social system. Understanding of each individual part can be gained only by looking at the functions it has in relation to the whole. Society is compared to the human body, to illustrate the fact that they are both systems that rely on the proper functioning of each constituent part in order to survive. In a human being, the heart has specific functions in relation to pumping blood around the body, but its function can only be understood in relation to the other organs, which transport oxygen to the blood and take waste products away from it. Similarly, functionalist theory emphasises the importance of looking at parts of society, such as the family, in terms of their function in, and maintenance of, the social system as a whole.

> *The function of any recurrent activity, such as the punishment of a crime, or a funeral ceremony, is the part it plays in the social life as a whole and therefore the contribution it makes to the maintenance of the structural continuity.*
>
> (Radcliffe-Brown, 1935)

There were many great civilisations in the past, such as the Roman, Greek, Inca and Aztec civilisations, but they all disappeared because some aspect of their structure began to falter and it eventually led to the downfall of the whole system. Functionalists are interested in this question: why do certain aspects of society exist, and what role, or function, does each aspect play in maintaining that society? This is important in terms of social influences and care practice, because if some social influences impact negatively on the functioning of society as a whole, then the government may need to intervene to address the impact of these social influences. If the government can be clear about what role these social influences play, it can make policies and procedures that aim to bring society back into balance again. For instance, with changes in the structure of the family since the mid-1970s, the role of looking after babies and young children is now not limited only to mothers. Society has adapted to the change of working mothers, and the function of rearing children is now shared with fathers and with care providers such as nursery schools and child minders, partly because governments have provided money to fund the growth of this provision. One of the reasons our society gathers so much statistical information is so that such changes can be recognised and steps taken to plan for and manage them.

This is the important aspect for Durkheim: it is crucial to have not just a clear knowledge about a problem or social influence, but to know also how we can change things to create social order, or harmony, in society again:

> *Consequently, to explain a social fact it is not enough to show the cause on which it depends; we must also, at least in most cases, show its function in the establishment of social order.*
>
> (Durkheim, 1938)

Consensus about norms and values was seen to be the ideal situation for a society, and it was seen as important that all the interconnected, inter-dependent parts should work together to maintain the cohesion necessary for an orderly, well-functioning society. This consensus model can be used to look at all levels and types of influence, including the family, social class and education.

Criticisms of functionalism

One of the main criticisms levelled against functionalists is that they fail to take adequate account of conflict in society. Functionalists do not see conflict as inherent in society but they do not ignore it altogether. Rather, they attempt to explain it in terms of the contribution that conflict can make to the maintenance of social order. Situations of conflict, such as a war with another country, or outrage at the sexual abuse of children, enable society to reconfirm what is important to it. In this sense, dysfunction is useful for society because it helps to clarify what is valued, for example freedom from abuse.

A further criticism is that functionalists, in concentrating on social functions and the social system, failed to take sufficient account of the individual in society. This is a general criticism of all macro-sociological approaches. Feminists have seen much of functionalist theory as being gender-blind and conservative, promoting traditional views of institutions such as the family, and in so doing perpetuating **patriarchy** (the role of women as housewives and mothers) and contributing to women's continuing inequality and disempowerment. Finally, through seeing society in terms of functions and harmony, functionalists have failed to emphasise change and the need for progress towards social justice.

Conflict theory

> *Society is like a more or less confused battle ground. If we watch from on high, we can see a variety of groups fighting each other, constantly forming and reforming, making and breaking alliances.*
>
> (Craib, 1984)

Unlike functionalist theory, which emphasises equilibrium, balance and shared values, conflict theories rest on the view that conflict between various groups in society is fundamental, because they have inherently different interests from one another. The interests of some groups are better served by the way in which society is organised than are the interests of others: some groups of people get a better deal from 'society' than other groups. This is not because some people work harder; it results instead from the way in which society is structured. In any group of people, whether a society or an organisation, there are limited resources and competition for these scarce resources. In society, for instance, there may not be enough decent jobs or houses for everyone, and there can sometimes be conflict in communities about who should get the chance to get the resources that do come up. Therefore competition, not consensus, is the main aspect of human relationships and, according to conflict theory, it is those who already hold power who will be more likely to succeed in this competition. Recognising this structured imbalance of power is key to understanding oppression by the dominant group.

In this section two major theorists who have put forward conflict theories will be considered. These are Karl Marx and Ralph Dahrendorf. **Karl Marx** (1818–83) was born in Germany and lived for a time in Paris, where he met Friedrich Engels, with whom he formed a lifelong friendship. He then moved to Brussels and finally settled in London in 1849. He is best known for his views about the importance of **economic structures** in determining the way a society operates. The Marxist approach put forward a view of society in which in capitalist society there is a fundamental conflict of interest between two groups: the ruling class (bourgeoisie), which owns and controls the means of production, for example factories, and the subject class (proletariat), which produces labour to work in the factories but which is exploited and oppressed by the ruling class. In Marx's view only when the means of production are communally owned (i.e. equally owned and shared by everyone) will classes and conflict disappear. For Marx economic class and ownership of the means of production were the most fundamental divisions in society and the source of conflicts of interest. Economic relations were the central facts that determined how the rest of the relations in society were structured.

The second conflict theorist to be considered is **Ralph Dahrendorf** (1929–2009). He too was born in Germany and subsequently moved to London, where he became Professor of Sociology at the London School of Economics. Dahrendorf took Marx's theories as a starting point but argued that changes took place in society in the twentieth century that necessitated a re-evaluation of Marx.

Dahrendorf sees functionalist theories as being utopian or idealistic in their analysis of society and proposes that at least one other way of looking at society is required. For Dahrendorf this is conflict theory. This theory emphasises **change** as continuous and normal in society. Dahrendorf believed that social **conflict** is the great creative force that carries along change. He goes on to state that 'Wherever there is social life there's conflict, and the surprising thing in society would not be the presence of conflict but the absence of conflict.' He is talking here not just about major conflicts like wars and revolutions, but also about what happens in your family's house, the local care home or the most recent reality TV show! Thus, so far two main concepts in the conflict model are **change** and **conflict**. For Dahrendorf a third important concept is **constraint**.

Unlike the functionalists, who suggest that agreement holds societies and organisations together, Dahrendorf argues that these are held together 'not by consensus but by constraint, not by universal agreement but by coercion of some by others'. Thus for Dahrendorf some groups in society coerce and others are coerced; some groups constrain, others are constrained. This has some similarities to Marx, who argued that the owners of the means of production constrain and coerce the workers. Dahrendorf differs from Marx in seeing the situation as much more complicated than this, in seeing sources of conflict other than economic ones and the possibility that in some situations a person may be the source of constraint and in other situations may be constrained. For example, a teacher might constrain students in the classroom but might herself be constrained in what she can teach by the education authority. The essential point to grasp is that in conflict theory, change and constraint, and not function and consensus, are points of departure in any analysis of social situations and the impact of social influences.

Criticisms of conflict theory

Dahrendorf again differs from functionalists in stating that conflict theory is not the only way of looking at society, in a way building in his own criticism of his theory. Functionalists usually claim that theirs is a comprehensive model and can be used to explain all social phenomena. But Dahrendorf (1964) states:

> *As far as I can see, we need … both the equilibrium and the conflict models of society; and it may well be that … society has two faces of equal reality: one of stability, harmony and consensus, and one of change, conflict and constraint.*

There is clear evidence that the divisions in society are much more complicated than they were in Marx's day: there was not then the large, professional middle class that there is today, and it is sometimes very difficult to identify who actually 'owns' the global multinationals that exist. Feminists and other campaigning groups have demonstrated that the way society is stratified, or structured, has to be seen as multi-dimensional: class alone no longer explains someone's position in society. Depending on the situation, society can also be seen to be divided along lines such as gender, race or age.

The divisions in society are also not static and fixed. Historically, the Suffragettes campaigned strongly against the government to achieve votes for women, but withheld their campaign during the First World War, when British society was united against Germany. After the war, they vigorously reinstated their campaign. There are many instances of this type of changing situation when it comes to alliances and divisions in society.

Symbolic interactionist theory

> *Symbolic interactionism is … the study of the self–society relationship as a process of symbolic communication between social actors.*

(Abercrombie *et al.*, 2006)

In contrast to the macro approach presented by functionalism and conflict theory, symbolic interactionist theory focuses attention on the meanings that individuals give to social actions. Here, interactions among individuals – rather than the way society is structured – are seen as the starting point. The importance of society is not denied but social structures are seen as changeable through individual actions and open to varying interpretations. Symbolic interactionism originated in the USA. Among the founders was **George Herbert Mead**. Mead (1863–1931) was an American philosopher whose ideas had a great influence upon sociology. Howard Becker's (b. 1928) **labelling theory**, also within the interactionist theory, is discussed later in this chapter in the section on discrimination.

In symbolic interactionism **symbols** are seen as the foundation on which interactions are built. A symbol can be defined as:

> *Any gesture, artefact, sign or concept that stands for, signifies or expresses something else …*

(Abercrombie *et al.*, 2006)

A word can be a symbol. For example, the word 'table' has a symbolic meaning – it stands for a particular set of ideas about a thing called a table, which is immediately understood by those using the symbol and includes some meanings and excludes others. What does the symbol 'table' mean to you? At home it might symbolise the place where you sit down to eat and chat, but also the place where you have to do your college homework. If this latter symbol takes on negative connotations (the work is piling up and never seems to get finished), the table may stop having the positive associations it used to have for you. In some situations it has positive connotations and in others it has negative, but it is still the same word. Other words can take on particular meanings because they become associated in popular consciousness with a particular event. Examples of this include Piper Alpha, Dunblane, Lockerbie and 9/11.

A gesture such as a handshake is also a symbol that signifies a particular meaning: in many societies this gesture is used as a welcome. This meaning is, however, culturally determined. The handshake on its own, without its symbolic meaning, would be meaningless to some people. If you try to shake the hand of a child, they often have no idea what to do or why they should do it. If you met someone from Japan, they might bow to you as a greeting. British people sometimes find it awkward to return the bow, perhaps because it symbolises subjection to them, has a religious connotation, or because they are just not familiar with the action.

Clothes are very potent symbols. Those of a teenager, in particular, say a lot about with what group – or subculture – they identify. For all age groups, clothes convey all kinds of messages about factors such as what you feel about yourself, how much you like to conform, or what your income is. You can 'dress up' or 'dress down' depending on what message you want to convey and you can broadcast all this on Facebook and other social media. And, as anyone living in a house with a teenager knows, piles of washed and unwashed clothes on the floor can symbolise freedom or disrespect, depending on which point of view you are taking! In care settings, many organisations have moved away from requiring staff to wear uniforms as it conveys messages about power and control that they don't want to project to service users.

One of Mead's central ideas was that individuals develop their interactions and their ideas through their ability to put themselves in the position of others. The process of imagining responses is called **role-taking**. If I see you crying, for example, my response will largely be determined by my imagining myself in your position. It is likely that my response will be appropriate because I have internalised how to respond to crying and can, in my imagination, take the role of someone crying and respond to it. This process of role-taking is also central to the development of a **concept of self**.

According to Mead, without symbols there would be no human interaction and no human society. It is the use of symbols that distinguishes human interactions from the interactions of other species. It is only through symbols that the responses of others can be imagined. The individual imagines the effect of **symbolic communication** (verbal and non-verbal communication, words, gestures, etc.) on others and so can anticipate their response. This is done through internal 'conversations' that individuals have with themselves, based on the imagined responses from other people – the **generalised other**.

Mead, in developing his thoughts about self, distinguishes between **the 'me' and the 'I'**:

> *The 'I' is the response of the organism to the attitudes of the others; the 'me' is the organised set of attitudes of others which one himself assumes. The attitude of the others constitute the organised 'me', and then one reacts towards that as an 'I'.*
>
> (Mead, quoted in Coser and Rosenberg, 1976)

This distinction between 'me' and 'I' is an important, though rather difficult, one to grasp. 'I' is the self-concept, 'me' is the definition of yourself in specific roles. 'I' has been built up from your reactions to others, their reactions to you and the way in which those reactions have been interpreted. This combination of social interaction and a person's definition of the situation gives rise to people making choices about which roles they take on and how those roles are performed.

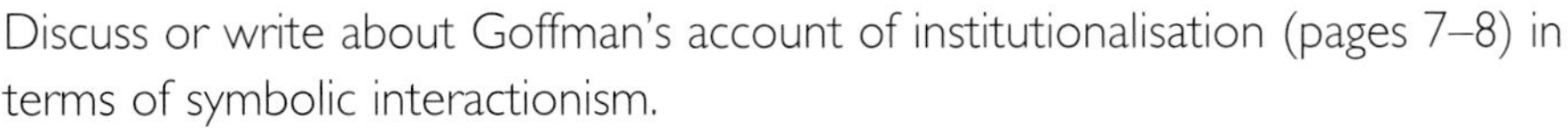

Symbolic interactionism and institutionalisation

In Chapter 1 you read about institutionalisation and the way this affects people.

Discuss or write about Goffman's account of institutionalisation (pages 7–8) in terms of symbolic interactionism.

Do you think Goffman's views of institutionalisation can be seen as contributing to symbolic interactionist theory?

Criticisms of symbolic interactionism

There are a number of criticisms that can be levelled against this micro-sociological approach, one of which is that there is insufficient consideration given to macro features such as the importance of historical aspects of society and the influences of institutions, power and class. Symbolic interactionists also, in the past, failed to explain the source or origin of the symbols upon which communication and interaction depend. Why do people shake hands when they meet? Does it matter? Is it important to look at why a type of behaviour started, or is it interesting just to have an accurate record of what people are doing and to understand what it means to them? Currently symbolic interactionists are concerned with moving away from a completely micro-sociological approach to address some of these criticisms.

Social constructionist theory

There are many versions of social constructionism in sociology. They originate from the work of Peter Berger and Thomas Luckmann in the 1960s (Berger and Luckmann, 1991), which was modified in the 1970s and later. Berger and Luckmann were affected by such thinkers as the French philosopher **Foucault** (Foucault, 2002). They have influenced sociological thinking in new directions and presented a theory of society based on the prominent discourses of any one particular period. They see '**truth**' as being contingent on a particular historical period, implying that the truth about society as people see it and construct it changes over time. There are three essential elements to most social constructionist theories:

1. They question whether there can be an objective reality outside of people's experience.
2. The way in which the world is understood is through social interaction.
3. Understanding is located in a particular cultural and historical time and place.

For Foucault '**discourse**' consisted of people's use of language, knowledge and power to structure society's truths. For example, models of disability have been subject to different discourses about disability, and the meaning of disability is not fixed but changes over time. It is socially constructed through the use of discourse so that in the past a medical model of disability dominated, where people were seen in terms of having problems as a result of impairments; in contrast a social model of disability based on personalisation sees society as the main disabling agent. The Paralympic Games in London in 2012 present an example of the social model approach to disability based on a discourse dominated by the abilities rather than the disabilities of people with impairments. This discourse depended on a change in the way language is used in relation to impairment and disability, advances in knowledge that enable people with impairments to participate as fully as possible in 'society' and changes in attitude and political action to promote a social model. Another example of a changing discourse is in relation to welfare benefits, where attitudes have fluctuated backwards and forwards depending on the dominant discourse of the day, from viewing benefits in terms of alleviating social inequalities to seeing people on benefits as 'scroungers'.

Activity *Welfare benefits*

Examine and discuss your own views about people who receive welfare benefits. What do you see as the dominant discourse in relation to welfare benefits? What changes do you think there have been in relation to this discourse and society's 'truth' about welfare benefit claimants in the last ten years?

Criticisms of social constructionist theory

The ideas associated with social constructionist theory enable analysis in terms of discourses based on language, knowledge and power at particular points in time. Its critics are often social realists who see that there are social facts that disadvantage people, whether or not they are socially constructed. For them disability is a social fact that in most societies disadvantages people.

Critics of Foucault's version of the theory also say that the association of knowledge and power is an assumption rather than a fact, and that often power is used based not on knowledge but rather on viewpoint or prejudice. It is also a very general theory and doesn't take account of all the nuances of social structure and relationships. As another way of looking at society, however, the idea of a discourse taking place at a particular time and place presents some interesting perspectives, especially in relation to social change.

Feminist theory

Macro approaches are criticised because they don't take account of an individual's power to influence society, and micro approaches are criticised because they don't take enough account of the importance of the way society is structured. The feminist theory adds another dimension to these critiques, because it maintains that all theories in the past have undervalued, or completely ignored, the importance of women's role in society. In this sense, it also stands as a useful reminder that the experience of many groups has been neglected by the mainly white, middle-class, heterosexual, male academics who developed early sociological theories.

Feminism as a theory sets out to bring to centre stage and to explain the position of women in society, and to focus attention on how women have been subordinated and oppressed. There are a number of differing strands of feminist thought, some of which take a micro-sociological and others that take a macro-sociological approach. The theory as a whole is closely linked to feminism as a social movement, which advocates equality of opportunity for women and men, and the eradication of the economic, social, political and sexual inequalities that exist between the genders. As a sociological theory, feminism has only relatively recently made its way into general sociological literature. For example, a book published in 1971 entitled *Sociological Perspectives: Selected readings*, edited by Thompson and Tunstall, had no mention of feminism, and out of 44 readings not a single one was written by a woman or addressed issues specifically related to women. Twenty years later, *Sociology: Themes and perspectives* by Haralambos and Holburn (1991), gave considerable attention to feminist thought.

In spite of the relatively recent emergence of feminist theories in sociology, feminist ideas have been around for a long time. Mary Wollstonecraft expressed an **equal rights** doctrine as early as 1792 in her 'Vindication of the Rights of Women'; the Suffragettes fought for votes for women at the beginning of the twentieth century; feminist writers such as Simone de Beauvoir in France and Germaine Greer in Britain gained prominence from the 1950s to 1970s. More recent feminist thinkers such as Dominelli (2002) have emphasised the diversity of feminist thought. Several strands of feminist thought can be identified, such as liberal feminism, radical feminism, Marxist feminism and black feminism.

The above developments can be referred to as the three waves of feminism:

- **Wave 1**: the beginnings of feminism, fighting for women's civil rights, especially equal rights to vote and to own property
- **Wave 2**: a more radical focus, seeking reform of society in order to promote an equality of power and to eradicate male domination of women from all spheres of life
- **Wave 3**: postmodern feminism, emphasising the diverse needs of different groups of women, for example black women, working class women, gay women, while retaining the main focus of eradicating all inequalities.

To understand more fully the ideas behind feminist theory, you have to look at ideas associated with **gender** and **patriarchy**. Many people have argued that differences in biology between men and women justify the domination of women by men and that they should occupy different roles in society. For example, one argument runs: because women can become pregnant and bear children, they should stay at home to look after the children they produce; this is their 'natural' role. Since it is their 'natural' role to bear and look after children and be at home with them, it is also 'natural' that they should do the housework while they are there. Women, it is argued, make unreliable workers anyway, always taking time off to have children or to look after them when they are ill.

Feminist theory seeks to give insight into why there is absolutely nothing 'natural' about this situation. Feminists claim that there is nothing in female biology that determines that women should perform childcare or housework or should be any less reliable than men, given the same opportunities and rights. In the 1970s, Ann Oakley gave research status for the first time to the subject of housework, based on the feminist principle that the 'personal is political'. (You can see that this approach reflects a micro-sociological approach: individuals *can* influence society.) Before this, such a subject would not have been considered worthy of sociological research. Oakley and others argue that, although 'male' and 'female' are biological terms, gender roles in society are culturally, not biologically, determined. Most feminist thinkers support this view and feel that confusion between sex (male and female) and gender (masculine and feminine) has been used as an excuse to promote the subordination of women, through placing them in roles that are given inferior status in society.

Figure 5.6 On the summit. This photograph shows a group of women on the summit of Carn Aosda, a Perthshire Munro, 8 March 2014, International Women's Day. International Women's Day was established in 1911 to demonstrate support for women and girls everywhere having the opportunity to achieve their potential.

Patriarchy, the systematic structuring of male dominance in society, reflects a macro-sociological approach, looking at the impact society has on the lives of women. For instance, in the health and social care sector in Scotland, although 85 per cent of the workforce is female, women make up just 28 per cent of the chief executives in the health service (*Herald Scotland*, 2014). And this is despite the fact that there has been sex discrimination and equal pay legislation for more than 40 years! In terms of decision making in society, only 20 per cent of MPs in the House of Commons were female in 2014. The Scottish Parliament fares a lot better, with women making up 35 per cent of MSPs, although this is still far from equal representation in positions of power, in spite of the fact that there is a woman as first minister. Some feminists would argue that if there is better representation of women in the policy-making process, then the laws that get made are more likely to reflect the interests and values of women. For instance, the Scottish Parliament has had a lot of initiatives on improving community care, reducing sexual violence against women and zero tolerance of domestic abuse.

Criticisms of feminist theory

There are criticisms of feminist theory from both within the ranks of feminism and outside them. Many people have criticised the second wave of the feminist movement for being 'colour blind' and not paying enough attention to the particular issues of black women and the racism they experience. Any person who is a member of more than one oppressed group should have all aspects of their life acknowledged in a full exploration of the multiple discriminations they face. There is still an on-going debate about whether you can talk about 'feminism', even at the most general level, as a single theory because there are more differences between women – for instance on the bases of race, class or sexuality – than there are similarities. All feminist writers agree, however, that there are gender divisions in society, that these are historically based and that they are still perpetuated today.

Feminists have also been criticised in the past for their emphasis on only the gendered oppression of women, and for neglecting the problems encountered by men by the social construction of masculinity. For instance, although more men are choosing to work in care settings, the workplace is still a very gender-divided area even within the care sector. Although only about one sixth of the care workforce in Scotland is male, men make up about a third of the workforce in criminal justice and residential children's services (SSSC, 2014). But how does this square with the fact that men still dominate the key positions in most of the large organisations in society? It points to the fact that you can't understand a social issue from one point of view only. Looking at gender alone is too narrow: it has to be matched by an analysis of the other dimensions of the issue, such as class, education and employment opportunities.

Activity *Table of main sociological theories*

Draw up a table showing the main sociological theories, giving the main theorists of each and **summarising** the most important points of each theory, the advantages and the disadvantages. You will then have this to refer to as you read the following sections. This will be a useful activity to help you learn the key features of each theory and will also help you when you are preparing your course assessments.

Sociological theory and main theorists	Main points	Advantages	Disadvantages

In the following section sociological concepts, perspectives and theories are used to help you understand the social influences of and on the family, inequality and poverty, and discrimination.

Social influences

So far this chapter has tried to give you different ways of seeing society, and different concepts, influences, perspectives and theories with which to look at what is familiar to you. In doing this you are developing what the American sociologist C. Wright Mills (1916–62) called '**the sociological imagination**'. With these concepts, influences, perspectives and theories, and the resulting sociological imagination, some social influences that are of particular relevance to care practice will now be considered in detail. As you saw earlier in the chapter, a social influence may be defined as an effect that is external to the individual and that is part of his/her social environment. Social influences have an impact on people's development and life chances. They have been touched upon briefly in Chapter 3 in the sections on strands of development (SPECCS). In this section the focus is upon applying sociological thinking about social influences to:

- the family
- inequality and poverty
- discrimination.

As with every separation of concepts there are also links among them, so that these influences are not entirely separate from one another, neither do they comprise all of the social influences that impinge on individuals' development and life chances. For example, a family in which a member experiences a disability may be discriminated against and may experience poverty because of unequal treatment, but this may also be influenced by the availability of good quality health care and appropriate educational provision. You should be mindful of potential links and other influences as each social influence is discussed.

The social influence of the family

> *The question 'what is the family' is frequently posed by sociologists and underlies the point that although in generic terms we talk about 'the family', in reality this can mean very many things to different people.*
>
> (Cunningham, 2014)

> *The family – that dear Octopus from whose tentacles we never quite escape.*
>
> (Smith, 1938)

> *The family as an institution is not a static entity, stereotyped in its forms, or unchanging in its functions. It is a dynamic system, susceptible to change; it's influenced in the short term by the personality, development and relationships of its members, and in the longer term by the pressures of economic events and historical processes.*
>
> (Herbert, 1986)

The first thing to recognise when talking about 'the family' is that there is not just one 'family type'. Today, there are many differing manifestations of the family. Families are part of the social structure and as such are affected by, and affect, the culture in which they exist. This culture is in turn influenced by many social, economic and historical forces, such as social class, ethnicity and regional differences. Scotland today is characterised by a great variation in family patterns and this has repercussions on how 'normal' families are defined.

Activity *Is there such a thing as a 'normal' family?*

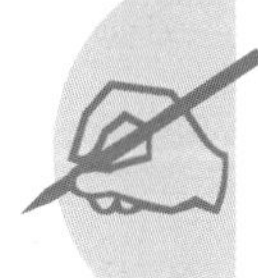

What do you see as a 'normal' family? Is there such a thing? What percentage of the twenty people you know best in your age group live in what you have defined as a 'normal' family?

A definition of the family, such as George Peter Murdock's quoted below, can no longer be seen as universally relevant. Murdock took a sample of 250 societies, ranging from small hunter-gatherer bands to large-scale industrial societies, and developed the following definition:

> *A family is a social group characterised by common residence, economic co-operation and reproduction. It includes adults of both sexes, at least two of whom maintain a socially approved sexual relationship, and one or more children, own or adopted, of the sexually co-habiting adults.*
>
> (Murdock, 1949)

Although this might have been the norm in 1949, even then it hardly encompassed all possible family types. Married or co-habiting couples in the absence of children, for example, can be regarded as a family in the support that they provide one another. A definition more applicable to the realities of modern Britain is taken from *Social Trends* (Office for National Statistics); this is its definition of a nuclear family (explained on page 225):

> *The definition of a family is a married or cohabiting couple with or without children, or a lone parent with one or more children.*
>
> (Office for National Statistics, *Social Trends,* 2009)

While there is a difference between a household and a family, household statistics present some interesting indications of the way in which families live in Scotland in the twenty-first century. The variety of household types in Scotland in 2013 is represented in Figure 5.7. This shows that just over a third of households in Scotland contain only one adult living alone, split as 18 per cent in single adult households and 16 per cent in single pensioner households. Small families without children account for almost one-third of households (small adult, older smaller), while around a quarter (23 per cent) are families with children aged under 16 (single parent, small family, large family).

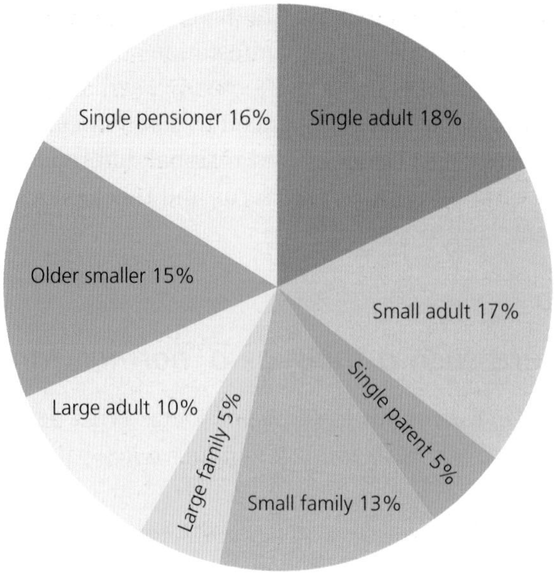

Figure 5.7 Household type in Scotland, 2013 (Source: Scottish Government (2014) 'Scotland's people')

How many of these categories would be included in the definition of 'nuclear family' given on the previous page?

The definitions used in Figure 5.7 are as follows:

- A **single adult** household contains one adult of working age and no children.
- A **single parent** household contains one adult of any age and one or more children.
- A **single pensioner** household contains one adult of pensionable age and no children. Pensionable age for the purposes of this figure is 60 for women and 65 for men.
- A **small family** household contains two adults of any age and one or two children.
- An **older smaller** household contains one adult of working age and one of pensionable age and no children, or two adults of pensionable age and no children.
- A **large adult** household contains three or more adults and no children.
- A **small adult** household contains two adults of working age and no children.
- A **large family** household contains two adults of any age and three or more children, or three or more adults of any age and one or more children.

Sociological concepts that relate to the family

Before going on to discuss the family in terms of different sociological theories there are some sociological concepts that contribute to an understanding of the family and the changes that are taking place within it. The first distinction to be made is that between the extended and the nuclear family. An **extended family** consists of all family members related by blood or marriage, beyond the nuclear family, and this has both vertical (grandparents, grandchildren) and horizontal (aunts and uncles, in-laws) dimensions. The **nuclear family** accords with the definition from *Social Trends* above and usually takes one of three forms: a couple in a socially recognised union and child or children; a single parent and child or children; or a couple without children, all sharing the same household. 'Socially recognised union' includes married and co-habiting couples, step-families, adoptive and foster families. Here are some of the available statistics relating to families in Scotland.

In 1976–80, the proportion of babies born in Scotland to **unmarried parents** was 10 per cent, which was a figure more or less unchanged from when records first started in 1855. By 2001–05, however, this figure had leapt to 45.3 per cent of all live births (General Register Office for Scotland, 2006) and by 2011 had increased again to 51 per cent (**www.gro-scotland.gov.uk**). In 2011, however, 21 per cent of households with children (aged 0–15) were single-parent households; the number of births registered solely in the mother's name actually fell, to 5.3 per cent in 2010/2011 (6–7 per cent in the 1980s and 1990s). These figures indicate that although fewer children may be born within a marriage, 79 per cent still live within a nuclear family where there is a partner present and the births of most children are registered by two parents.

Since **civil partnerships** became legal in 2005, there has been a wider social recognition of gay partnerships. Although the numbers are small, 343 partnerships were recorded in the first six months of the Act being passed (General Register Office for Scotland, 2006) and 554 civil partnerships were recorded in Scotland in 2011. Gay Marriage came into effect on 16 December 2014 with the passing of the Marriage and Civil Partnership (Scotland) Act 2014. This has enormous symbolic importance as same-sex unions and marriages are now officially recognised by the State. Another symbolic change was brought about by the Adoption and Children (Scotland) Act 2007, which enables both civil partners to legally adopt as a couple. Although it had never actually been illegal in Scotland for a gay person to adopt a child, the Act caused considerable debate in the Scottish Parliament.

To clarify some of the changes in the family in Britain up to the 1990s, studies by Willmott, reproduced in O'Donnell (1993), are summarised below. In 1957 Peter Willmott and Michael Young published a now-famous study of family life in Bethnal Green, London. At that time this was a fairly stable working class community where most residents had lived for a long time and over 90 per cent of residents had some relatives living in the district. **Kinship** was a very important element in people's lives and kinship contact from and to the extended family, in the form of face-to-face support, was a common part of life, with a high proportion of married women with children seeing their own mothers on a daily, or at least weekly, basis.

In a later study Willmott makes the point that, by the 1980s, although enormous changes had taken place in what were old established areas and in the way society functions, the role of kinship and of the extended family continued to be very important in the lives of a high proportion of the population. In a study of a London suburb (Willmott, 1986, reprinted in O'Donnell, 1993) the proportion of couples seeing relatives in their extended family at least weekly was precisely two-thirds. O'Brien and Jones updated Willmott's study in 1996 and discovered that 'kin contact and association do not appear to have changed significantly since Willmott's study in the 1950s' (quoted in Haralambos and Holborn, 2004, p.489).

Willmott suggested three broad kinship arrangements in Britain:

- The **local extended family** has relatives living near each other providing mutual aid on a continuing basis. This kind of arrangement applied to approximately one in eight of the adult population of Britain, being more common in Scotland, the Midlands and the north of England than in southern England.

- The **dispersed extended family** is where members of the extended family still maintain contact and, although they are not all living in one locality, support is still provided both in an emergency and on a regular basis. Research evidence from many sources suggests that this operates for about half of the adult population.
- The **attenuated extended family** is a term used to describe people who still have an extended family but maintain only limited contact with it, either from choice or because distance or finance prevents this, or for a mixture of other reasons. For example, many students break away for a time from their family of origin (though they often return in the holidays), and for them friends matter more and family less than at other stages in their lives.

Families today have to be looked at in their widest sense, as 'extending' as well as 'extended'. Many people live with people who are not blood relatives, but who are part of a 'step', 'half' or foster family. Indeed, many people are part-time members of two different family groups: generally one that includes their biological/adoptive mother and another that includes their biological/adoptive father. There is a whole new twenty-first century vocabulary associated with families to include post-divorce and separation families, blended families, friends as family, same-sex unions, ethnic minority families and ageing families, which add new dimensions to how the influence of the family is viewed and analysed. The internet, video calling and texting play a major part in enabling extended families to communicate with one another and these complement the more traditional telephone conversation.

Activity *Drawing your own 'extended family'*

Look at your own family and draw a diagram to illustrate it. Does it include just the people with whom you share a house? How many of the people are actually related to you by blood? Do you feel this makes a difference to the relationships within the family?

The evidence points to the family, in all its different forms, as an important influence in its continuing relevance to people's lives. But what about the influence of the family in terms of sociological theories? How can different theories enhance our understanding of this major social influence? The five theories outlined earlier in the chapter are now returned to and assessed in terms of their contribution to the understanding of the influence of the family in Britain today.

The family and functionalist theory

Functionalist sociologists concentrate on looking at the family in terms of its functions both for society and for the individuals within that society. Some functionalists have made the leap from trying to demonstrate that the family is universal to saying that if the family is universal then it must also be necessary. For example, Murdock (1949), quoted above, suggested that the family is found in every society and has **four main functions**, which he called sexual, reproductive, economic (providing food and shelter) and educational (socialisation).

Activity *The MacDonalds and the Ahmeds*

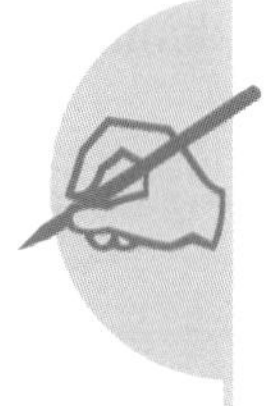

Read the case study of the MacDonald and Ahmed families in Chapter 7 and say how you think these families achieve the four main family functions suggested by Murdock: sexual, reproductive, economic (providing food and shelter) and educational (socialisation).

In a similar way to Murdock, Talcott Parsons (1937) argued that there are two 'basic and irreducible' functions of the family: primary socialisation (i.e. early childhood socialisation, which serves to internalise culture and develop personality) and the stabilisation of adult personalities through emotional security and performance of appropriate social roles. There is an impact for both the individual and for society when a family is disrupted, however, for example through separation, divorce or death. In their Research Briefing on 'Divorce in Scotland', the Centre for Research on Families and Relationships (2002, p.3) quotes evidence from the West of Scotland Twenty-07 study, a longitudinal survey of the health and social circumstances of a youth cohort living in Glasgow:

> *The form of family disruption may be significant, as outcomes vary depending whether the loss of a parent is through separation or death. For example, the proportion of young people who used drugs was 20 per cent for those living with both parents, higher (37 per cent) among those losing a parent through separation – but higher still (47 per cent) for those losing a parent through death. Early pregnancy too was more common among those whose parents were separated (14 per cent) than among those living with both parents (6 per cent) – but higher again among those losing a parent through death (40 per cent). This study also found that young people reporting more conflict with parents were more likely to have health problems and lower self-esteem.*

Although living in an intact family is a functional arrangement for society, a 'good' divorce, where there is not too much conflict between the parents, may be less harmful for the children than a bad marriage where there is conflict over a period of time. Walker (in Davies, 2013, p.114) emphasises that it is the relationship between couples that is important and that where children are subjected to poor quality couple relationships their health and quality of life are at risk of being adversely affected. Remember though that, from the earlier discussion of socialisation, the family is only one of the influences on young people. Among teenagers especially, behaviour and attitudes are also greatly influenced by peers and the media.

Both Murdock and Parsons have been criticised for presenting a rather idealised picture of family life, especially since their theories implied that families are harmonious and integrated. There was little consideration of the problems that can beset many families, such as divorce, single parenthood and step-parenting, or of diverse family patterns and cultures in a multicultural society, or of the ways different families allocate and perform social roles.

Some of these criticisms have been partly met by later functionalist sociologists, who appreciate the problems that families may experience and the changes that have taken place in family structures, but maintain that families in some form or another still perform useful functions today. Sociologists such as Ronald Fletcher (1988) and Young and Willmott (1957) maintain that family functions may have changed but they have not diminished. Young and Willmott, using their research in London, claim that the family:

> *... can provide some sense of wholeness and permanence to set against the more restricted and transitory roles imposed by the specialised institutions that have flourished outside the home.*
>
> (Willmott and Young, in O'Donnell, 1993)

Fletcher maintains that the functions of the family have increased in detail and importance. The family's role in socialisation is as important as ever, the family has a responsibility for the health and welfare of its members, and is a major consumer of goods and services. Steel (2012), while not favouring any particular theory, points to the family's continuing importance to people and to society as a source of identity, security and reassurance in spite of its changing nature and diversity. She is, however, aware of 'the dark side' of family life, when families are dysfunctional to the point of causing harm to the individuals in them.

The family and conflict theory

By contrast with the functionalist view, which emphasises the family as a positive force, conflict writers present a theory that views the family as serving the needs of some sections of society more than, and often at the expense of, others. For example, from a Marxist viewpoint the family favours the interests of the owners of the means of production. Marx's friend and colleague Friedrich Engels was a major proponent of this view. He saw the monogamous nuclear family developing alongside and supporting capitalism. For Engels, a nuclear family structure provides the owners of the means of production with a way of passing wealth from one generation to another through the male line. At the same time workers are stabilised within families, which inadvertently perpetuates the capitalist system because they are dependent on their waged labour to support themselves and their families.

Later Marxists have emphasised that in modern society the family consumes the products of the capitalist system and that people must continue in paid employment in order to maintain their families. They depend upon the products produced through their labour and perpetuate the need for them, which gives the owners of the means of production (capitalists) the power to continue to make a profit.

The somewhat different emphasis of Dahrendorf's conflict theory provides a more complex and complicated analysis of the family in conflict terms. If you look back at the account of Dahrendorf's theory (page 214) you will be reminded that the three central concepts are change, conflict and constraint. Change in Dahrendorf's view is a natural social phenomenon. Society and its parts are in a perpetual state of change, a phenomenon that is not adequately accounted for if society is viewed using functionalist theory. Change in the family is illustrated in many ways and is affected by social influences, including cultural attitudes: increases in the divorce rate; increases in the number of step-families; the presence of single-parent families as an accepted part of the social structure; the emergence of gay and lesbian families; multicultural families. All illustrate changes in the family that are not inherently good or bad, or necessarily functional or dysfunctional. They are just part of the inevitable movement that is always taking place in society.

Constraint upon the family is illustrated through laws and social policy, and through the promotion of norms and values. For example, parents have legal responsibilities to their children as outlined in the Children (Scotland) Act 1995, and most religions continue to promote heterosexual marriage and the procreation of children within marriage. Conflict theorists believe that many social influences, including laws, norms and values, constrain individuals and, by doing so, prevent individual creativity, diversity and achievement.

When Edmund Leach (1971) made the following statement he was expressing a conflict theory analysis of the family:

> *Far from being the basis of the good society, the family, with its narrow privacy and tawdry [grubby] secrets, is the source of all our discontents.*

He goes on to say that within the family '[the] parents fight, the children rebel', and his solution is not that dissimilar to that of Engels when he says that:

> *... children need to grow up in larger, more relaxed domestic groups centred on the community rather than on mother's kitchen ...*

Dobash and Dobash (1980), in a Scottish study of domestic violence, said:

> *For most people, and especially for women and children, the family is the most violent group to which they are likely to belong. Despite fears to the contrary, it is not a stranger but a so called loved one who is most likely to assault, rape or murder us.*

Over three decades later, this is still the case. Of the 60,080 incidents of domestic abuse reported to police in 2012–13 in Scotland, 80 per cent involved a female victim and a male perpetrator, and 17 per cent involved a male victim and a female perpetrator; the remainder involved same-gender perpetrator and victim (Scottish Government, 8 October 2013). These figures don't represent the full picture: domestic abuse is still among the crimes least likely to be reported to the police, and emotional abuse is rarely reported. Scottish Women's Aid (2010) estimates there are at least 70,000 incidents of domestic abuse annually in Scotland, with child abuse also present in 30–60 per cent of these situations.

Conflict theory, however, does not account for the fact that many people continue to live harmoniously within nuclear families and to see their family as a major source of comfort and emotional support. These theorists do not acknowledge that the family can provide the emotional stability from which individual creativity and achievement can emerge. Conflict theory fails to explain why, despite the faults of the family, only a small proportion of the population has no contact with any other family member.

The family and symbolic interactionist theory

One of the most relevant features of a symbolic interactionist theory in relation to the family is its part in the development of a self-concept. If you look back at the account of this theory, you will see that the starting point is the way in which the individual interacts with society. The individual's experience of family is one of the social influences on the construction of the self. For most people the family influences our definition of 'the self'. Individuals learn the symbolic meaning of family and family roles initially through play. They gradually acquire knowledge of the expectations and attitudes of others about family roles (Mead's 'generalised other'). Their experience of roles, including gender and family roles, enables people to be members of 'a community' or of society. There are, however, still choices the individual 'I' can make about which roles to take on board and how these roles are to be performed.

The interactionist view, in seeing individuals as both influenced by their social environment and actively influencing this environment, explains the diverse ways in which family roles are performed, or even whether they are chosen at all, even within the same family environment. The symbolic interactionist view of the family differs fundamentally from the functionalist view in that it emphasises the part the individual plays in creating his or her own social world, while at the same time recognising that this world is also being influenced through the performance of social roles.

The symbolic importance of language is also relevant when considering the family. Many women now retain their maiden name after marriage, and couples make a variety of arrangements about what surname their children should have. These decisions just weren't available to most people 50 years ago. Another example is that the terminology used in the Children (Scotland) Act 1995 has changed the way post-divorce arrangements for children are spoken about. It talks in terms of the child having 'residence' (with the main parent/guardian) and 'contact' with other relevant people. Previously, people spoke in terms of one parent having 'custody' of the child and other people as having 'access'. That was the language of prisons, and implied more of a conflictual 'us and them' situation, rather than the partnership approach that is being encouraged today, which puts the child's needs, rights and opinions at the centre of the discussion. The language reflects, and helps to create, these new social arrangements. The language itself can be seen as a social influence.

Activity *Family roles in the MacDonald and Ahmed households*

Now look at the case study of the MacDonald and Ahmed families in Chapter 7 using the symbolic interactionist theory, paying particular attention to Andy and Tanveer.

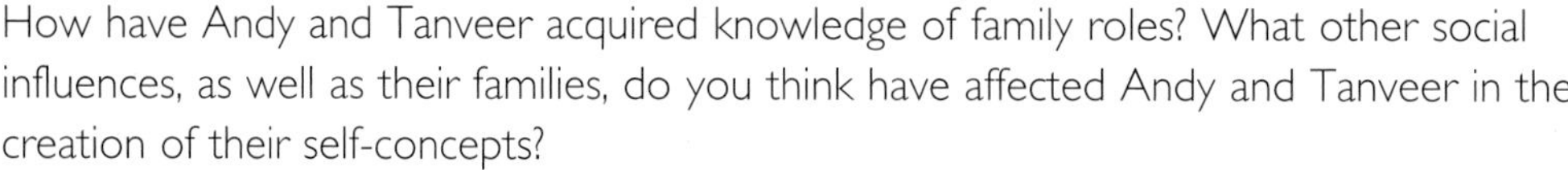

How have Andy and Tanveer acquired knowledge of family roles? What other social influences, as well as their families, do you think have affected Andy and Tanveer in the creation of their self-concepts?

The family and social constructionist theory

A social constructionist view of the family takes into account changes in the meaning, structure and role of the family, emphasising that the way you view family changes over time and is subject to the language, knowledge and power structures of society. The meaning is socially constructed through a 'discourse'. Some of the discourses about the family use language and knowledge to present a view of the family that is much broader than the nineteenth and twentieth century views, and incorporate a new vocabulary about family structures, for example blended families, same-sex unions and post-divorce families. Language and power, however, are used also to portray a much narrower view of the family, where both parents are heterosexual, married and bringing up their children. This image of the family is still promoted through TV advertising (the 'cereal box family') and through some politicians and prominent individuals.

The family is still a very prominent concept in Scottish society, even if its meaning has changed.

> *The family … should be afforded the necessary protection and assistance so that it can fully assume its responsibilities in the community.*
>
> *The child, for the full and harmonious development of his or her personality, should grow up in a family environment, in an atmosphere of happiness, love and understanding.*
>
> (Scottish Government, 2013)

The family and feminist theory

Feminist theorists have had a field day with the family as a social influence, backed up by some very substantial evidence that, even in the twenty-first century, women still perform the majority of the housework and childcare, still experience most of the violence that occurs in the home and are far from equal in their status as family members or as members of the workforce. Patriarchy and oppression are alive and well, and feminist theory of the family focuses on the relationship between women, the family and society. As discussed previously, it is closely related to the political stance of pursuing equality and empowerment within the family and elsewhere.

Gender is the starting point for examining what happens in the family from a feminist point of view. Ann Oakley (1985) was one of the first researchers to identify the power imbalance between men and women when it comes to participation in housework and childcare. She found that few marriages could be defined as egalitarian. Although there was greater equality among middle class than working class families, in only 15 per cent of the families she studied did men have a high level of participation in housework, and in only 25 per cent did men participate in a high level of childcare. In 2005, the picture had changed little. The Living in Britain survey found that 74 per cent of men in Britain didn't do any of the four main household tasks (grocery shopping, cooking, cleaning/vacuuming, washing/ironing), and that this figure rose to 82 per cent if just men in Scotland were counted, and 93 per cent if those men were aged between 16 and 29 years old. Rosemary Bennett (2014), reporting in *The Times*, states:

> *Women do twice as much housework as men, and the bulk of the most dreaded chores, according to a major poll on the subject.*

Feminists would argue that it is this subjugation of women into carrying out time-consuming and tiring tasks that makes it more difficult for them to have the time and energy to be active participants in other areas of community and work life.

Oakley showed not only that women did most of the housework and the childcare, but also that these tasks are associated with culture. Women are socialised to perform these roles and it continues to be in the interests of men to keep women in these subordinate roles. The role of mother/wife, even in an age of enlightenment, is still passed from one generation to the next:

> *... the female is chronically disadvantaged from the start by the socially constructed framework of values and norms that constrain her options.*
>
> (Allan, 1985)

Women still undertake a disproportionate amount of unpaid labour within the home and are much more likely to view their contribution as being unfair.

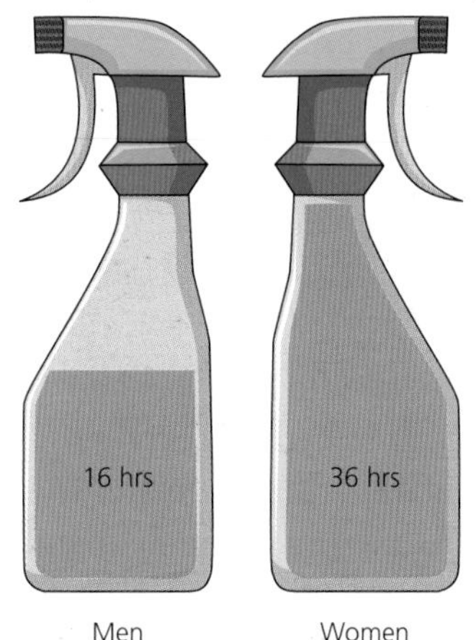

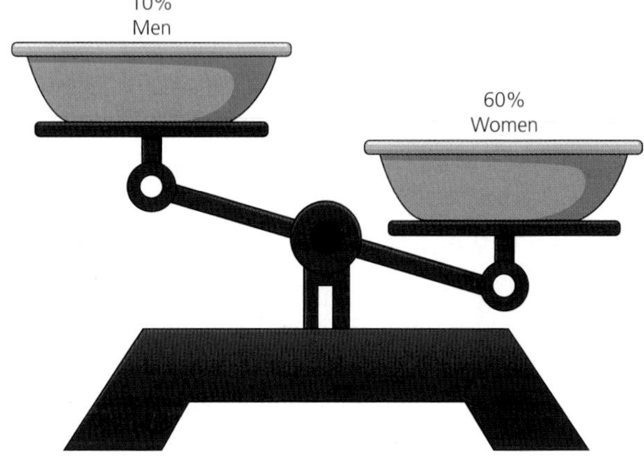

Women report spending an average of 13 hours on housework and 23 hours on caring for family members each week; the equivalent figures for men are 6 hours and 10 hours.

Both sexes view their relative contributions as unfair; 60% of women report doing more than their fair share (compared with just 10% of men), while 37% of men report doing less than their fair share (compared with just 6% of women).

Figure 5.8 Household work, 2013 (Source: Park *et al*, 2013, p.30)

Lena Dominelli (1997) discussed housework in terms of black women:

> *Black women have, therefore, carried the burden of doing the housework for the world. This included working as domestic servants for white middle class women ... Consequently black women's oppression is not the same as white women's even if they share the same gender and class.*

There have, however, been other social changes related to the division of labour within families. With one in five women being the major breadwinner in their household, many couples have decided that the best childcare arrangement is for the man to stay at home. Five thousand men in Scotland in 1996 were 'stay-at-home' dads, but by 2003 this number had risen to more than 20,000 (Wilson, 2003). Mark King in the *Guardian* (25 October 2011) reports on a study by an insurance company:

> *There are now ten times as many stay-at-home dads in the UK than a decade ago ...*

The government has recognised this change in attitude about the more active role many men want to play with their children and has responded by legislating for improved paternity leave. Statutory Paternity Pay and Leave was introduced in Britain in 2003 and was extended in the Work and Families Act 2006 to enable fathers to take Additional Paternity Leave and Pay. Evidence shows that involvement of the father in childcare during the first eighteen months of their child's life can have strong beneficial effects on the child's cognitive development, especially if the mother is working (DTI, 2006).

The social influence of social inequality

Inequality

Social inequality occurs when conditions exist that are more advantageous to some sections of society than others. Sociologists argue that it is not just coincidence, nor a matter of individual psychology, that certain people are more likely to experience inequality. The area in which you are born and brought up, the education you receive, the social class position of your family, whether or not you have an illness or impairment, the services available to you, your income or lack of it, your housing status, your gender, your nationality – all of these may reflect social inequality and have an impact on your development and life chances, though they do not necessarily have to determine them.

Inequality is demonstrated by the fact that certain people and groups are more likely to experience deprivation than others. The Scottish Index of Multiple Deprivation (SIMD, 2012) examines different aspects of deprivation at a very detailed local level in Scotland. This provides a basis for a long-term Scottish Government strategy to measure and reduce deprivation. It clearly demonstrates that people living in certain geographical areas experience poorer life chances, in a number of different ways, compared with other geographical areas, while also emphasising that not all people living in areas of deprivation experience deprivation and that not all people who experience deprivation live in areas of deprivation.

The SIMD indices measure deprivation in seven different 'domains', or categories:

- employment
- income
- health
- education, skills and training
- geographic access to services
- crime
- housing.

Each of these has a number of specific items against which different geographical areas can be compared. For instance, one of the 28 indicators of whether an area is likely to be deprived on the 'Income' category is the proportion of people on Income Support or income-based employment and support allowance. An indicator of likely deprivation in the 'Education, skills and training' category is the number of pupil absences from school. An indicator of possible deprivation in the 'Health' domain is the standardised mortality ratio, the ratio of the number of deaths in a population and the number of deaths that would be expected in the light of average death rates. As you can see, there is a wide variety of factors that, when combined, are likely to indicate whether an area experiences deprivation. The full list can be accessed at **http://simd.scotland.gov.uk**

Education has always been seen as one possible route out of the cycles of deprivation that exist in deprived communities, but educational attainment varies widely between schools in different areas.

Once again the league tables illustrate the gap between schools in affluent areas and those in more deprived parts of the country. While more than half of pupils leave the best performing schools in East Renfrewshire – a largely prosperous local authority in the south of Glasgow – with five Highers or more, there are secondaries in parts of Scotland's largest cities where not one child secured the same result.

(*The Scotsman*, 20 December 2013)

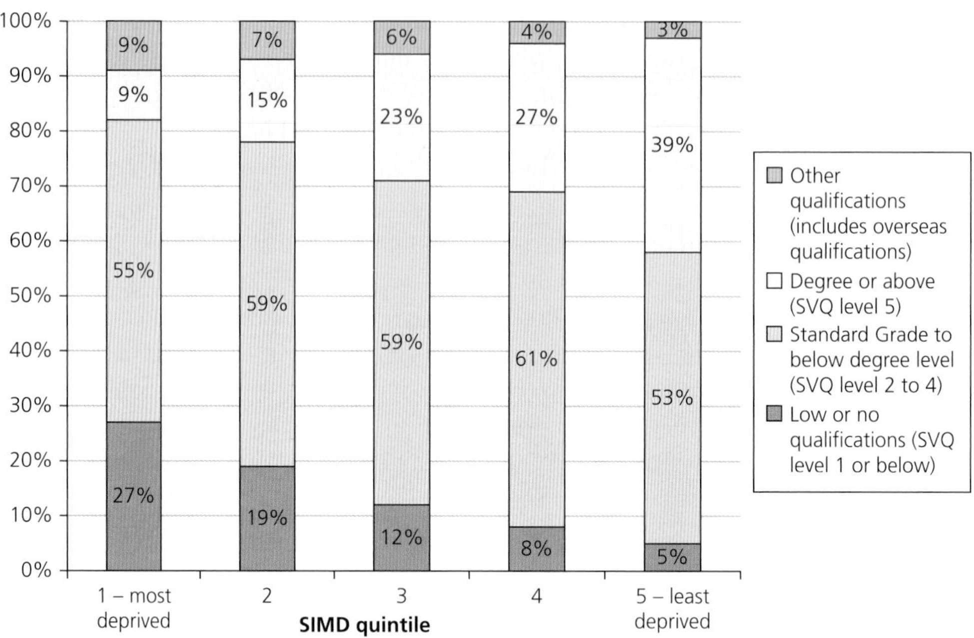

Figure 5.9 Qualifications and deprivation. In 2011 the proportion of the population aged 16–64 qualified to degree level or above was over four times lower in the 20 per cent most deprived areas compared to the 20 per cent least deprived areas (8.9 per cent compared to 39.4 per cent). (Source: Annual Population Survey, 2011)

A Joseph Rowntree Foundation Report (Sosu and Ellis, 2013) indicates that the attainment gap between children from deprived areas and those from less deprived areas starts very early – by age 5 it is 10–13 months – and that lower attainment in literacy and numeracy is linked to deprivation throughout primary school. Thus, some people find it difficult, from an early age, to get their foot on to even the first rung of the ladder of educational success. Some young people leave school without even basic literacy and numeracy. If you can't read by the time you leave school, it limits not only your job opportunities in later life, but also many other factors such as your health (e.g. being unable to read health promotion literature or prescription advice) and social opportunities (e.g. being unable to read newspapers or websites).

Social inequality is related not only to where you live; it is also closely linked to poverty and discrimination. These are the subject of the next two sections of this chapter.

Activity Up-to-date statistics

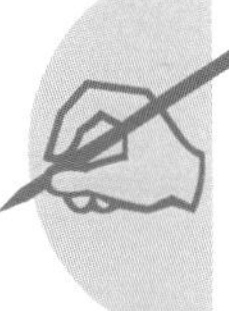

The statistics in Figure 5.9 are clear indicators that inequality exists in Scotland. The problem with statistics, however, is that they quickly go out of date. Carry out an internet search to provide yourself with up-to-date information about inequality in Scotland.

While you can experience the adverse effects of social inequality and not necessarily be poor, poverty is a major aspect of social inequality as both a cause and a consequence. It is also associated with many of the difficulties that people who use care services face, whether or not other aspects of social inequality are present. For these reasons it is considered in detail below. Other social influences are also present to a disproportionate degree in terms of social inequality, for example disability and old age. These factors are also closely allied with the social influence of discrimination, however, and are considered in the following section of the chapter.

Activity Poverty

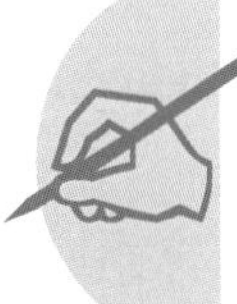

Think about, discuss and write down your own views about people who have low incomes and/or live on welfare benefits. Why do you think they are in this position?

Poverty

Nicola Sturgeon, elected as Scotland's first woman First Minister in 2014, has stated that tackling poverty is among her main priorities. Poverty? In Scotland? This acknowledges the existence of a problem that many people would like to sweep quietly under the carpet and pretend doesn't exist in the twenty-first century. The evidence, however, is striking, though it varies depending on your definition of poverty. A distinction is made between **absolute poverty**, defined by Bartholomew (2006) as a lack of the basic necessities such as food, clothing and shelter, and **relative poverty**, which is measured against prevailing living standards. Relative poverty is usually defined as an income 'below 60 per cent of the average income necessary to secure a decent "socially acceptable" standard of living' (Cunningham and Cunningham, 2014, p.32). This definition has the advantage of being a comparison with current living standards and also of being a measure of social justice. If an unequal distribution of wealth is diminished then the number of people in poverty should decrease. The more there is an unequal distribution of wealth in a society, the greater is the number of people living in relative poverty. In terms of both the absolute and relative definitions there is poverty in Scotland. The continuing prevalence of foodbanks testifies to the need to supplement one of the most basic needs: **food**.

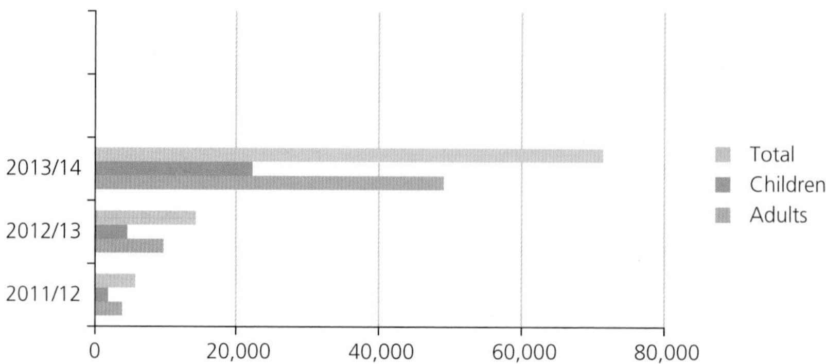

	Total	Children	Adults

2013/14
2012/13
2011/12
0
20,000
40,000
60,000
80,000
Total
Children
Adults

Figure 5.10 Foodbank use in Scotland, April 2011 to April 2014 (Source: **www.trusselltrust.org**)

In an article in *The Courier* on 20 November 2014 Alan Jones writes:

> *Gaps in the social security net are one of the main reasons people are turning to foodbanks … many users face a number of challenges, including ill health, caring responsibilities, mental health problems and relationship breakdown. The study [Cooper* et al. *(2014)] also found many are unable to work or have lost their job … Rachael Orr, head of Oxfam's UK poverty programme, said: 'Foodbanks are both a lifeline for people at a time of crisis and a symptom of fundamental failure in our society'.*

In terms of relative poverty the figures are also of concern. National statistics for Scotland (Scottish Government, 2014) estimates for 2012–13 indicate relative poverty levels as follows:

- 16 per cent of all individuals
- 19 per cent of children
- 15 per cent of working-age adults
- 15 per cent of pensioners.

A study by the Joseph Rowntree Foundation of poverty and **social exclusion** in Scotland (Aldridge *et al.*, 2013) indicated the following significant trends in poverty indicators in Scotland:

- Since 2008, the number of under 25s who are unemployed has almost doubled to 90,000.
- Among those without dependent children there was a rise in the number living in low-income, working families, from 125,000 to 150,000.
- The number of people working part-time, who want a full-time job, has risen from 70,000 in 2008 to 120,000 in 2012.

- Health inequalities in Scotland are not only stark but growing. A boy born in the most deprived 10 per cent of areas has a life expectancy of 68 – eight years below the national average and fourteen years below that of boys born in the least deprived areas. For girls the difference is eight years.

While poverty and social inequality are not the same thing, poverty is a major factor in most of the indicators of social inequality. Not all of our problems would go away if poverty were eradicated, but there would be a more equal starting point for, for example, the attainment of educational goals, adequate housing, and gaining employment.

Sociological explanations of poverty

Different sociological theories provide different perspectives in relation to poverty. While one theory alone cannot provide a full explanation, when taken together the theories provide a multi-dimensional view, with consequent indications of what may be done to alleviate it. These explanations place the causes of poverty within society and encourage thinking that does not blame individuals.

Functionalist theory and poverty

Functionalist theory emphasises the functions that different aspects of society play in the structure of that society. While it allows for some change to take place over time, it emphasises structure and the different components of that structure as essential for maintaining social stability. Even negative aspects of society may serve important functions.

Activity *The functions of inequality and poverty*

What functions do you think inequality and poverty play in society?

You may have thought of some of the following:

- In terms of the stratification of society, functionalist theory seeks to justify a need for there to be a group of people at the top who do one kind of specialised work and for a group of people at the 'bottom' who do the work no one else wants to do for a very low salary, or who don't work at all in times of economic difficulty and carry the consequences of this on behalf of 'society'.
- In being poor, people provide jobs for those who support them and who deal with the problems that result from poverty: police, social workers, health workers, etc.
- Poverty enables rich people to stay rich.
- Poverty enables everyone else to feel better about themselves and provides a comparison with a situation into which they don't want to get.
- Poverty provides **scapegoats** for the ills of society.

None of this, of course, justifies the existence of poverty, but it does provide a perspective about why it may continue to exist. Functionalist language also can often be discriminatory as a way of maintaining the status quo. Can you distinguish this in the statements above?

Conflict theory and poverty

In terms of conflict theory poverty is seen as the inevitable consequence of a capitalist society, based on the power of some sections of the population to control wealth at the expense of other sections. Those with the least power and the least control end up in poverty. Poverty may be partially alleviated by welfare benefits, but these simply serve the function of giving poor people just enough to live on without providing a means of escape. Only radical change in the way society is organised and structured can overcome poverty and there is a need to understand poverty in a structural way in order to overcome it and its consequences.

Symbolic interactionism and poverty

Symbolic interactionism provides a way of looking at poverty in terms of the difference it makes to people's lives. It examines people's interactions and how they may develop coping mechanisms to deal with the effects of poverty on their identity. It examines the symbols, such as words and gestures, that people use to reach a shared understanding of their interaction. Sociological works and many novels recount how individuals negotiate the effects of poverty, sometimes in ways that are labelled as socially deviant. Labelling is part of symbolic interactionism. It provides symbols for the behaviours and identities that result from poverty. The label 'poor', for example, can interact with the individual's self-concept; it can be incorporated into it and affect the individual's interactions with others in society, and society's interactions with that person. If you have the label 'poor', certain behaviours (crime, drug abuse, alcohol misuse) may be associated with this, and you may incorporate them into your own identity; there may be other interactions and symbols that lead to a different resolution. Symbolic interactionism doesn't attempt to explain why poverty exists but it is useful in terms of examining the influence of poverty on identity and consequent actions, and the way in which other people react to those who are labelled 'poor'.

Social constructionist theory and poverty

For adherents of a social constructionist theory, poverty is seen to create a discourse about poverty that changes over time and that is based neither wholly on fact nor wholly on perception but is socially constructed through the use of language, selected knowledge and power. Power is not necessarily associated with wealth but with a complex interplay of factors linked with stratification and social class, reinforced through language and the use of selected knowledge in favour of some people rather than others. This theory falls between structural and interactionist approaches and looks at how poverty is socially constructed, and maintained and reinforced through complex interactions of social institutions and individual perceptions.

Activity *Feminism and poverty*

Feminist theoretical explanations of poverty combine different sociological explanations. Use your reading and thinking to explain poverty from a feminist perspective.

The social influence of discrimination

> *... but some aspects of sexual identity are still challenging for many people. Transgender and intersex are two such aspects, with campaigners reporting that discrimination within institutions and the public at large is a very real problem.*
>
> (*Scotland on Sunday* editorial, 2 June 2014)

> *Even though you're gay, I will always treat you the same way as I do now ... You're a great teacher ... You shared a personal secret, which was very brave.*
>
> (Letter from Becky Barnes to her teacher, 17 December 2014, reported in *Pink News*)

> *I went to the Jordanian–Syrian border ... I was not expecting that there would be women without shoes, there would be children without shoes, with no coats, with no idea of where they were going ... All they want is peace. They just want a place where they are treated with equality ...*
>
> (Malala Yousafzai, 2013, p.281)

> *An actress with dwarfism who could not reach the chip and PIN machines at post office counters has had her discrimination case settled by the company ... The Post Office ... has put flexible leads on the machines.*
>
> (*Scotland on Sunday*, 14 December 2014)

In Chapter 2 you were introduced to the concept of discrimination. Only once you have understood this concept is it possible to optimise anti-discriminatory and anti-oppressive practice. Discrimination affects people's development and life chances and is a social influence upon them. This chapter provides you with an opportunity to take a renewed look at discrimination, this time from a sociological perspective. The family and poverty have been examined using different sociological theories. You should now consider contrasting theories and analyse discrimination in terms of these, with a view to suggesting actions that care workers can take to combat discrimination based on your sociological understanding.

What is discrimination?

You saw in Chapter 2 that:

- Discrimination is treating someone differently. Although it can be either positive or negative, it is negative discrimination that is being discussed under the heading 'discrimination'.
- Discrimination is the unequal and unfair treatment of an individual or group.
- Discrimination is based on prejudice towards people who are seen as being different.
- Prejudice is learned from picking up negative attitudes from our families and society.
- Discrimination is built into the way we run our social, political and economic institutions.

- Discrimination can be conscious or unconscious.
- Discrimination occurs at different, interrelated levels: personal, cultural and structural.

Sociological explanations of discrimination

Functionalist theory and discrimination

It is difficult to appreciate that discrimination may have any functions in society apart from very negative ones. Functionalist theory, however, bases its explanations on the positive functions of social influences. For functionalists, who are looking at the functions of things for a whole society rather than for particular individuals, discrimination could be seen as advantageous in some circumstances. This is not to advocate the existence of discrimination, but is one possible way of explaining why discrimination is often perpetuated. Many of the same functions apply to discrimination as for those relating to poverty. Some of the functions could be seen as:

- maintaining current structures by discriminating against those who would seek to change them or who, by their very presence in society, mean that change or adaptation have to take place
- creating jobs for people who work with or on behalf of people who are discriminated against
- discriminated-against groups reinforce the 'normality' of everyone else
- discriminated-against groups can be scapegoats for the ills of society, saving society the trouble of looking for the source of problems within itself
- discriminating against an out-group or out-groups can serve to promote the cohesion of the in-group.

Conflict theory and discrimination

An explanation of discrimination in terms of conflict theory maintains that those who are powerful in society misuse discrimination as a tool in bolstering and maintaining that power. If some groups of people, through processes of stereotyping and prejudice, are made to look 'bad' in some way, then treating them unfairly enables those in power to justify discrimination as being in the interests of society. For Marxist conflict theorists, capitalism exacerbates the misuse of power by ensuring that discriminated-against groups are generally less wealthy, poorly educated, receive poor quality services and are treated unequally in an already unequal society. For conflict theorists like Dahrendorf, discrimination can be an expression of the misuse of power at any level of society as a tool in demonstrating superiority by one group over another or others.

Symbolic interactionism and discrimination

In focusing on the self–society relationship and symbolic communication, symbolic interactionism is useful in examining how stereotypes and stigma can lead to prejudice and discrimination against certain groups. Becker (1963) emphasised how the theory is especially useful in looking at how labels are applied to people and are then incorporated into identity. Prejudice usually means an attitude of hostility or antipathy towards a social group. This can result in a negative stereotype for that social group, for example people with a particular disability or from a particular country or who have committed a certain kind of act. Labels, which are an aspect of symbolic communication, are then applied to that social group, which can have a negative impact and can lead to discrimination. These labels may be applied consciously but the discrimination resulting from the application of the label may happen at an unconscious level. People are no longer seen as 'whole' people but instead are seen as the label that is applied to them. This in turn can affect their image of themselves. Thus labels like 'black', 'disabled', 'criminal' and 'poor' are seen as defining social groups. Assumptions are made about all people in those groups, about their abilities, interests and personalities, that limit their ability to express their own individuality and to build self-esteem. Labels often reflect divisions in society and the unequal distribution of power, and they change over time, thus also relating this theory to conflict and social constructionist theory.

Social constructionist theory and discrimination

Social constructionism, with its focus on discourses about knowledge, language and power, provides a basis for looking at how the discourse about discrimination can change over time. For social constructionists there is no real dividing line between scientific knowledge and social knowledge, as knowledge is seen as being socially constructed. The workings of knowledge, language and power actually provide some hope in the field of discrimination. An understanding of the language of discrimination, more analysis of how discrimination occurs and the voices of some of those in power promoting more equal opportunities have led to a deconstruction of some of the foundations of prejudice and some forms of discrimination. This is not to say that this situation will stay the same or that there will not be changing forms of discrimination in the future, or that some forms of discrimination have gone away. Legislation and its active implementation, for example the Equality Act 2010, however, reflects the social knowledge that discrimination cannot be tolerated in a so-called civilised society. People in power, though, often attempt to construct a social reality that is in their own interests. It is therefore up to all groups in society, including care workers, to change the social reality.

Activity *Social knowledge*

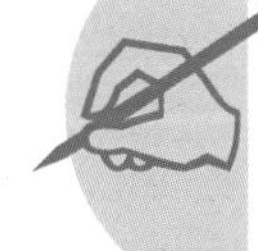

What kind of social 'knowledge' do you think a former Cabinet Minister was trying to convey when he said the following to a taxi driver?

> *You've been driving a cab for ten years. I've been in the Cabinet, I'm an award-winning broadcaster, I'm a Queen's Counsel. You think that your experiences are anything to mine?*

(*The Telegraph*, 2 February 2015)

Feminist theory and discrimination

In relation to discrimination feminist theory understandably focuses on the position of women in relation to discrimination from several perspectives. It challenges the assumptions of functionalism that it is functional and in the interests of society as a whole for women exclusively to perform certain roles, such as housework and childrearing. These assumptions and the structures that society has constructed around them have discriminatory elements built into them. For example, the way child care is structured in Scotland still favours the careers of men over women through unequal maternity and paternity leave; there are on-going assumptions by large sections of society that women (not men) 'should' stay at home with their children, especially when they are very young.

In terms of conflict theory feminist theory points to the conflicts in society, especially the use or misuse of power by men, that prevent women from reaching their full potential. From a symbolic interactionist perspective feminist theory points to the use of symbolic communication in creating labels that discriminate against women. Social constructionism examines the discourses that society creates using knowledge, language and power to discriminate unfairly against women, while also providing an analytical framework to examine how the discourse is changing.

Applying your knowledge and understanding

How can you apply your knowledge and understanding of social influences and sociology to the care context?

The family

In relation to the family you can:

- maximise your understanding of how sociological theories can contribute insight into the social influence of the family and the social influences on the family
- recognise that the family can have a negative as well as a positive impact on family members if, for example, there is a misuse of power or labelling of some family members
- ensure that you do not have a stereotype of what a family should be, and that you recognise from where your own stereotypes may have come
- ensure that you have a good knowledge of the resources that can assist families in achieving their positive functions, while guarding against discrimination in the way resources are used
- recognise the inter-relationships between the social influences of family, poverty and inequality, and discrimination
- think about and critically reflect on how you can optimise the use of your knowledge and understanding about sociology and social influences in relation to families with which you work
- keep up to date; read relevant research or develop your own.

Inequality and poverty

In relation to inequality and poverty you can:

- maximise your understanding of how sociological theories can contribute insight into the social influences of and on inequality and poverty. It is especially important to understand the social structural aspects of inequality and poverty caused by an unequal distribution of resources and the way power is exercised in society. While recognising that there may be individual factors that contribute to individual people being poor, poverty is predominantly a structural problem, requiring structural solutions

- understand and work to counteract the negative influence that poverty can have on people, especially as poverty influences many other difficulties and problems that people experience
- recognise and counteract your own stereotypes about poverty and inequality so that you work with all people with respect, and promote social justice
- build an excellent knowledge of the resources you can use to counteract the negative influences of poverty and inequality. This includes knowledge about: services in the statutory, third and private sectors; welfare rights; credit unions; community-based projects
- believe that change can happen and advocate for change with and on behalf of service users. This may involve advocating on behalf of service users with housing departments, assisting service users to challenge decisions about benefits, supporting people in accessing health and social services, or referring them to independent advocacy agencies that can act on their behalf (see independent advocacy in Chapter 6)
- decide whether you wish to work at a political level through taking issues to local councillors or acting through political party membership, or through taking part in national campaigns or protests
- keep up to date; read relevant research or develop your own.

Discrimination

In relation to discrimination you can:

- maximise your understanding of how sociological theories can contribute insight into the social influence of discrimination and social influences on discrimination. It is especially important to understand the social structural aspects of discrimination caused by socialisation and an unequal distribution of power in society, and also to understand unjustified labelling of and by some sections of the population. By definition discrimination is the unfair treatment of people in society. While recognising that there are differences among people and groups of people in society, there is no justification for discrimination
- develop anti-discriminatory practice and promote equal opportunities. You can do this by:
    - increasing self-awareness so that you treat everyone with respect for their dignity and promote social justice
    - challenging prejudice and discrimination when they occur
    - using organisational strategies to promote positive action, a clear equal opportunities policy, diversity training and anti-discriminatory practice

- recognising how services and service providers can discriminate and be oppressive in the ways they operate, and how accessing independent advocacy can assist in overcoming such tendencies (see independent advocacy in Chapter 6)
- using structural strategies through the use of legislation and campaigning for changes in legislation, and through the work of political and other pressure groups
- keeping up to date; reading relevant research or developing your own.

SUMMARY

At the beginning of the chapter, attention was given to defining sociology and some key sociological concepts and influences. Five sociological theories were considered: functionalist, conflict, symbolic interactionist, social constructionist and feminist.

Functionalist theory emphasises a view of society as a system made up of interrelated parts, which perform functions in relation to the whole. 'Society', according to this theory, is seen in terms of consensus and agreement rather than conflict and change. Conflict theory, on the other hand, rests on the view that conflict is fundamental, inevitable and even desirable between various groups in society that have differing interests from one another. Both the functionalist and conflict theories can be regarded as macro or large-scale approaches, which take as their starting point the influence of society on individuals. Symbolic interactionist theory focuses attention upon the meanings that individuals give to social actions, and the active part an individual plays in creating their own reality. This is an example of a micro-sociological approach. Social constructionist theory has elements of both a macro- and a micro-sociological approach and emphasises changing discourses in society related to language, knowledge and power. Feminist theory sets out to explain the position of women and to focus attention on such issues as the subordination and oppression of women in society. Feminist sociology may take a macro- or a micro-sociological approach, in combination with a central focus on the role of gender in any issue.

All of these theories were used to examine the social influences of and on the family, poverty and inequality, and discrimination. The chapter provided opportunities for you to apply your thinking to care situations.

Activity Snapshot: sociological theory and social influences

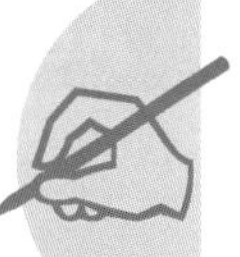

Now that you have had an opportunity to look at social influences from a theoretical perspective, summarise your understanding in a table like the one below. You can do this individually or as part of a group discussion.

Theory and influence	The family	Inequality and poverty	Discrimination
Functionalism			
Conflict theory			
Symbolic interactionism			
Social constructionism			
Feminism			

Activity Defining sociology

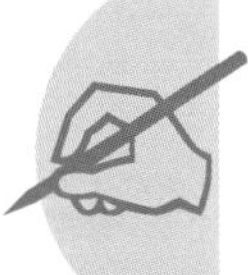

You were asked at the beginning of the chapter what you would answer if a friend asked you 'What's sociology?' How would you answer that question now?

Activity: Sociological theory: the MacDonalds and the Ahmeds

Assess the relevance of any one sociological theory in understanding the social influences of and on the family, poverty and inequality, or discrimination in either the MacDonald or the Ahmed family, described in the 'Case study: A tale of two families' in Chapter 7. If you are working in a group situation, you could divide into a number of sub-groups, with each sub-group considering a different theory.

Suggested reading

Books

Cunningham, J. and Cunningham, S. (2014) *Sociology and Social Work*. **London: Sage.**

A book that focuses on the practical applications of sociology; while the applications are to social work, much of the book is relevant also to those working in care settings.

Haralambos, M. and Holborn, M. (2013) *Sociology: Themes and perspectives*, **8th edition. London: Collins.**

A more academic and thorough discussion of sociological ideas touched on in this chapter.

Websites and media

BBC Radio 4, *Thinking Aloud*, every Wednesday 16:00–16:30 (check for other times) – focuses on the latest social science research. It is introduced by Laurie Taylor, formerly Professor of Sociology at the University of York.

The British Sociological Association www.britsoc.co.uk – see the publication 'Discover sociology' on this website.

CHAPTER 6
Positive care practice

We must always put people and what is best for them at the heart of what we do. We must see the person and not the budget, the person and not the target, the person and what they need, and not the worker constrained by their job description. We must innovate and change, and approach things differently and jointly with all our colleagues.

(Harry Stevenson, 2014)

Introduction

This chapter aims to enable you to develop knowledge, skills and understanding of the processes of positive care practice. You are introduced to approaches to assessment and care planning that are person-centred and that focus on achievable outcomes. Ways of implementing care plans are explored. Useful frameworks are introduced. Some of these have been included in Scottish Government policy documents and legislation, such as Getting it Right for Every Child (2006), and Self-directed Support: A national strategy for Scotland (2010) which promotes the personalisation agenda discussed in Chapter 1, and Promoting Excellence: A framework for all health and social services staff working with people with dementia, their families and carers. Sections on safeguarding, advocacy and self-directed support supplement the discussion of care practice. The importance of the value base, communication and relationships discussed in Chapter 2, and attachment and resilience discussed in Chapter 3, are emphasised within this chapter.

Personalisation is central to current policy and practice in relation to health and social care. It is a concept that is used in many different ways, sometimes synonymously with being person centred and outcomes focused as discussed in this chapter, sometimes synonymously with the self-directed support agenda empowering individuals to direct their own support as far as possible, and sometimes in the sense of providing personalised services which are tailored to meet the needs of the individual. All are compatible with one another and with people having more choice and control over the services they receive. Within personalisation there is an emphasis on the integration of services, of service users having control not only in terms of having choice and access to universal services but as far as possible over their budget and how it is spent.

The material in this chapter is relevant to Care: Values and Principles (Higher). It also covers material that will be useful to learners studying Care: Values and Principles at National 4 and 5 levels, Scottish Vocational Qualifications SVQ2 and SVQ3 in Social Services (Children and Young People) and Social Services and Healthcare, and for HNC Social Care and HNC Health Care.

By the end of this chapter you should be able to:

- ★ understand the processes of positive care practice
- ★ think in a person-centred way
- ★ practise competent and imaginative assessment, care planning, implementation and evaluation
- ★ explain needs, wants, wishes and dreams in relation to the assessment process
- ★ explain assessment and tools of assessment
- ★ work with individuals to develop achievable outcomes
- ★ explore approaches to care planning and explain the care planning process
- ★ explore ways of implementing care plans
- ★ demonstrate an understanding of self-directed support and personalisation, advocacy and safeguarding
- ★ understand evaluation through monitoring and reviewing progress made in the achievement of outcomes.

Positive care practice

The foundations of good practice were laid in Chapter 2, through the development of a sound value base and the ability to build helpful, supportive relationships with people. These are really important, since without them care practice is just a chore without the interests of people at its centre. On their own, these are not enough, however, to promote the most positive practice. The best practice needs care workers to develop an approach that:

- has an outcomes focus
- builds solutions with and around people, their families and carers in a personalised and person-centred way
- empowers people, putting them in control as far as possible
- enables people to get the right help at the right time
- supports change and flexibility where current provision is not the best way to reach outcomes
- involves everyone working together
- is imaginative and creative.

This approach requires care workers to develop knowledge, skills and understanding of the helping process based on assessment and the development of outcomes, care planning, implementation and review. This should aim to give service users as much power in their lives, as much choice and as much say about how they wish to lead their lives as possible, while at the same time safeguarding them from potential harm or abuse. Unfortunately care practice doesn't always achieve this, but when it does it can be transformative and life-changing.

Activity *Positive care practice*

Discuss or write about the situations below and make suggestions about what could have been done to improve life for the people involved. You may wish to make further suggestions as you continue to read the chapter.

> *I have just lost my mum, who had Alzheimer's. I have often been upset, disappointed, furious at the responses people had towards her. The carers at her home were kind, and helped a great deal, but there was no real empathy or understanding of how they as individuals/an organisation could enhance my mum's quality of life. There is not enough interest – Mum's home felt like a benevolent holding pen and she gradually declined. They could have brought out so many qualities in her. I am in mourning and I'm angry …*

(**www.whoseshoes.wordpress.com**, April 2014)

> *Everyone got together, staff and family, and did your meeting and got my future sorted out without me. When I got my plan typed up the four things I wanted had been left out, but some things staff wanted were there.*

(Sanderson *et al.*, 1997)

Care practice is part of a process that begins with **assessment**. Initially it involves working with the individual and relevant others to explore needs and wants, with a view to identifying outcomes to work towards. **Needs** refers to those things that it is considered the person's right to have, whereas **wants** refers to things that a person would like, wishes for, dreams about and/or that would make life easier. The dividing line between needs and wants is rather a blurred one. Person-centred work takes into account not only those things that are considered to be needs, but also the wishes and dreams people have. A good plan will attempt to incorporate both while recognising that for service users, as for anyone else, it is impossible to have everything you wish for. A lot of what people do in life, however, is probably about working towards not only meeting their basic needs but about improving their life and achieving at least some of their wants, wishes and dreams.

Once written, the **care plan** has to be implemented, i.e. put into action, and it should be constantly evaluated through processes of monitoring and review. The mode and timescale of evaluation should be built into the plan. If evaluation indicates that the plan is not meeting agreed outcomes, then it should be changed. Flexibility is essential in this process, and frequent opportunities should be presented to the service user to discuss and evaluate the plan of care. Implementation in this chapter is examined in terms of a positive care practice approach using different strategies to achieve outcomes, and including the optimisation of using four environments: helping and therapeutic, physical, organisational, and community.

Figure 6.1 illustrates the care planning and helping process in the form of a tree. The roots of the tree represent values and principles, communication and other skills, and knowledge, some of which are explained in other parts of this book. The trunk of the tree represents the relationships that are made with service users and other relevant people, emphasising especially the qualities put forward by Carl Rogers (1991) of empathy (understanding), congruence (genuineness) and unconditional positive regard (acceptance), discussed in Chapter 2. The crown of the tree is the assessment, care planning, implementing and reviewing process. This may lead back to reassessment and the adaptation of outcomes, or to decisions that do not require further involvement with care services. It is a process that continues for as long as the service user needs and/or wishes it to continue. Before proceeding to a more detailed consideration of assessment the concepts of 'needs' and 'outcomes' are discussed. An understanding of these is vital to working with service users in the assessment process.

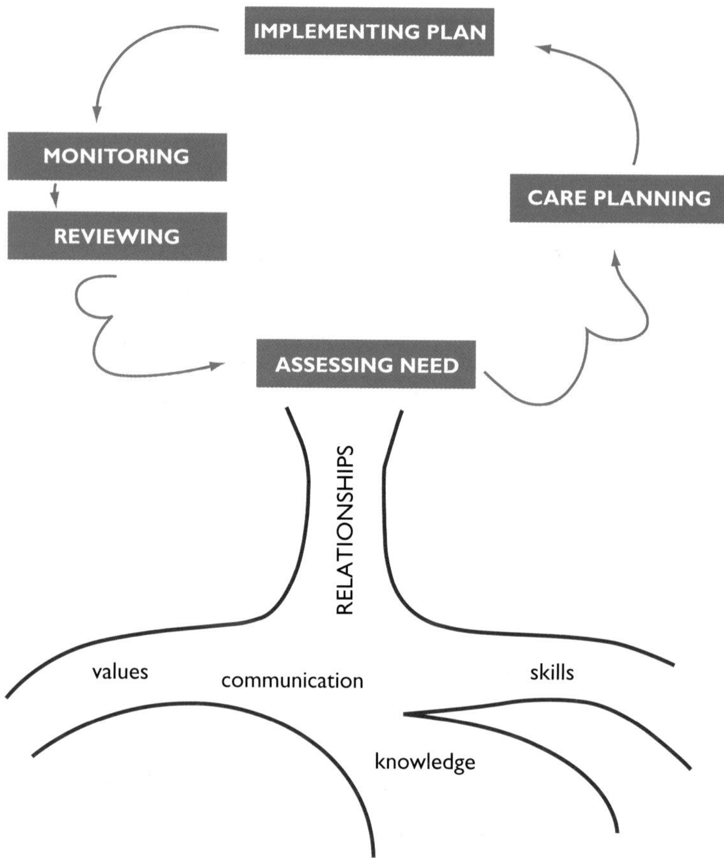

Figure 6.1 The tree as a model of care

Needs

This section reminds you of some of the things it is important to consider when examining need. The term 'need' is used here to incorporate many kinds of need, including those identified in Maslow's hierarchy (see Chapter 4), ranging from physiological to self-actualisation, and needs that reflect aspects of development in terms of SPECCS (social, physical, emotional, cognitive, cultural and spiritual). Another model, which includes and expands upon both Maslow and SPECCS, and is useful in a consideration of needs in a helping context, is the **PROCCCESS** model (Miller, 2005).

This model is examined in further detail below. The categories of need examined in the PROCCCESS model are as follows:

- **P**hysical needs
- **R**elationship needs, with carers and other professionals
- **O**rganisational and operational needs
- **C**ommunication needs
- **C**ognitive/intellectual needs
- **C**ultural needs
- **E**motional needs
- **S**ocial needs
- **S**piritual needs.

Physical needs

Everyone has physical needs, which are associated with keeping the body in good working order and as healthy as possible. For people who need some help it is essential to identify those needs that the individual is unable to meet and to provide enough help to meet these, while at the same time maximising independence, maintaining dignity and promoting empowerment. The quotation below gives an example of providing adequate housing as a way of enabling people, including informal carers, to meet the needs, especially the physical needs, of children with physical disabilities.

> *The home was often these children's most restrictive environment. Often they simply could not use their equipment such as walking or standing frames around their homes because of the cramped and confined conditions.*
>
> *Parents were worried that their children were not getting the exercise or therapy they believed they need because of space constraints, and the two mothers of visually impaired children complained that their children spent a lot of time colliding with furniture and doors.*
>
> (*Community Care*, 1998d)

Compare this with the experience of Debbie after moving to a new, specially built home:

> *Within 24 hours of being in this house it was like – Wow! She was a different child. Her confidence increased overnight. I can't describe to you the difference in Debbie.*
>
> (*Community Care*, 1998d)

Meeting physical needs for housing, however, also has to be balanced with meeting other needs. The example below illustrates the links between meeting physical needs and meeting social and cultural needs. In an article about single people who have been homeless or have mental health problems Gerard Lemos states:

> *Making a flat or a house a home depends almost as much on who or what is nearby as it does on the flat itself. Being near family members and friends, places of worship and interests, groups and activities are what makes an area feel like your community.*
>
> (Lemos, 2006)

Relationship needs with carers and other professionals

One part of the care planning process that is often neglected is the need for service users and care workers to build up relationships with the providers and organisers of care. Informal carers such as parents, partners and friends, professionals such as doctors, social workers and community nurses, and other people with whom the service user interacts, such as neighbours and befrienders, are all potentially important components of the planning process. In person-centred planning, which is explained in greater detail later in the chapter, the service user chooses who is to be part of the planning process. In other situations, especially where statutory requirements must be met in relation to children or people with mental health problems, there are some people who must be part of the planning process and others who can be chosen by the service user. Some of these links can continue to provide support throughout the helping process as part of support networks or circles of support.

Organisational and operational needs

A knowledge of organisations that have the potential to provide for need, support and protection, and of the operations necessary to access their services, is a vital part of the care worker's repertoire. The more a care worker knows about what resources and opportunities can be utilised or may be available, the greater the choice that can be given to the service user. Sometimes all that is needed is information about how to access various forms of help, for example information about self-directed support, what benefits are available, where there is a community or resource centre, or which college runs appropriate courses in computing. Armed with this information, the service user may then be able to pursue avenues of interest or care independently. Among the agencies that are able to provide a great deal of useful information are: Citizen's Advice Bureaux, found in many locations around Scotland and the rest of the UK; Department for Work and Pensions (for UK benefits); social work or combined departments; health centres; and other organisations listed at the end of this chapter and at the end of the book.

Communication needs

Although communication needs could be included in the section on cognitive/intellectual needs they are considered separately here, mainly at the suggestion of service users who feel that this is an often neglected area. Many people experience some form of communication difficulty or disability, such as a hearing or speech impairment, or have a first language that is different from that of the care worker. It is important that their communication needs are met, for example by providing signers for someone who is deaf and communicates by signing, and/or by learning some signing yourself.

CASE STUDY

Joan

Joan, a social work assistant on a disability team, wanted to gain a qualification. She is deaf and communicates by signing. She visited her local college, where she was offered a place on a course and the assistance of a signer. Joan successfully completed her course and is now keen to further her education by taking an Open University degree. By meeting Joan's communication needs, her cognitive needs were also achieved and Joan was enabled to move towards self-actualisation.

Cognitive/intellectual needs

If you look at Chapter 3 you will see that there are different cognitive needs at each stage of development. A young child needs education, usually at school, and stimulation at home, especially through play and communication. An adult also needs opportunities to continue to develop cognitively and these should be explored as part of the planning process. Whenever possible, people should be enabled to access resources that are available to everyone. Many colleges at present provide special courses for people with a learning disability. It is often assumed that these students would be unable to access mainstream courses when in fact additional support rather than special courses may fulfil their needs. Care workers can be advocates for people to access resources in the community that contribute to the fulfilment of cognitive needs. Remember, however, that cognitive needs are not just about gaining qualifications and learning new things. For some people, meeting cognitive needs may be about what television programme to watch, what website to access or what meal to eat. Cognition is about making decisions and formulating opinions, in whatever way this is relevant to the person.

Cultural needs

Cultural needs are often seen as part of social needs but are in danger of being neglected if not considered separately. Culture includes values, language and customs. The care worker should try to familiarise him/herself with the different cultural practices of those with whom he or she works and should take these into account in assessment and care planning. Different cultural groups have different practices in relation to diet, physical care and coping with death. For **Muslims**, for example, Islam forbids the eating of pigs in any form, as well as other animals unless they have been slaughtered ritually (halal). During the month of Ramadan a Muslim fasts from sunrise to sunset, although those who are sick are not expected to fast. A Muslim who is dying may wish to face towards Mecca. In **Jewish** families there is a tradition of circumcising their newborn sons. An example of the way in which such cultural practices can cause difficulty is provided by Neil Pollack, who is Jewish, and his wife, who isn't. When they announced to Neil's parents that they had decided not to have their son circumcised they were told that he would therefore not be recognised as their grandson. His mother said: 'Your wife is immaterial here. You can't betray 6000 years of Jewish tradition' (Pollack, 2007). Fulfilling cultural needs is not always straightforward!

Emotional needs

Emotional development depends on the fulfilment of emotional needs. These include the need for love, belonging, self-esteem and for opportunities to develop a positive self-concept. Exploration of emotional needs rests very much on spending time getting to know the service user, listening actively to his/her verbal and non-verbal communication and, from this, gaining a picture of the individual's emotional life and the extent to which their emotional needs are fulfilled. The time and patience required to explore the significance of relationships and how the individual sees and feels about him/herself can have spin-offs in many areas of life.

The account below, provided by a care student about a man who attended a resource centre, provides a good example. The service user had no speech and couldn't say how he felt. Other care staff had said this was not a great concern!

> *I thought about making up a chart of faces with different expressions so that the service user could show me how he felt and we could start working together and getting to know each other. Doing this would promote effective care practice for the service user as he would be getting to know how he feels and how he can deal with it … Within two weeks I was getting results and he was showing me and telling me how he was feeling.*

Social needs

Social needs include the need for relationships and for opportunities to build these in a variety of contexts. When you look at the opportunities that service users have to develop social relationships, how far do these meet their social needs and is there any support needed to develop these? Have community links been thoroughly explored in order that service users have opportunities that are as far as possible equal to the opportunities open to all citizens? The answers to these questions provide indicators for planning and implementation.

CASE STUDY

Mary and Jean

Here is an example contributed by a student with the permission of the service users.

Mary has a physical disability that restricts her movement, and is a wheelchair user. She also has a mild learning disability. She loves the cinema and going to pubs, and enjoys going to church on Sundays. She has a good friend Jean, who lives in the same supported living house and with whom she enjoys going out. Jean also has a learning disability but is able to walk and is physically quite fit. Because of Mary's mobility problems and her inability to travel independently she has few opportunities to go out socially with her friend. I asked if I could be of any help in enabling Mary and Jean to do something they would enjoy together. They discussed this and said that they would love to go to see the film *Braveheart*.

I discussed this with the care team and it was agreed that I could arrange this outing with maximum help from Mary and Jean, and that I would accompany them to assist with Mary's wheelchair, but would sit with them only if they wanted me to. The outing was a huge success and enhanced their relationship with one another, fulfilling both social and emotional needs.

Spiritual needs

Spiritual needs could perhaps have been encompassed in the discussions of emotional and social needs, but there is a danger then that they would be given insufficient emphasis. Spiritual needs include the need for contemplation, for the pursuit of religious belief and/or the sharing of ideas about the meaning of life and mortality. Mary, in the case study above, fulfilled some of her own spiritual needs through attending church, though it wasn't always possible for her to achieve this need because someone had to organise this and accompany her. In their book, *Spiritual Well-being of Adults with Down Syndrome*, Margaret Crompton and Robin Jackson (2004) emphasise the importance of assessing and meeting spiritual needs through attention to spiritual well-being:

> *Every individual, irrespective of intellectual or physical ability, race, religion or any other attribute, has the right to respect for and nurture of spiritual well-being. Failure to ensure this may cause impairment of the whole life development and experience.*

Other considerations

Before proceeding to a consideration of assessment, there are other things that underpin and should be taken into account in the assessment process. These include:

- wants, dreams and nightmares
- gifts and strengths
- opportunities
- risks
- outcomes.

Wants, dreams and nightmares

Wants refer to things a person would like but doesn't necessarily need, though it does depend on how you define 'want' and 'need' and where you draw the line between the two. It used to be the case that if you had a roof over your head and enough food and clothing, you could be considered to have your needs met. Happily we have progressed beyond this to legislate for needs to be met in many additional areas of life and at a level beyond that of mere subsistence. **Dreams** can be seen as wants that perhaps don't seem realistic in the immediate future but are things that can be imagined as making life more satisfying and uplifting. They are worth having because they present possibilities for the future that could just be achieved with the will, the 'right' support and enthusiasm from everyone involved in the helping process. **Nightmares** are those things that an individual definitely does *not* want to happen. Assessment needs to identify those things that shouldn't happen as well as those things that should.

CASE STUDY

Vicky

Vicky, aged 33, has learning difficulties, lives with her parents and is supported to choose opportunities in which to participate at a community resource centre and within her local community. She has various wants, dreams and nightmares, identified in Table 6.1.

Table 6.1 Vicky's wants, dreams and nightmares

Wants	Dreams	Nightmares
To live in a flat away from her parents	To share a flat with her boyfriend, John	To live in a large institution
To have a mobile phone	To have a computer and to learn to use it	To be cut off from her friends and family
To manage her own care budget through direct payments	To earn enough in a job to live on	To be dependent on others for all decisions that relate to her
To have a holiday abroad every year	To go abroad with John to a place they choose	Not to have any holidays

Gifts and strengths

Assessment in the care planning process considers gifts and strengths as part of looking at needs. Gifts in this context refers not to exceptional talents, such as singing well, but to the recognition that every individual is unique, has a personality, a presence and characteristics that distinguish him or her from everyone else. These gifts need to be recognised so that they can be used and built upon in care planning. Judith Snow in Sanderson *et al.* (1997) has written beautifully about how giftedness can be seen as based on presence and difference:

> *Everyone has gifts – countless ordinary and extraordinary gifts. A gift is anything that one is or has or does that creates an opportunity for meaningful interaction with at least one other person. Gifts are the fundamental characteristics of our human life and community.*
>
> *There are two simple gifts that all people have and that every other gift depends on. The first is presence. Since you are here you are embodying the possibility of meaningful interaction with someone else.*
>
> *Secondly, you are different from everyone else – in countless ways. Difference is required to make meaning possible … human interaction arises from presence and difference. You are different from the next person in hundreds, perhaps thousands, of ways – in your body, your thinking, your experience, your culture, your interests, tastes and desires, your possessions, your relationships, and more. Therefore you are a bundle of hundreds, perhaps thousands, of gifts. So is everyone else.*

Strengths are the other side of the same coin. Gifts may be seen as strengths, but strengths go beyond the meaning of gifts in being the positives that the individual has to bring to a situation and that can be used to help achieve outcomes for that individual. A strength may be defined as a good or beneficial quality or attribute. It may include skills, knowledge, abilities, and may form the foundations, alongside gifts, for strengths-based practice discussed later in the chapter.

Opportunities

Opportunities are things that can be used to produce a favourable outcome. They may exist already or they may have to be created. They may be the gifts and strengths of an individual as outlined above or they may exist outside the person in the form of resources; they may be here within this agency or they may be outside in the wider community. Resources refers to anything that can be helpful: money, people, services in the statutory, third and private sectors including day centres, education and respite care. Opportunities are important in assessment and care planning because they present the means by which the plan can be put into action. A care worker needs to work with service users, carers and others to build up a picture of what these opportunities are, what needs to be done to access them, create them or fight for them.

The assessment and care planning focus should be needs-led but must also be realistic in terms of what may be possible. This doesn't mean abandoning dreams, which should be fought for, but it does mean that a worker has to be honest both with herself and with the service user about what opportunities exist or are likely to exist. The one great resource that a good care worker needs to develop is reflective thinking (see Chapter 7), since many care plans can be implemented using all available resources imaginatively. Befrienders, volunteers, shared carers, everyday facilities in the community such as sports centres, libraries, colleges, coffee shops and pubs, family members, friends, can all be useful resources in providing opportunities for fulfilling many needs.

Risks

The assessment of risk should be an integral part of the assessment process. It requires balanced and, where possible, shared decisions about meeting needs, freedom, dignity, safety and protection. Care provision often has a tendency to be risk averse for many reasons, especially fear of the consequences if something goes wrong. However, when you considered choice in Chapter 2 emphasis was placed on the value and normality of taking risks. Risk assessment should focus on minimising the consequences of risk where there is a real risk of harm, by putting in place sensible and agreed controls, not excessive ones. You need to be aware of legislation and agency policy in relation to risk, ranging from health and safety legislation to protection legislation for children and adults (see Chapter 1). There is useful information on many websites including the Health and Safety Executive at: **www.hse.gov.uk/healthservices/sensible-risk-assessment-care-settings.htm**.

Outcomes

> *At an individual level outcomes can be framed in terms of steps a person needs to take in order to improve aspects of their lives.*
>
> (CCPS, 2010)

In order to provide the best possible outcomes for people it is necessary to understand what outcomes are and why they are so important. The above understanding of need is vital but care practice needs to go beyond meeting need to moving towards practice that achieves what people *want* to achieve, their own priorities, in ways that can enable them and us to assess the degree to which their priorities have been fulfilled. This is where outcomes come in. They provide us with statements about what success would look like in terms of what matters to an individual. An example provided by CCPS (2010) clarifies the difference between an outcome and an output:

> *A person is assisted to prepare a meal for his/her friends. The output is the meal. The outcome is an improved social network and greater self-esteem and confidence.*

Helen Sanderson has for many years been associated with person-centred work and on her website (**www.helensandersonassociates.co.uk**) has set out an eight-step process for developing outcomes:

- Step 1: **Check**
  - Do we know what matters to this person?
  - Do we know about their future aspirations?
- Step 2: **Now**
  - What is working and what is not working, viewed from different perspectives?
- Step 3: **Prioritise**
  - Develop outcome statements in order of priority (not too many, e.g. three to start with)
- Step 4: **Success**
  - What would success look like if we were to address what is not working and move towards aspirations?
- Step 5: **Test it**
  - Is it an outcome? (not an embedded solution)
  - Does it change what is not working or build on what is working?
  - Does it take the person closer to their aspirations?
  - Do we know what is important to the person about this issue?
- Step 6: **What's stopping you?**
  - What is getting in the way (or stopping this from happening now)?
- Step 7: **Action**
  - Create clear goals and SMART* actions for the outcome
  - Assign resources
  - Repeat for each outcome on your list of priorities
- Step 8: **Record**
  - Record in the plan and review.

*SMART stands for: Specific, Measurable, Achievable, Realistic, Time-bound.

Assessment

It is vital that care workers are able to contribute to the assessment process so that the needs, preferences and priorities of the service user are taken into account as fully as possible in providing a service to them. Assessment is the first step in the care planning process. It involves examining needs, wants, opportunities and priorities as a basis for identifying outcomes and developing a care plan that aims to ensure the service user reaches a quality of life that is as good as it possibly can be. Right at the centre of this process, guiding its course as much as possible and making decisions, is the service user. A good assessment will also take into account other people in the service user's life, especially carers and family members, but the focus of this assessment should always be the service user him/herself. Under Community Care, Disability, and Carers' and Children's legislation other people in the service user's life may be entitled to assessments and plans in their own right in order that their own needs are promoted.

Activity *Assessment and care planning*

Before proceeding to a more detailed examination of the elements of assessment, think about, and if possible discuss, the ten essential points about assessment and care planning identified below. Most of these have been contributed by care students during their first placement or after they have worked in a care service for the first time. A fresh pair of eyes often sees things more clearly than people who have worked somewhere for years! Would they be your priorities? Do you have other suggestions?

Assessment and care planning should ensure that:

- **the individual is put first** – assessment and care planning should be done with, and not of, the service user and be available to him or her. The aim is to empower and optimise the participation of the service user in developing agreed outcomes for the care plan
- **the value base is really important** – with respect for the dignity of every individual and promotion of choice, rights, empowerment, protection and anti-discriminatory practice at the forefront
- **you develop a care plan that meets the person's needs** – there is no one 'right' care plan, and assessment and care planning should be tailored to individual needs. The plan should be needs-led and the outcomes needs-focused, not service-led. '**Needs-led**' means focusing on a full examination of needs; 'service-led' is the way in which, in the past, people were assessed for a particular service for which they had been referred. Service came first in the past, needs second
- **you remember care planning is ongoing** – there should be in-built evaluation of the helping process and monitoring of progress in relation to agreed outcomes, with opportunities to change the care plan in the light of its implementation
- **you provide the right environment**, for example for someone who has dementia or is in a wheelchair – the right physical environment is important, but also remember the right helping, organisational and community environments
- **the individual is in control** – you need to keep reminding yourself of the personalisation agenda, that this is the service user's care plan, not yours, and that *they* should be, as far as possible, 'in the driving seat'. This requires the plan to be specific about who is responsible for what, and to outline the responsibilities, as well as the rights, that the service user has in the process

- **everyone is working together towards agreed outcomes** – assessment and care planning are collaborative processes, with people working together and in partnership towards the same outcomes, for example the service user, carers, families, care workers, managers, social workers, GP, dietician, community nurse, school/education, etc. Remember that confidentiality may be an issue and should be respected where legal and possible
- **you take into account cultural preferences and beliefs** – not only should these be taken into account but you should try to find out about and understand the cultures and beliefs of service users and carers
- **communication and empathy underpin your practice** – using language and other forms of communication, listening and developing helpful relationships, are all part of this process. It is also important to try to put yourself in the service user's shoes and imagine how it is for them
- **you guard against labelling, stigmatising or making a scapegoat of a person** – for example, if Joe is described as 'difficult' in an assessment this is a label that can lead to stigma (a negative sign), which can lead to scapegoating (being unjustly blamed for everything that goes wrong).

Tools of assessment

Assessment builds up a picture of needs, gifts, strengths, dreams and nightmares in order to develop outcomes. There are some tools available to the care worker that can help in building this picture over a period of time. Some of these are a necessary requirement of the agency, and some can make the process enjoyable rather than a chore. The emphasis is on building relationships as a prerequisite to good assessment and on taking time, rather than attempting to complete an assessment and plan in one or two short meetings. Below is an account of some of these tools, which are examined in terms of their merits and disadvantages.

Getting it Right for Every Child

In relation to children and young people the Scottish Government has developed and promoted the use of Getting it Right for Every Child (GIRFEC), which presents a consistent way for people to work with all children and young people. GIRFEC contains the National Practice Model for assessment, planning and action. Many of the tools presented in GIRFEC are transferable to working with families and adults. It presents a very useful approach, which is fully set out by the Scottish Government (2012) in 'A guide to Getting it Right for Every Child'. The section below about GIRFEC is contributed by Francis Scott and Debbie McIntosh of Aspire Scotland Ltd., an organisation described in Chapter 1.

The Getting it Right for Every Child (GIRFEC) framework can be viewed as an outcomes-focused approach, in which the outcomes can be either single and specific or complex. The GIRFEC National Practice Model focuses on the well-being of children and young people and includes eight areas of well-being: **safe, healthy, achieving, nurtured, active, respected, responsible and included** (**SHANARRI** for short).

It is believed that in order for children or young people to grow and develop they must experience the positivities within these areas of well-being. In addition, these well-being factors are fixed within the setting of the '**four capacities**' of the Curriculum for Excellence (CfE). These capacities are: **successful learner, confident individual, responsible citizen, effective contributor**. SHANARRI and the CfE capacities are illustrated in Figure 6.2.

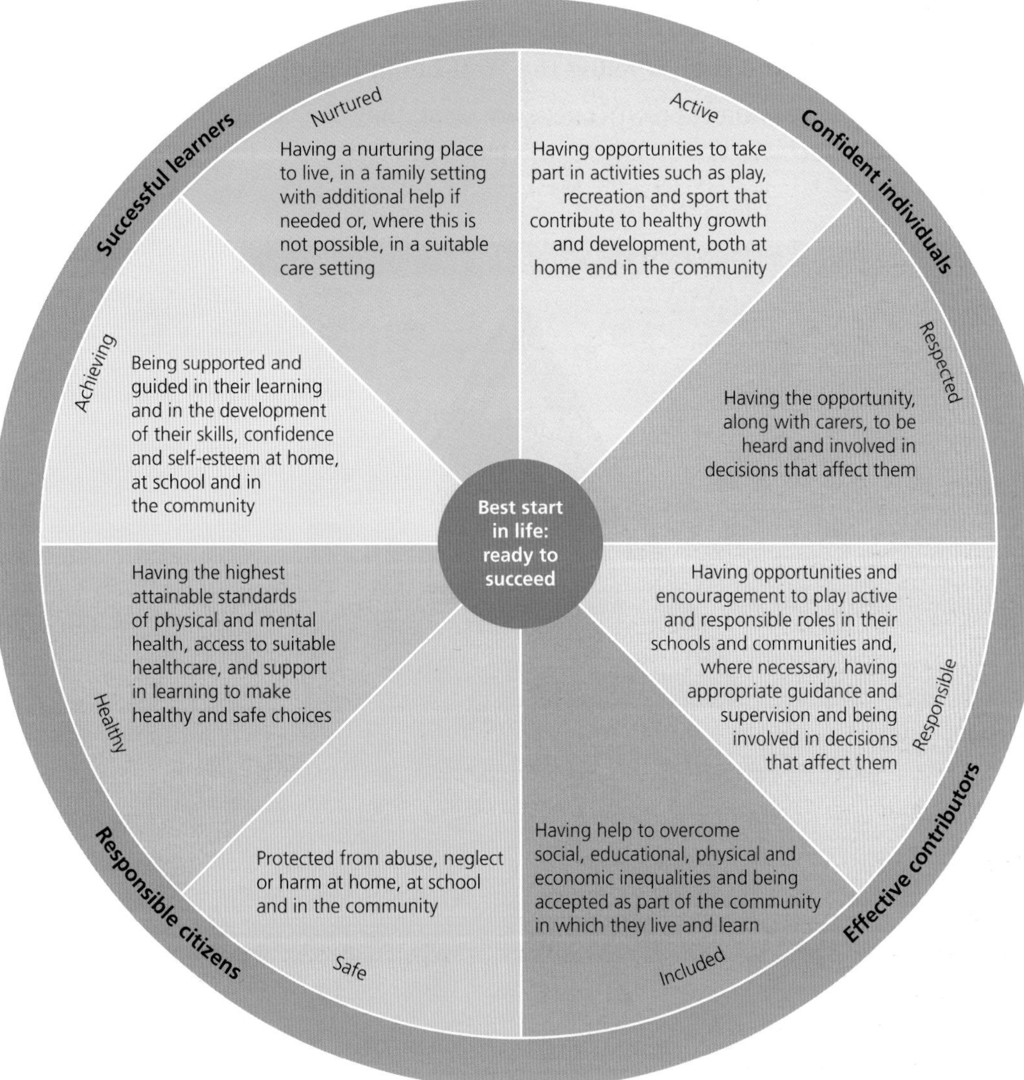

Figure 6.2 SHANARRI Well-being Wheel

The GIRFEC National Practice Model involves the following four phases in relation to assessment:

1 **Observing and recording using the Well-being Wheel**:

This means using the well-being indicators in the Well-being Wheel to record and share information that may indicate a need or concern, and taking any early action at this stage if possible.

2 **The My World Triangle**:

The My World Triangle (see Figure 6.3 below) helps practitioners to understand a child's or young person's whole world. It can be used to explore their experience at every stage, recognising there are connections between the different parts of their world. In assessment, it can be used to explore needs and risks.

3 **The Resilience Matrix**:

Used in more complex situations, the Resilience Matrix helps practitioners to organise and analyse information when they need to.

4 **Planning, action and review using the Well-being Wheel**:

When the child's or young person's needs are clear, they can be summarised using the SHANARRI Well-being Wheel to develop a plan of action.

(Scottish Government, 2012a)

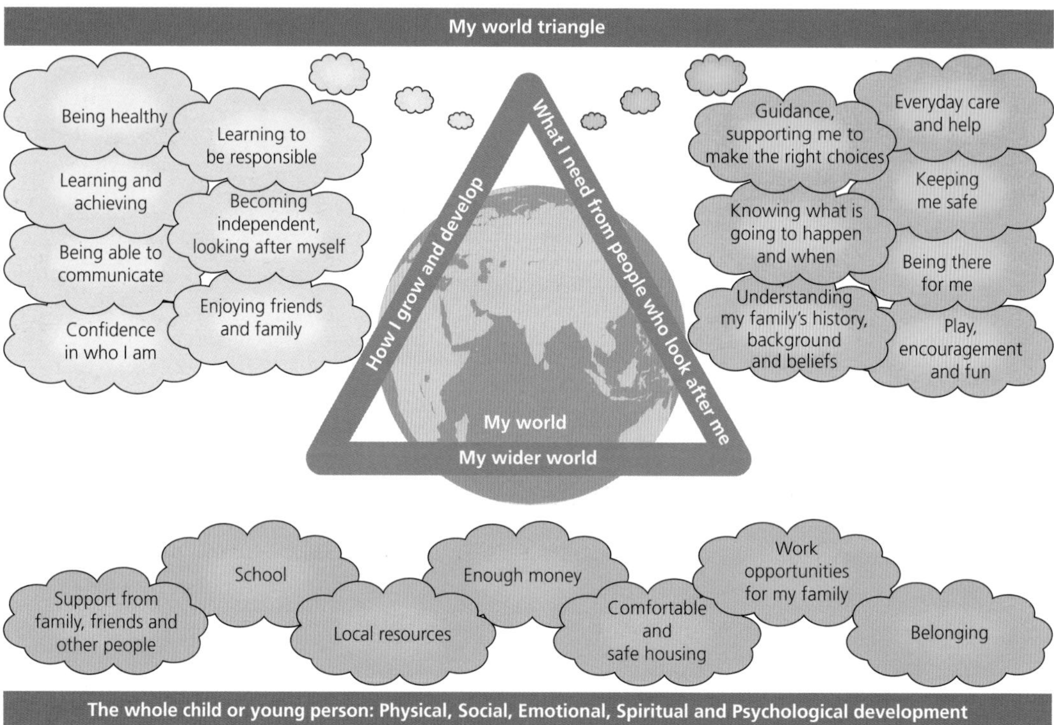

Figure 6.3 My World Triangle

Phase 1: Observing and recording using the SHANARRI Well-being Wheel

The SHANARRI Well-being Wheel enables practitioners to structure, organise, plan and share relevant information regarding a child or young person using the eight well-being indicators. In addition, it also allows us as workers to record any areas of concern that may require a more detailed analysis using the Resilience Matrix.

As a practitioner the following five questions should be asked if you have any concerns about a child or young person:

1 *What is getting in the way of this child's or young person's well-being?*

2 *Do I have all the information I need to help this child or young person?*

3 *What can I do now to help this child or young person?*

4 *What can my agency do to help this child or young person?*

5 *What additional help, if any, may be needed from others?*

(Scottish Government, 2012)

Phase 2: The My World Triangle

The My World Triangle looks at the strengths and pressures that the child or young person may experience under three headings: **My wider world, What I need from the people who look after me, How I grow and develop**.

These three headings allow us to obtain information relevant to the young person, such as health needs, learning needs, opportunities, etc., thus providing us with a detailed overview of that child's or young person's whole world.

Phase 3: The Resilience Matrix

The Resilience Matrix enables you to capture how resilient a child or young person is by interpreting and inputting their experiences into four categories: **Resilience, Vulnerability, Adversity, Protective factors**. Inserting relevant information into these four areas helps to analyse how resilient or vulnerable they are.

With the aid of the Resilience Matrix practitioners are able to assess and analyse whether a child or young person has strengths or vulnerabilities. This can then form an action plan based on the collated information as well as incorporating the eight areas identified on the Well-being Wheel.

Activity *Resilience Matrix*

With reference to the case study of Kristyna below, input the key factors into the Resilience Matrix template (Figure 6.4) and discuss it with your peers.

Kristyna

Kristyna is 15 years old and engages in various risk-taking behaviours, such as associating with a negative peer group, smoking, taking illegal substances and staying out all night. She can present as aggressive when her demands are not met and struggles to reflect back over her behaviours or to link her behavioural choices to the consequences. Despite this, Kristyna has been able to maintain one good friendship (this friend is not part of the negative peer group with which she chooses to associate herself), has a sense of humour and when in a positive frame of mind has the ability to express her thoughts and feelings appropriately.

Kristyna has had a traumatic and stressful childhood, has witnessed seriously violent domestic abuse, and has herself experienced physical and emotional abuse. Due to the levels of aggression displayed by her dad, and her mum's refusal to leave him, Kristyna was placed into her grandparents' care. When her grandfather died, however, her grandmother was unable to care for her due both to her own health needs and to Kristyna's increasingly challenging behaviours. Kristyna continues to have regular contact with her grandmother but refuses contact with her parents. She regularly attends education; she struggles with the more academic subjects, however. She regularly attends dance, art and cooking classes, in which she seems to excel.

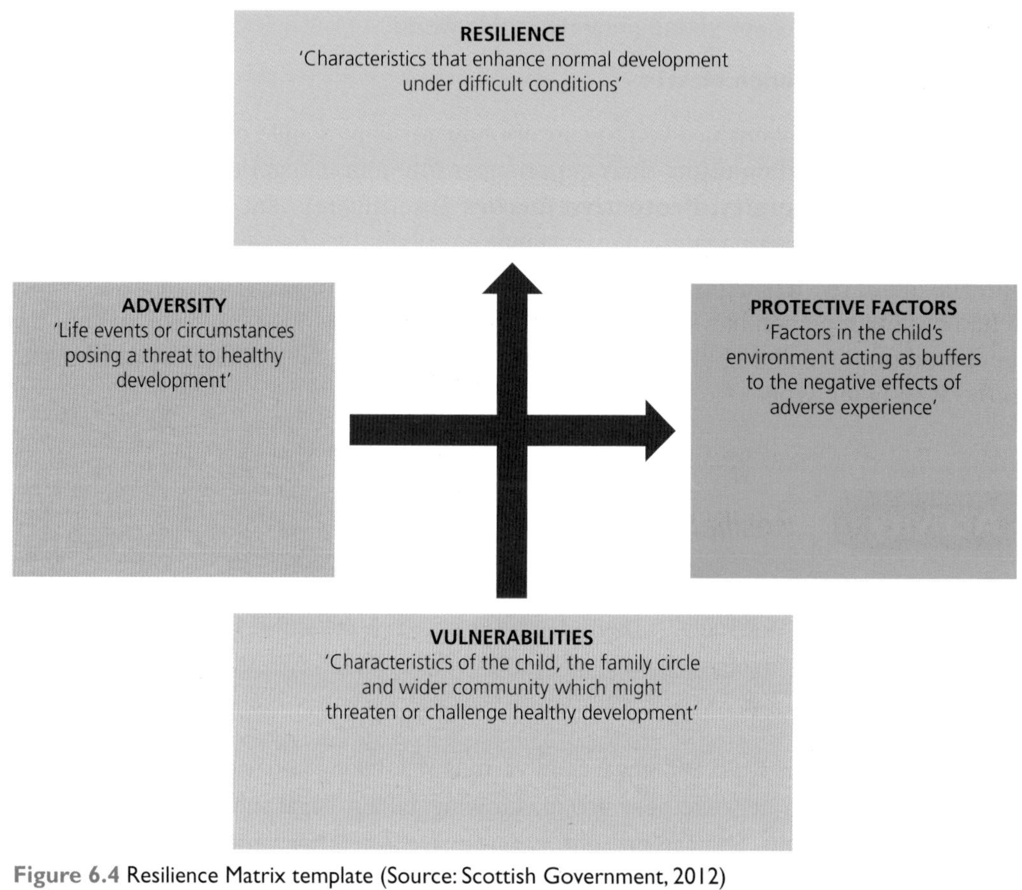

Figure 6.4 Resilience Matrix template (Source: Scottish Government, 2012)

Phase 4: Planning, action and review using the Well-being Wheel

This section brings everything together and forms an action plan based on the child's or young person's needs. It also identifies expected outcomes under the eight well-being indicators (SHANARRI), taking a multi-agency approach to forming the individual's care plan. This plan can be reviewed and adjusted over time, taking into account new and changing needs of the child or young person. The relationships among the different parts of the GIRFEC National Practice Model are illustrated in Figure 6.5.

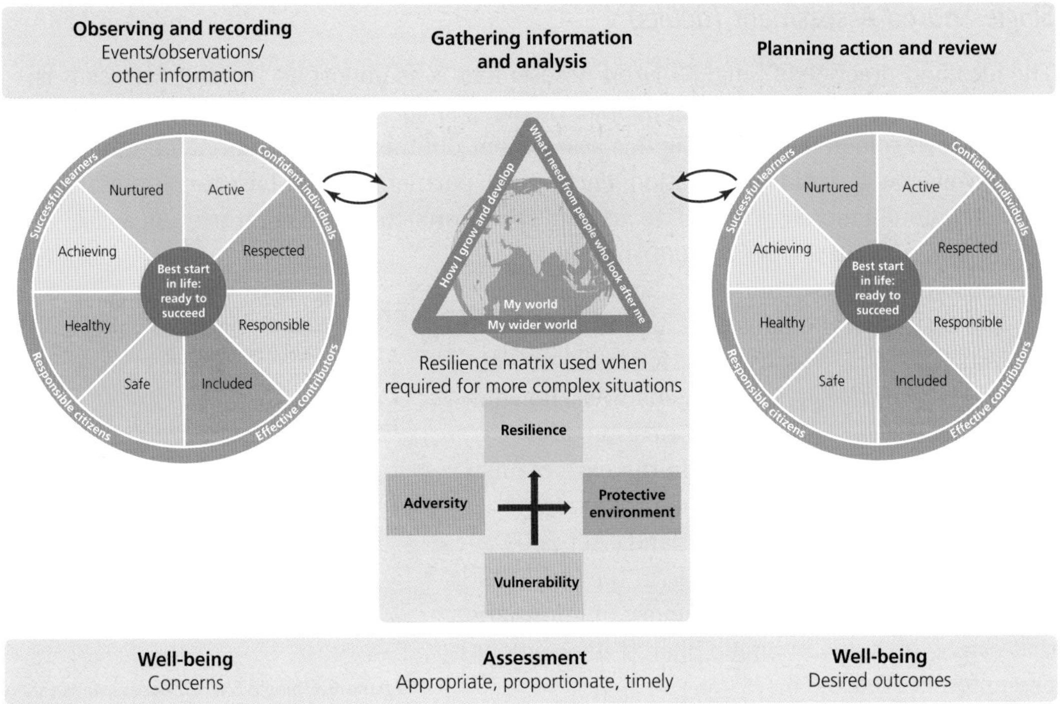

Figure 6.5 National Practice Model

Single Shared Assessment (children and young people)

The Single Shared Assessment requires various professionals to contribute to one document, where information between all agencies or professionals involved with the child or young person can be shared. This document can be built on over time and can contain information, knowledge and skills in relation to the child's or young person's needs. The information gathered is key to determining and forming the best level of support, which is implemented through individual care plans that focus on outcomes and resources.

The Single Shared Assessment is completed by a lead professional, normally the social worker. A multi-professional approach, which includes health, education and any significant others, provides input to fully complete and meet the needs identified within the plan. Co-ordination, collaboration and communication are key to this process.

The National Residential Childcare Initiative (NRCCI) Report (2009), states that:

> *... the commissioning report describes careful assessment as a cornerstone of an 'outcomes' approach. It argues that unless there are clear and valid baseline measures of some kind then evidencing precise 'outcomes' of placement will not be possible.*

Therefore it is important that all agencies involved with the child or young person contribute to the Single Shared Assessment.

Single Shared Assessment (adults)

The idea and practice of Single Shared Assessment is as important in adult care as it is in the care of children and young people. Having a single assessment and one person taking a lead role in co-ordinating this assessment optimises the potential for service user involvement, avoids duplication, encourages partnership and has the potential to promote a much more collaborative and holistic approach to care practice. As a care worker you may play a role in contributing to the Single Shared Assessment and in helping to put into operation the outcomes agreed in the assessment. A single assessment for an adult with the capacity for decision making involves the adult consenting to the sharing of information among those working with him or her. In the case of an adult who lacks this capacity, the protection of the Adults with Incapacity (Scotland) Act 2000 provides for decisions to be made in the interests of the person concerned. A summary of information that can be included in Single Shared Assessment is presented in Figure 6.6.

Single Shared Assessment may include information about:

- service user's perspective
- carer's perspective
- relationships
- spiritual, religious, cultural matters
- risk and safety
- immediate environment and resources
- personal care and physical well-being
- mental health
- clinical background
- disease prevention
- senses
- communication.

Figure 6.6 Single Shared Assessment (SSA)

The SSA uses agreed core data and should result in the development of outcomes and a personal plan.

Assessment meetings

An assessment meeting can take many forms. In person-centred planning, for example, the service user can invite those people whom he or she chooses to a meeting (or if necessary, more than one meeting), at which needs, dreams and strengths and the people who are to be part of their implementation are discussed, with an aim of making a plan that is truly focused on this individual. Another form of meeting is a multi-disciplinary one, attended by the service user and as many people involved in his or her care as possible. Meetings need to be as non-threatening as possible and relaxed so that everyone feels confident enough to make a contribution. Meetings have the advantage of bringing many people together but are only one aspect of the assessment/care planning process. They can be rather formal occasions unless a determined effort is made to avoid this.

At one assessment meeting I attended, the chair of the meeting began by taking this opportunity to discipline the service user. Why do you think this defeated the purpose of the meeting? The service user was immediately put on the defensive, his mother was furious, other people at the meeting felt extremely uncomfortable and were completely taken by surprise by this approach. Although efforts were made to rescue the situation, the participation of the service user and his mother was effectively lost. When you read the section on person-centred planning (page 271) you will see an emphasis on meetings being facilitated rather than chaired, with a facilitator representing and advocating for the service user where necessary. Some situations may require both some formal structure and a degree of advocacy, for example when assessment and planning are taking place with a child or adult at risk.

Assessment documents

Assessment documents have their uses but should never be the be-all-and-end-all of the assessment and care planning process. They are only a tool. Local authorities and Health Boards have Single Shared Assessment documents using agreed data sets, which summarise useful information in terms of personal details and components of need. Components of need may include:

- service user's perspective
- carer's perspective
- any disagreements between the two perspectives
- relationships
- risk and safety
- immediate environment and resources
- personal care and physical well-being
- people contacted as part of the assessment process
- a summary of needs, wishes and dreams
- a summary of outcomes to be carried forward to the care plan.

Other organisations build on these data sets or develop their own according to the needs of the service users with whom they work. A data set may be defined as a set of criteria for collecting specified information. Computers have made the sharing of information and everyone using the same pro forma and data sets much easier, but care needs to be taken that this does not exclude service users and carers from the process. With younger people especially, they may find it interesting, even exciting, to participate in their computer-generated assessment, planning and action process. They are enabled to have a visual view of how outcomes are decided, worked towards and achieved, and the opportunity to contribute their view, entering this themselves whenever possible.

Checklists

Checklists are sometimes used in care practice to establish, for example, what a service user can do in relation to a set of tasks, as a way of planning what needs to be achieved to make progress. They may be used, for instance, with people with learning disability to establish a baseline from which a plan in relation to defined tasks can be made, such as handling money, making a meal or planning a journey. These checklists have many of the pitfalls that have already been seen to apply to other documents. They are only as good as the questions asked and there is a danger that they can become the main focus of work when they should be only one tool in the assessment process.

Observation

Observation doesn't mean that a person's every move and action needs to be watched and recorded, but instead that a care worker's and others' observations of the service user can be of relevance in the assessment process, especially in situations where the service user has difficulty in communication. Observed changes in behaviour, difficulties in relating to some people more than others, observations of likes and dislikes, can all be important aspects of assessment. If, for example, you are working with a child who has a learning disability and whom you observe becomes very agitated and exhibits challenging behaviour when there is a lot of noise, you may build into the care plan opportunities to have quiet times away from other service users.

Asking questions

As with observation, asking questions is a very straightforward way of obtaining information if the service user or those being asked have the communication skills to provide adequate answers. This method is quick and is a very good way to obtain factual data. Categories of the Single Shared Assessment form a good basis for asking questions. Asking questions can, however, be seen as rather threatening and sometimes people give the answer they think you would like to hear rather than what is really concerning them. There may be issues of power or fear transferred from other situations, which can limit the use of questions, or the questions themselves may not be sufficient to elicit information about what is really worrying the service user. As you saw in Chapter 2, it is usually better to use open questions beginning with the words 'how', 'what', 'when', 'where' or 'why' than closed questions which only have the answer 'yes' or 'no'. Often information is just as well gained through one of the other more informal ways set out below, which may in the end produce a more accurate picture.

Diaries and scrapbooks

Diaries record day-to-day events of significance. A care worker can suggest to a service user that he or she keeps a diary for perhaps a period of two weeks, writing down (with help, if necessary) all of the things that are important during that time: activities, people, classes, outings and so on. In this way a picture of the service user's everyday life and the network of people who are important to him/her can be built up as a basis for assessing need and looking at things that should and should not happen in the plan of care.

CASE STUDY

Stephen

A care worker worked on a diary with Stephen, a boy of 13 residing in a care and education centre. Stephen enjoyed going over his day, and the care worker realised from the diary just how important routine was to Stephen. One of the most vital parts of the day was a morning shower, without which Stephen felt very uncomfortable. Keeping the diary not only enabled the care worker and Stephen to identify needs and activities that should be incorporated in the care plan, but as a spin-off it improved their relationship with one another and gave Stephen the opportunity to improve his literacy skills in an enjoyable way.

A diary may also be a useful tool for the care worker to keep, recording events in relation to a specific service user over a set period of time. In this way it may be possible to identify patterns of behaviour, triggers for challenging behaviour, issues that are of importance, social contacts, likes, dislikes and needs that have not previously been evident. Carers too, for example family members or carers in shared care situations, can facilitate the assessment process through the use of diaries from which needs can be identified. Shared care refers to situations where people offer care in their own home to share that care with family members and provide them with regular, planned breaks.

Where communication, especially written communication, is difficult, a scrapbook of pictures could be built up as a shared exercise, enabling the service user to identify needs and people of importance through photographs and magazine pictures.

Shared activities

Sometimes needs can be identified when the focus isn't on assessment at all but on an enjoyable activity shared between service user and worker.

CASE STUDY

Linda

When Linda and her care worker went to the cinema together they had a good chat afterwards about the film and all sorts of other things too. Linda talked about her family, how she wished she could see her sister more often, her great love of the cinema and going bowling and swimming. She mentioned her key worker several times and expressed a dislike of one particular night shift worker. All of this contributed to building up a picture of her needs, which could subsequently be included in the assessment and help in developing her care plan. Sharing activities could also alert you to potential difficulties and issues of safeguarding.

The above are not the only ways in which information for an assessment can be gained. You may be able to think of others that work just as well. These ways do, however, provide a start and a basis on which an assessment can be developed and a plan of care formulated.

Before proceeding to a consideration of care planning, one recently implemented action which is proving useful in many care settings and which can be achieved alongside assessment and amended as care planning and implementation take place, is the development of one-page profiles. These are explained below.

One-page profiles

One-page profiles provide an entry point for person-centred, personalised care. They can be done by service users, carers and care workers as a way of introducing themselves. They can identify service users' most important needs and requirements. One-page profiles are based on the answers to at least three questions:

- What do others like and admire about you?
- What is important to you? (What I like, what I don't like.)
- What is good support for you?

You can vary or add to the questions according to the needs of the situation but these three areas should be covered in one way or another. Profiles can be written collaboratively with service users, by service users on their own, or with or by people who know service users well. It is useful to include a photograph on the profile.

You can find more information about one-page profiles on the SCIE and Helen Sanderson websites: **www.scie.org.uk** and **www.helensandersonassociates.co.uk**.

Care planning

Care planning is the agreement about the what, who, how, when and where of outcomes to be worked on as a result of the assessment process. It should be written down and agreed with the service user and all of the relevant people involved, and outcomes should be as **SMART** as possible: **Specific**, **Measurable**, **Achievable**, **Realistic**, **Time-bound**.

Plans can be staged according to which outcomes are to be met in what timescale. For example, there will be some outcomes to be met immediately, some in one month, some in three months, some by next year and some that will be worked towards at some point in the future. The essential features of a care plan, from the above definition and the preceding discussion of assessment, are that:

- It is the basis for action (not just a paper exercise).
- It is written down.
- It is outcomes focused.
- It is shared with the service user.
- It is a contract – providers and users agree about what is to be done by whom.
- It is a practical activity.
- All team members should be working to this plan, and the plan is the service user's, not theirs.
- The plan should state specifically what is to happen, who should be doing what and in what timescale.
- Monitoring and review of the plan should be built into the planning process.
- The plan should clearly identify any statutory/legal requirements, implications or constraints. For example, some care plans for children incorporate a supervision requirement that is legally enforced by the Children's Hearings or the courts. Any other likely constraints that may affect the care plan should be detailed.

Models used in the care planning process

The above discussion has drawn heavily on two models of planning: the exchange model and person-centred planning. Both of these emphasise the importance of placing the service user at the centre of the planning process. Person-centred planning goes much further than this, however, and presents exciting possibilities for the service user to make supported choices, ranging from who attends planning meetings to how the future is to be lived.

The exchange model

The exchange model is described in Coulshed and Orme (2012) and emphasises an exchange among service users, carers and workers of their knowledge and skills, including knowledge of methods of helping and of resources and skills in the process of problem-solving. The model recognises that a person with needs and those in their network know more about their problems than any worker who comes along to help them, though workers have their own areas of expertise. The process of producing a plan is an exchange among everyone involved and should be multi-disciplinary in nature. A plan emerges that is a balance-sheet of everything that has been presented. One person, usually a key worker or social worker, co-ordinates the plan and negotiates agreements about who is to do what, for whom, in what timescale. The focus is on the social situation and on everyone in the service user's network. Smale *et al.* (1993) summarise the main tasks of this model as being:

- to facilitate full participation in the process of decision making
- to make a 'holistic' assessment of the social situation, and not just of the referred individual
- to help create and maintain the flexible set of human relationships that make up a 'package of care'
- to facilitate negotiations within personal networks about conflicts of choices and needs
- to create sufficient trust for full participation and open negotiations to actually take place
- to change the approach to all these broad tasks as the situation itself changes over time.

Person-centred planning

> *Person-centred planning is a process of continual listening and learning, focusing on what is important to someone now and in the future, and acting upon this in alliance with their family and friends.*
>
> (**www.helensandersonassociates.co.uk**)

Much of the text of this section is based on material from Ritchie *et al.* (2003), and is used with permission.

Person-centred planning has developed from ideas presented by O'Brien and Lovett (1992), mainly in relation to people with learning disability who were then beginning to find a place 'in the community', often after spending many years in hospital. Some of its central ideas, however, can be transferred to care planning in general and can be useful with any service user who wants and is in a position to make changes in his or her life. It is an exciting advance on traditional models of care planning, moving away from professionals organising the process, towards placing as much control and decision making as possible in the hands of the service user, in line with the Scottish Government's personalisation agenda. Various forms of care planning are based upon the person-centred approach, including Personal Futures Planning and Essential Lifestyle Planning, and many agencies, among them Edinburgh Development Group (**www.edg-sco.org**), are embracing person-centred planning as central to their work. The potential of this approach for empowering service users is enormous and exciting and for this reason it is given considerable space in this section of the book. Unlike the exchange model, the focus is well and truly on the service user, rather than on a social situation and a plan that must account for the needs of many people. The roots of person-centred planning are illustrated in Figure 6.7.

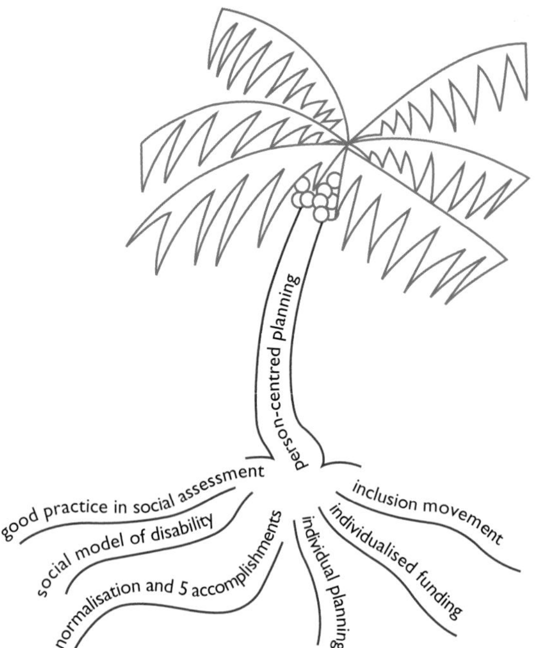

Figure 6.7 The roots of person-centred planning (Source: Ritchie *et al.*, 2003)

Person-centred planning is often very visual, using diagrams and charts to assist in building a plan. Figures 6.8, 6.9 and 6.10 show some of the ways in which visual material is used in the planning process, illustrating 'building a shared understanding', 'relationship circles' and 'when a meeting is needed'.

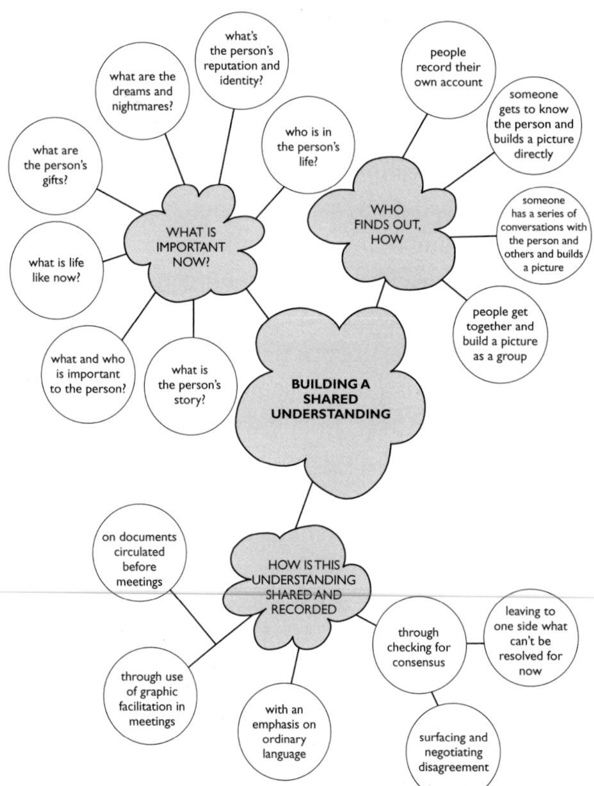

Figure 6.8 Building a shared understanding (Source: Ritchie *et al.*, 2003)

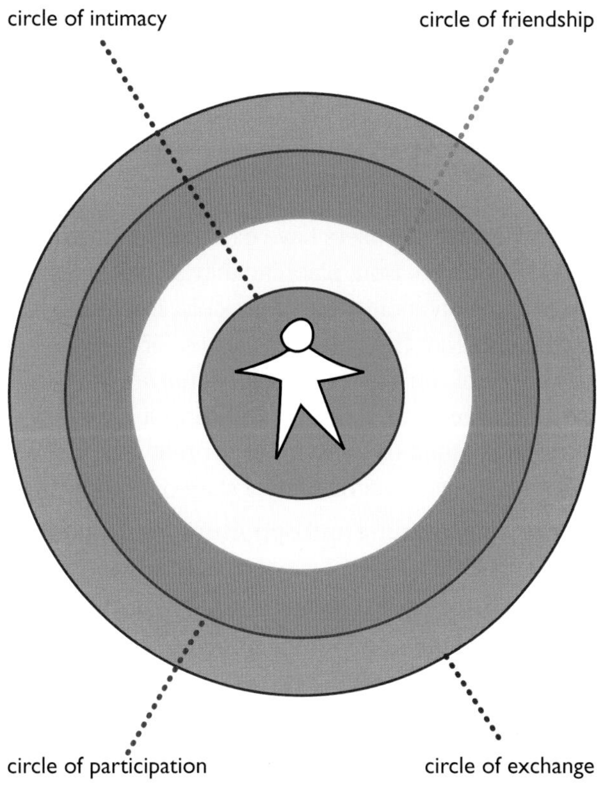

Figure 6.9 Relationship circles (Source: Ritchie *et al.*, 2003)

We need to look creatively at these issues with the person and think about how decisions can be made in the most empowering way.

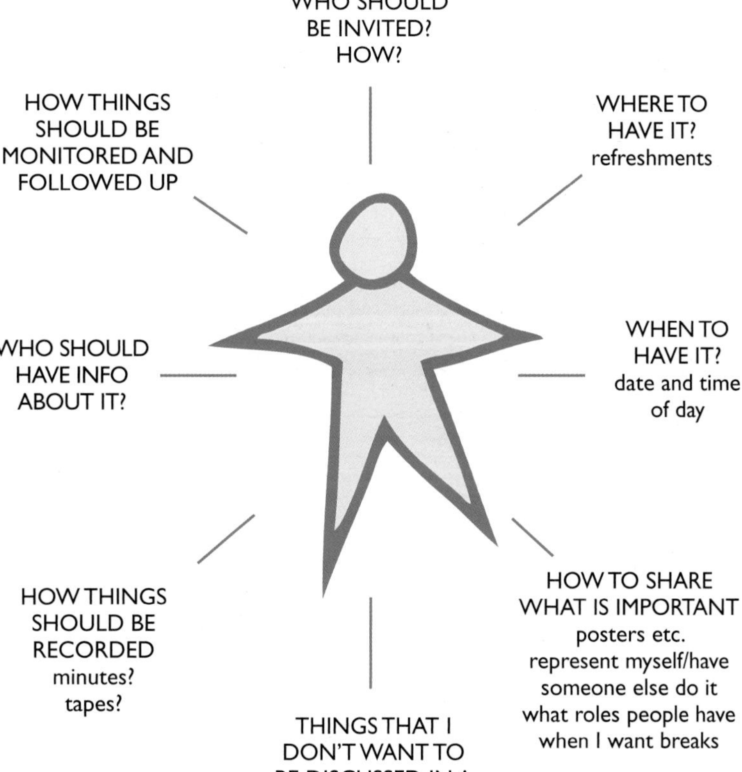

Figure 6.10 When a meeting is needed … (Source: Ritchie *et al.*, 2003)

Three ways of working that are essential to the person-centred planning (PCP) process are now considered:

- sharing power
- building a shared picture
- building a capacity for change.

Sharing power is not always easy, especially when service users have experienced many years of powerlessness in institutional settings. For this reason, planning may also have an educational element, showing and informing the person about what is possible. It may also require enormous patience and a very positive belief that the person is capable of growth and participation. The use of visual materials is one of the ways in which people are both empowered and can begin to **build a shared picture** of their future. **Building a capacity for change** may involve investigating and utilising community resources in creative and new ways. Here are some ways in which agencies share power and build up a shared picture:

- Edinburgh Development Group (EDG) provides training and opportunities for young people to develop person-centred plans.
- Ritchie (2003) advocated looking at the best possible day and the worst possible day for the person, going right through a 24-hour period and looking at every detail.
- Helen Sanderson has developed PCP tools such as 'Top Tips and Short Stories'.

The important thing about PCP is that it is about the big things *and* the small details of life, such as what the individual likes for breakfast.

Person-centred planning is a comprehensive way of planning with people. There may still be some formalities to be completed in order to access some aspects of the care plan. It will probably still be necessary, for example, to complete documentation for a Single Shared Assessment, but the process of getting there in person-centred planning is unique to this service user, who is being empowered to make these changes in his or her life. It is completely compatible with other models such as personalisation and self-directed support, and an outcomes focus, which have relied heavily on person-centred thinking.

Table 6.2 provides a summary of what person-centred planning is moving away from and what it is moving towards.

Table 6.2 Moving towards person-centred planning

Moving from ...	Moving towards ...
Clinical descriptions of people	Seeing people as human beings
Professionals being in charge	Sharing power
Professionals inviting people to meetings	The person choosing who attends meetings
Meetings in offices at times to suit professionals	Meetings in a venue chosen by the person, when it suits her/him
Meetings being chaired	Meetings being facilitated
Not asking what the person wants	Encouraging the person to dream
Assuming inability	Looking for gifts in people
Filing plans away	Giving the plan to the person
Writing notes of meetings	Graphic facilitation of meetings
Professionals putting the plan into action	All participants having some responsibility for implementing the plan

Implementing care plans

Positive care practice aims to implement the care plan in ways that respect worth and dignity, empower and include the person as much as possible, promote rights, personalisation and welfare, and safeguard individuals from harm and abuse. GIRFEC calls this part of the process 'action', which is what it is. It is taking action to implement the outcomes identified in the assessment and care plan. A lot of people think of implementation and the 'helping' that goes along with it as a very active process of doing things for other people. From the value base, skills and qualities already explained, however, you will have realised that helping is really about empowering and enabling people to do as much as possible for themselves. It is about empowering them to make decisions and to have the same opportunities as are available to most other people. This should always be considered to ensure that helping does not become patronising, discriminatory or demeaning. With these factors in mind, a positive approach to implementing care plans is explained below. This sets out some useful skills that aim to improve the service user's quality of life and enable them to work towards achieving their identified outcomes.

Below are some of the suggestions made by a group of care students on placement when asked what skills and methods they used to implement plans. Before reading this, it is useful for you to think about the skills you already have.

- 'I use empathy when I'm helping people, just imagining what they may want and how they're probably feeling.'
- 'I always demonstrate respect so that people aren't embarrassed when they need help.'
- 'I talk to the young people, get to know them first.'
- 'I try to motivate the older adults I work with by providing some interesting activities and a choice of things to do.'
- 'I play with the young people and try to help with their socialisation and their education plan.'
- 'Communication, communication, communication – verbal and non-verbal; anything that works.'
- 'I assist people to the toilet and with bathing, always being careful to find out how much they can do for themselves first, and I always talk to them and ask how their son or daughter is, or whoever is important to them.'
- 'I write up notes in the log at the end of the day and attend the handover meetings so that I know what is being achieved in the care plans and so that others have an idea about what has happened during my shift.'

- 'I take one lady shopping. It sometimes takes us an hour to get out of the house because she's quite slow at getting ready and the other care staff seem to think this isn't relevant work. I think this is what the job is all about. We go to the local shop for anything she needs, then we'll go for a coffee and take our time, then a walk back in time for lunch. Admittedly you can't do that every day, but it's an important part of care work.'
- 'I've been helping a group of children with life story books so that they have a reminder about who has been important to them and about important places, holidays and so on.'
- 'I've been making a scrapbook with some older adults to represent old times. We have some amazing conversations about some of the pictures. Some people in their eighties and nineties remember the Second World War.'
- 'I used to be a hairdresser and when we're going on an outing I ask if anyone wants their hair done. Lots of them do. While you're doing their hair or their nails you talk to them and they tell you all sorts of things they never would usually, because they're so relaxed.'

What do you notice about the above examples? Most of them illustrate skills that are part of everyday life: talking to people, playing with children, making scrapbooks, going shopping. The importance of the value base and communication are emphasised again and again and are an essential part of all care work.

Building on these foundations, a useful model for implementing care plans is presented below. You will see that this rests firmly on the foundations of value base and communication discussed above and set out in Chapter 2.

A positive care environment approach

Implementation can be considered in many ways but one useful framework that promotes assessment, planning, implementation and review in person-centred ways is the 'positive care environment approach'. A 'positive care environment' is a broad term that embraces optimising the use of the different environments of care. The term 'environment' is used in the sense of circumstances that work for the individual, and the underpinning knowledge, skills, values and understanding that are brought to different environments by everyone involved. The focus remains firmly on working with service users to optimise their quality of life, build on their strengths and work towards achieving outcomes identified in the care planning process.

Four environments are considered, illustrated in Table 6.3. These environments overlap, interlink and are inextricably connected with one another. For the purposes of clarity, however, they are discussed separately.

Table 6.3 Positive care environments

Care environment	Description
Helping and therapeutic environment	• Working with service users and carers towards positive outcomes • Range of choices and ways of working • Builds on: value base, communication skills, personalisation and self-directed support, person-centred planning • Psychological and sociological theoretical base, for example concepts of attachment, resilience and loss
Organisational environment	Includes: • Ethos, including aims, objectives and mission statement • Teamwork, partnerships and collaboration • Involvement of service users • Leadership and management • Promotion of good quality assessment and care management • Safeguarding and protection from harm and abuse • Supervision and mentoring • Supporting learning and development
Physical environment	• The physical environment matters, whether it is the service user's house, a resource centre or residential unit or anywhere else • If it is a building, the location, accessibility, decor and state of repair are all important, with maximum decision making in all of these by service users
Community environment	• Links with families and the local community • Use of community resources and opportunities by service users • Links with other similar groups locally, nationally, internationally, electronically • Care settings as a community resource

The helping and therapeutic environment

The helping and therapeutic environment involves working directly with service users and carers to improve their lives. Several theoretical frameworks that you have already examined are relevant here and you may wish to refer back to them. For example, attachment theory and thinking in relation to resilience in Chapter 3 direct you to taking these into account when using any of the ways of helping discussed in this chapter. Attachment-based practice emphasises everyone's need for a close and loving relationship with at least one other person, especially in early life, and ideas about resilience emphasise the importance of building resilience in helping people to cope with difficulties.

In determining how to work with service users and carers, they should be as involved as possible in deciding how agreed outcomes should be reached and how success should be evaluated. For example, if one of the outcomes is that the service user increases the links in their network of informal support, you may together agree that choosing two additional community opportunities, or meeting a friend twice a month for a cup of coffee, may achieve this outcome. You may agree that the way to get there is to build on strengths or by the use of a behavioural approach or referral for counselling. Below are some suggested ways of working with service users towards positive outcomes.

Attention to the importance of daily life

The enormous importance of attention to how the tasks of everyday life are achieved is often underestimated. These everyday tasks often provide the greatest opportunities for establishing warm and genuine relationships with service users, sharing activities and using their potential for working with difficult behaviour or developing social skills. One care worker I spoke to said that one of her outstanding memories was of helping a child to tie his shoelaces on his first day at school. It was so important to him that someone cared about how he looked and realised how important this day was to him. The help was as symbolic as it was practical. It set the seal on an on-going and productive helping relationship. The importance of the symbolic relates to the discussion of symbolic interactionism in Chapter 5. Staff who see having to assist people with everyday tasks as a chore, whether at meal times or to get up in the morning, cannot be cheerful about such tasks. They do not make an effort to converse or make these events pleasant, and this sets the tone for a bad day. It is poor practice.

The establishment of a daily routine incorporating specific tasks that have to be achieved can also be of great importance to some service users. This can provide structure to previously unstructured lives and enhance skills in daily living. Where these skills are lacking a behavioural approach (discussed below) could be used, where everyday tasks can be modelled by the care worker and practised by the service user. The care setting provides the ideal opportunity for this in an environment that is comfortable for the user and with someone with whom he or she has a close and trusting relationship. The importance of crucial events in everyone's lives is also often undervalued in care services. The way in which these events are approached can make the difference between people feeling good about their lives and people feeling absolutely dreadful.

Building on people's strengths

There is a lot of literature in the field of mental health relating to strengths-based approaches. Without getting too technical, these approaches can be transferred to working with people in almost any context. Strengths-based work involves identifying and promoting a person's strengths as a way of finding solutions to things that are problematic for them or that are preventing them leading a satisfying life. This is not different from a person-centred or outcomes approach, but builds on these to focus on strengths. For example, a focus on people's strengths can point to ways of achieving outcomes.

To begin your thinking about strengths McCormack (2007) suggests the following activity:

Activity *Strengths*

Write down what you consider to be your weaknesses. Once you have done this, rate your feelings of self-esteem on a scale of 1 to 10, with 1 being low self-esteem and 10 being high self-esteem.

Now do a similar exercise in terms of your strengths. Write down what you consider to be your strengths. Once you have done this, rate your self-esteem on a scale of 1 to 10.

Findings indicate that when people focus on their strengths their self-esteem is higher than when they focus on their weaknesses.

The activity above provides a starting point for a focus on strengths. Strengths-based practice uses strengths as a basis for making progress. Table 6.4 shows some examples where the same circumstances can be seen either as a problem, or as a strength which can then be used as a platform for making progress.

Table 6.4 Strengths-based practice: problem or strength?

Problem	Strength
Person never goes out.	Person uses the home environment as a source of support.
Person finds it difficult to stay in.	Person prefers being out of the house and in their local community.
Person drinks too much.	Person is trying to find a way of coping with difficulties but has periods of abstinence.
Person withdraws when there is a stressful situation.	Person copes with stress by withdrawing but is usually sociable.
Person always looks untidy and unwashed.	Person copes with many difficulties in her own way.

A behavioural approach

Building on the cognitive/behavioural approaches discussed in Chapter 4, ways of working with individuals who present behavioural difficulties have been developed. These rely on changing behaviours that present difficulties to the individual and/or those in their environment through learning new and more rewarding, less damaging behaviours. Workers help individuals to achieve this through processes of modelling new behaviours, and rewarding and reinforcing new behaviour when it is appropriate. Two case studies, contributed by Joanne Gaughan of TRFS (The Richmond Fellowship Scotland) illustrate this process.

Activity *Using a behavioural approach*

From the case studies of Mary and Sean below, identify the main components of a behavioural approach. In what circumstances do you think it is most effective?

Mary

Previously, Mary found a wide range of situations very difficult and would display challenging behaviour. Mary was at risk of losing her tenancy because she shouted at her neighbours in the street, and she has had years of being excluded from places where she has socialised. Mary was verbally and physically aggressive to staff on an almost daily basis. She also relied on staff support to do most activities.

Our experienced staff, including those who had a Personal Development Award in Management of Behaviour Support – a year-long course run by our own Positive Behaviour Support Team (PBST) – began to build a more comprehensive package for Mary.

Interventions: Staff began to monitor Mary's behaviour and looked at what triggered her challenging behaviour and what things helped her to relax and become calm again. In analysing this, staff began to recognise why Mary had developed this behaviour; this meant they were able to tailor any plans that were drafted to address her needs in a different way. Staff were also able to help Mary when she became anxious so that she didn't end up being challenging so frequently.

Outcome and progression: Staff are now able to calm Mary down as quickly and safely as possible and have a much greater understanding of how she is feeling. Staff are confident in their support due to the appropriate set ways of handling situations that Mary finds difficult. The staff approach is about increasing the activity in people's lives and teaching them ways of coping with situations they find difficult.

This process has made a big difference to Mary's quality of life. Mary has started:

- using public transport on her own more
- going into town without support
- attending a cookery course and working in the kitchen at her social club
- being involved in a drama production at the Citizen's Theatre, where she attended rehearsals for 10 weeks without support staff and then put on two performances for over a hundred people.

Mary's social worker commented: 'I've never seen Mary looking so confident before.'

Mary's neighbours have also commented that she is 'very quiet these days' and Mary proudly talks about how she is 'not shouting in the street anymore.'

The last words go to Mary: 'The new plans helped me feel I am not inferior to other people.'

Sean

Sean has a dual diagnosis of a learning disability and mental ill health, and presented with very challenging and aggressive behaviours. Sean would strike staff and others in the community.

Due to Sean's dual diagnosis and the severity of the incidents there had been involvement from the police and 'Violence Case Conferences' were held. These conferences discussed issues around moving Sean to the State Hospital, Carstairs.

When The Richmond Fellowship Scotland began supporting Sean, staff put in place a behaviour support plan to support Sean to learn about emotions and to be able to share his feelings with staff. Following this, a reinforcement plan was implemented, which meant that if Sean had not hit out and had learned to cope with his feelings better, then he was able to work towards a 'reward event' of his choosing.

The staff team was supported to understand what triggered Sean's behaviour and how to communicate more effectively. This work by the staff team resulted in the number of incidents dropping significantly.

It is now three years later and Sean is enjoying a much fuller life within the community. Sean's quality of life within a community setting has improved and progressed, so much so that he is also in employment and is in a steady relationship with a girlfriend.

Creative opportunities that contribute to achieving outcomes

Enabling service users to choose an activity from a range of opportunities is a splendid way of getting to know the service user group, for them to get to know you, of adding interest, challenge, development of skill and enjoyment to the lives of those with whom we work. It can also be very therapeutic, in the sense that it helps to relieve stress, raise self-esteem, has spin-offs in other areas of life, and can be included in the care plan as a way of contributing to achieving outcomes. Similarly, holidays can have lots of spin-offs apart from being, in general, thoroughly enjoyable experiences. They can be an occasion for:

- enabling service users to choose where to go and what they want to do
- planning
- gaining new experiences
- sharing
- feeling free from the constraints of everyday life
- staff and service users to get to know one another in a relaxed and friendly way
- sharing memories after the event, which gives a sense of bonding to those who participated.

Using activities can also contribute to implementing the behavioural approach discussed above.

The Duke of Edinburgh's Award

The Duke of Edinburgh's Award scheme has been used successfully with many young people, including young people experiencing difficulties in their lives. The following section about the scheme has been contributed by Jamie Mitchell of The Duke of Edinburgh's Award Scotland.

The Duke of Edinburgh's (DofE) Award is a flexible tool to structure the learning and personal development of young people, including looked-after young people. A major principle of the DofE is that it is 'achievable by all'. This is realised in the programme by allowing participants to go through the four sections of the Award at their own pace, taking into account the personal circumstances and goals of the individual. Young people set their own goals for each of the four sections: Volunteering, Physical, Skills and an Expedition. Sections can be taken one at a time or all at once, depending on to what the young person is capable of committing. Young people are encouraged to progress not only through their sections, but through the increasingly challenging levels of the Award: Bronze, Silver and Gold. Young people record their progress via eDofE, a secure website that helps them, and their leaders, to keep track of what they have accomplished. Once they have completed their level, participants can create an Achievement Pack, a document that contains the highlights from their DofE programme. This record of achievement is useful for participants and workers alike as a means of demonstrating their personal development journey.

CASE STUDY

The Duke of Edinburgh's Award

Young people at the Good Shepherd Secure/Close Support Unit are given the opportunity to do their DofE Award as a means of working towards something based on their own interests and as a way to improve their self-esteem and self-worth. Young people meet with a well-being activity facilitator, who helps them design a DofE programme. They generally start with twelve sessions to work towards their Award, but facilitators often see them continue on past this for upwards of 70 sessions. Cycling features strongly at Good Shepherd. Not only is it used for the young people's Physical section, but they learn life skills for their Skills section by learning how to take care of and repair their bicycle. Because the amount of time they commit to the DofE is flexible, young people see it in a different light from formal learning and become extremely committed to finishing their DofE. The staff at Good Shepherd see the difference in the young people in their care, saying that their health and well-being improves along with their employability and citizenship.

CASE STUDY

DofE: Calum

Calum is a DofE participant with the physical disability hemiparesis. He started his Bronze DofE programme while in hospital for depression, which was related to the struggles he faced in coping with his disability. Doing his DofE Award helped him gain confidence in his abilities in multiple areas of his life. His Volunteering with a conservation project helped him see his connection to the community; his Physical section helped him to keep his body healthy; and his Skill, photography, boosted his confidence through the knowledge that he was capable of capturing great photos. Re-engaged with his personal development, Calum was able leave care and return to school and complete his Highers. After finishing his Bronze Award he progressed through his Silver and Gold Awards and believes he has become a better and stronger person as a result of his DofE Awards.

Table 6.5 The Duke of Edinburgh's Award
(Source: CfE: H&W Across Learning Principles and Practice and The Handbook for DofE Volunteers)

Learning through health and well-being enables young people to:	Taking part in the DofE programme allows young people to:
make informed choices in order to improve their mental, emotional, social and physical well-being	develop a DofE programme that is personalised to suit their circumstances; supported by DofE volunteers they make informed decisions about the various sections of their programme
experience challenge and enjoyment	experience an enjoyable, fulfilling and rewarding programme, which is non-competitive but requires personal challenge
experience positive aspects of healthy living and activity for themselves	set their own challenging goals, collect evidence of their progress towards them and reflect on their learning at the end
apply their mental, emotional, social and physical skills to pursuing a healthy lifestyle	take part in a balanced programme of activities developing mind, body and soul (through the Skills, Physical and Volunteering sections, respectively)
make a successful move to the next stage of education or work	move through Bronze, Silver and Gold levels, with each level requiring a greater commitment and responsibility from the young person
establish a pattern of health and well-being that will be sustained into adult life, and that will help to promote the health and well-being of the next generation of Scottish children	establish routines around volunteering and physical activity. Many young people continue their involvement in activities beyond their DofE journey, or continue their commitment to DofE by becoming a DofE volunteer themselves!

Figure 6.11 Young people enjoying themselves and developing their skills (Source: Duke of Edinburgh's Award Scotland)

Music, arts and creative activities

Music, arts and other creative activities can enhance the lives of individuals in helpful and therapeutic ways. Sally Magnusson (2014) wrote a wonderful book about her mother who had dementia. She found that when nothing else could reach her mother, music could. Singing with her helped her mood and enabled her to retain memory. She advocates everyone being encouraged to have access to music that has meant something to them. Although dementia can be very difficult to cope with you can help people to feel better by offering music through the day or the night, and at difficult times. For example, if bathing is a difficult time, music that the person likes could be played.

Harry MacFadyen provides a lot of concerts for the charity 'Music in Hospitals', which organises music for all sorts of care homes and hospital wards. In the photographs below he plays his music and some of the residents of Dalvenie Gardens in Banchory join in his songs. Harry says:

> *A very cheery lot and they loved everything that I did and many sang along to all the old favourites like Loch Lomond and the Miles tae Dundee, Song of the Clyde and many, many more.*

Figure 6.12 Music as therapy

At an event entitled 'Living Well with Dementia' held in Dundee in 2014, the dementia choir Total Recall sang a selection of lovely songs. Many people with dementia who were attending the event joined in, remembering the words to many of the songs, even though they may have found other communication rather difficult. One man, who had seemed lost and had been uncommunicative all morning, suddenly brightened up when the music started and sang the words to the songs he remembered. His daughter who was with him cried to see him enjoying himself so much. She hadn't seen this response for months.

Similarly, arts and crafts can have huge benefits. Alzheimer Scotland is working with people with dementia to develop a new Alzheimer's Society tartan. Participants are working on different designs, one of which will be chosen to represent the society. This activity provides social, cognitive, cultural and spiritual benefits.

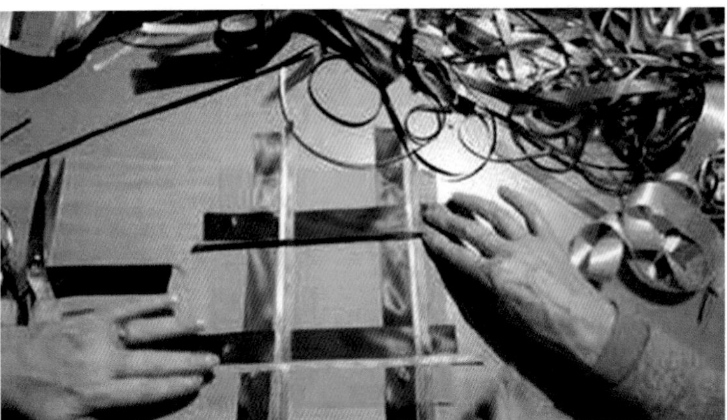

Figure 6.13 Developing the Alzheimer's Society tartan

Availability of specialist therapeutic approaches

Other approaches, such as using counselling skills, social work and psychological approaches, and group work, lend themselves to being implemented within a care environment both by trained and experienced care workers and by specialists in particular approaches. Care workers have a role to play in supporting the work of other professionals. It is so easy for care workers to be bypassed unless they can articulate their work to these others in the multi-disciplinary team and can demonstrate their skill, understanding and value base. The value of 'the other 23 hours' can be overlooked by professionals who come in for an hour or two (or less) for a therapeutic purpose. They may then attribute all of the progress to their own input, unless the care workers themselves can demonstrate their value and participate fully in the assessment, planning, implementation and evaluation process.

Care workers have many advantages over others involved in the care of the service user. They are often with him or her for more hours of the day and night than anyone else, they get to know his or her preferences and habits and can implement plans along with the tasks of everyday life. All of this gives care workers a unique advantage for helping in the context of optimising the benefit of therapeutic approaches. This is compatible with personalisation, with assisting individuals to work towards outcomes, with Adrian Ward's discussion of opportunity-led work below, and also with behavioural work discussed above.

Opportunity-led work

> *The concept of opportunity-led work is a framework that has been designed to enable workers to think through the stages of handling and responding to the many unplanned moments and events in a day's work in order to make their responses more productive and helpful.*
>
> (Ward, 2006)

Opportunity-led work is an approach developed by Adrian Ward to build on what happens during the course of every day. Many things that take place in a care service offer opportunities for working productively with people if they are thought about, even just a little and quickly. The skill lies in building up processes and a bank of questions to ask yourself. It involves thought and using your experience to advantage, rather than responding to every issue and event reactively.

For example, a young person, Josie, during the course of an evening discussion in a children's home, becomes very angry and leaves the room. The key worker instinctively gets up and follows her out shouting, 'What do you think you're doing? Come back NOW.'

Is this a good response? Perhaps not. The drawback is that it was not associated with even the quickest of thought processes. It was just a reaction. Such responses lose any advantage that may be gained from what is potentially an opportunity to improve quality of life.

Ward advocates a four-stage process in working with events that happen during the course of everyday work, an approach that can be practised until it becomes second nature. The stages are:

- observation and assessment
- decision making
- action
- closure and evaluation.

The first stage is crucial since it consists of weighing up what is happening, who is involved and what is likely to happen next. Questions associated with the key words what, why, how, when and who, can enable the worker quickly to weigh up the possibilities of the situation and to begin to make decisions about what to do. Action will depend on decisions about the answers to the questions posed: for example, what is happening, who is involved, who is affected, what the priorities are, what is actually possible, and what is ethical. The worker needs to examine the desirable result and how to get there given the current and future timescales. Consideration also needs to be given to what *shouldn't* happen under any circumstances and avoiding this, for example shouting back when someone shouts at you, giving straight back what is received, hitting back, swearing in response to swearing. Strategies include what is called 'first aid': dealing with the immediate situation, together with a decision about whether or not a longer-term strategy is required.

In the immediate situation, here and now, 'first aid' has to be administered through:

- working on a one-to-one basis, for example through what Redl (1966) has called 'emotional first aid on-the-spot' to help the individual express and leave behind anger, sadness or anxiety
- supporting the individual through the group, for example helping the group to be sensitive to this person's situation or distress and/or supporting group activities 'in order to override the disruptive effects of one member'
- managing the group through focusing on key individuals, for example by drawing the group's attention to how one individual may have been discriminated against without the group being aware that this is what they were doing
- managing the group, for example by establishing ground rules and reminding the group when these are breached.

There are some specific strategies in addition to these that may be used in a conflict or difficult situation:

- offering alternatives – for example, 'You can come back and join us now or when you feel you are ready.'
- preventing the build-up of tension through defusing the situation, for example being sensitive enough to know that when Josie clasps and twists her hands together she will quickly lose control unless you change the subject or introduce an activity
- allowing and helping people to climb down with dignity, for example if Josie has often caused offence in a group situation, giving her the opportunity to apologise quietly afterwards to those concerned.

This short-term emotional first aid may be all that is needed, but it may also be necessary to use some of the other longer-term strategies associated with more specialised therapeutic intervention.

Activity *Josie*

In the light of the above guidance, think about what might have been a more positive response to Josie than shouting 'What do you think you're doing? Come back NOW' when she left the evening discussion. Consider your answer if you know that:

- she usually comes back after she leaves
- she can react violently to any form of direct criticism
- she usually values the group discussions.

Advocacy

The following section is contributed by Mike Martin of Mike Martin Associates and the Open University in Scotland. Although he writes about 'independent advocacy', care workers can to some extent be advocates for the people with whom they work.

Care workers have divided loyalties, however, and must also be accountable to their organisations. If service users, carers and/or care workers feel that independent representation is needed a referral can be made for independent advocacy. An explanation of this is provided below.

Independent advocacy

> *Advocacy is about making sure that the views and opinions of people are heard and respected, and that they are treated as individuals, and as valued members of society. It is also about making sure that they have influence over decisions that affect their lives, so that their needs are met, and their rights and interests protected.*
>
> (Powerful Partnerships training materials, 2006. Powerful Partnerships was an Edinburgh-based independent advocacy organisation for people with learning disabilities, which ceased operation in 2013.)

The 'independent' part of independent advocacy means that an organisation or individual providing advocacy is separate from any organisation providing services to the person being advocated for. This independence is important because it recognises that people may need someone to support them if they are in conflict with or affected by an agency that has power or influence over what happens to them.

Advocacy can potentially support any individuals who, or groups that, use social or health services, but is most often associated with people who lack capacity or have limited capacity to manage their own affairs, for example: children, older people with conditions such as dementia, those with a learning disability or mental health condition. Recognition of the importance of independent advocacy for people with learning disabilities and/or mental health conditions was achieved when access to it was enshrined in law in s259 of the Mental Health (Care and Treatment) (Scotland) Act 2003. Sub-section (1) of this states:

> *Every person with a mental disorder shall have a right of access to independent advocacy; and accordingly it is the duty of:*
>
> *a) each local authority, in collaboration with the (or each) relevant Health Board, and*
>
> *b) each Health Board, in collaboration with the (or each) relevant local authority,*
>
> *to secure the availability, to persons in its area who have a mental disorder, of independent advocacy services and to take appropriate steps to ensure that those persons have the opportunity of making use of those services.*

While this should guarantee access to and availability of independent advocacy across all local authority and Health Board activities in Scotland for specific groups, it will also extend to those using private or voluntary sector services.

It is important that people who provide health or social services recognise their potential position of power and influence over those whom they support, and that they and their employers therefore have a duty to signpost vulnerable service users to independent support.

Before looking at what independent advocacy is and what it does, it is helpful to consider what it is *not*. The following may be important and valuable activities, but they are different from and are not advocacy: counselling; befriending; **advising** someone what they should do; speaking for someone when they are able to speak for themselves rather than supporting them to do so; persuading people to do what services want.

The Scottish Independent Advocacy Alliance (an umbrella membership organisation that represents independent advocacy organisations across Scotland, and seeks to ensure that any vulnerable person has access to independent advocacy) lists on their website what independent advocacy is. It is:

- *about standing alongside people who are in danger of being pushed to the margins of society*
- *about standing up for and sticking with a person or group and taking their side*
- *a process of working towards natural justice; listening to someone and trying to understand their point of view*
- *finding out what makes them feel good and valued; understanding their situation and what may be stopping them from getting what they want*
- *offering the person support to tell other people what they want or introducing them to others who may be able to help*
- *helping someone to know what choices they have and what might be the consequences of these choices*
- *enabling a person to have control over their life but taking up issues on their behalf if they want you to.*

(**www.siaa.org.uk/independent-advocacy**)

There are a number of different forms of advocacy and different organisations tend to specialise in one form or another. An individual may access or benefit from a particular form depending on their needs and the reason why they require advocacy. While there are differences between the forms of advocacy, they are not necessarily mutually exclusive (for example, legal, citizen and crisis advocacy might come together to support an individual in particular circumstances):

- **Citizen advocacy**: where an independent member of a local community builds a long-term one-to-one relationship with someone, and helps them to speak up for themselves
- **Crisis or issue-based advocacy**: where an independent member of the public helps someone to speak up for themselves for a specific issue or occasion; this sometimes is carried out by a citizen advocate or alongside citizen advocacy
- **Group or collective advocacy**: this is where a group of people unites to campaign on issues of common concern to them, and is typical of organisations such as Alzheimer Scotland, ENABLE, or the Scottish Association for Mental Health; an example in the field of learning disability is People First, which has groups of people with learning disabilities who take on a range of issues across the UK

- **Legal advocacy**: usually associated with lawyers and solicitors, acting as people with legal training skilled in helping people to exercise or defend their rights, often in particular theatres such as the courts or tribunals
- **Professional advocacy**: where the advocate is paid for
- **Self-advocacy**: this is where someone acts on their own behalf to present their case. Self-advocates express their own needs and views, and seek to play a more active part in their affairs and in their community. This is what many of us aspire to, though while we work towards being able to do this we may need others to advocate for or with us on the way
- **Volunteer advocacy**: where someone advocates on a voluntary and unpaid basis, usually representing an organisation and on a time-limited basis.

Activity *Different forms of advocacy*

James

James is 32 and has Down's syndrome. He lives at home with his parents and attends a community resource centre, previously called a day centre, three days per week. He has been at the same centre since leaving school and, although he is now offered a choice of day opportunities, he thinks he could work part-time, perhaps in a garden centre. While James loves his parents, he really wants more independence, and would like to move into his own flat. He would like to access education but was previously deterred by having to do the same curriculum for many years.

(Mike Martin, personal communication, 2014)

Thinking about James, can you suggest how some different forms of advocacy might support him? What might an advocate do to support James, and with whom would they need to engage? Why is it that independent advocacy might be needed?

Self-directed support and personalisation

Self-directed support presents opportunities for service users and carers to make decisions about how to organise their support and aims to give maximum decision making to service users within a framework of personalisation. Personalisation, discussed in Chapter 1, was originally formulated as part of the development towards self-directed support but is now seen as having relevance beyond the self-directed support agenda, as a method of supporting people in ways that are person centred and increase their choice and control. In Chapter 1 the various options open to people for how their care is delivered under the Social Care (Self-directed Support) (Scotland) Act 2013 were outlined. The options are:

- Option 1: direct payment
- Option 2: the person directs the available support
- Option 3: the local authority arranges the support
- Option 4: a mix of the above.

The Act also provides a power to authorities to support unpaid carers, and duties to provide information to help people make an informed choice. The Act is about how support is funded and organised. Action still rests upon assessment, planning and outcomes but in options 1 and 2 the individual directs their own support following the assessment process which determines the level of funding. In option 1 the individual also directs how their funding is spent through receiving a direct payment. This may be used, for example, to employ a personal assistant or to achieve outcomes in other ways, including opportunities available to everyone in society such as going to the theatre or for a massage. For more information visit the Self-directed Support in Scotland website (**www.selfdirectedsupportscotland.org.uk**) and the personalisation resources on the Social Care Institute for Excellence (SCIE) website (**www.scie.org.uk/publications/guides/guide47/files/guide47.pdf**).

The organisational environment

As important as the helping and therapeutic environment, is the way that an organisation is run and managed. The following are among the organisational factors that contribute to a positive care environment:

- ethos – the values, mission, vision, aims, objectives and outcomes
- teamwork, partnerships and collaboration
- leadership and management
- attention to safeguarding and the protection of everyone from harm and abuse
- supervision and mentoring
- providing and supporting learning and development.

Ethos

All staff should be given some guidance by those in responsible positions about for what their organisation is striving (its mission and/or vision), what values and ideas guide the thinking behind the care that is provided, and what the aims, objectives and outcomes of all the work and thought should be. This is the ethos that establishes the organisation's culture. Preferably both staff and service users should have a say in how this is developed. Some agencies have set out their ethos very clearly for everyone to read; others seem never to have thought about it, except perhaps in terms of aiming to make ends meet or make a profit. Below, I reproduce statements that encompass all or part of the organisations' ethos. These should be read critically and could be adapted to meet the needs of your own agency. The first statement is from Kibble Education and Care Centre for young people:

> **Kibble** *is committed to its vision of being at the forefront of effective and innovative services for young people at risk. Service integration is one of the key underpinning principles of this vision …*

> **Aspire Scotland**: *Our aim is to re-build confidence and resilience to better prepare a young person for their life ahead.*

> **Bield Housing Association Ltd vision**: *A Scotland where people of all ages are respected, make their own choices and are able to lead independent and fulfilling lives.*

Glasgow City Council Social Work Services:

> **Our Vision:** *Our vision is to provide high quality services that protect children and adults from harm, promote independence and deliver positive outcomes for Glasgow citizens.*
>
> **Our Service Aims:** *In order to achieve our Vision, we have developed six core Service Aims to provide sharper focus for our strategic planning activity:*
>
> - *Focus on the person through an approach committed to personalisation, independence,* ***social inclusion*** *and choice.*
> - *Design and deliver services around the needs of individuals, carers and communities.*
> - *Ensure transparency, equity and fairness in the allocation of finite resources.*
> - *Focus on building a culture of continuous improvement with the aim of driving up the quality of services.*
> - *Ensure services are an integral part of a whole public sector approach to support vulnerable people and promote social well-being.*
> - *Ensure a competent, confident and valued workforce to deliver high quality professional services.*
>
> **Our Values:** *Our Values drive everything we do, every day, for every service user. A set of Values provides a framework for our collective leadership of Social Work Services, by setting out the common norms of behaviour among employees. These common behaviours will, in turn, support the achievement of our Vision. The Values we set out here are also closely aligned with those of the Scottish Social Services Council (SSSC):*
>
> - *Protect the rights and promote the interests of service users and carers.*
> - *Promote the independence and self-determination of service users.*
> - *Respect the rights of service users while protecting them from harming themselves or other people.*
> - *Foster a culture of rights and responsibilities among service users, carers and communities.*

Teamwork, partnership and collaboration

> *... teamwork should never be regarded as an optional extra in this sort of work: it is the heart of the matter ... A worker who initiates and tries to sustain a large amount of individual work without reference to the team is actually undermining the strength of the team ...*
>
> (Ward, 2006)

Teamwork, partnership and collaboration are about everyone working together to achieve the best possible results for service users and carers, both within the organisation and across boundaries with other organisations and disciplines. It is only in this way that needs can adequately be met and aims and objectives implemented. Some things that contribute to effective teamwork, partnership and collaboration are:

- everyone feeling valued
- communication that is transparent, open and inclusive
- flexibility, which includes open-mindedness and a willingness to share and learn from others
- working in partnership to share ideas, work practices and relevant information, while also respecting confidentiality and boundaries
- having opportunities to share in decision making and the allocation of work
- feeling that everyone is pulling together to reach the same place
- having opportunities to discuss how things are going and how improvements could be made
- positive meetings that tackle the needs of service users and staff members
- regular meaningful supervision
- a willingness to address and resolve conflicts through discussion and negotiation within a no-blame culture
- supportive leadership and management.

Leadership and management

> *Leaders are those who in some way embody, articulate, channel and construct the values …*
>
> (Grint, in Martin, 2003, p.24)

> *Conventionalists and rationalists wear a metaphorical hard hat. Leaders must be different and wear sombreros.*
>
> (Bennis, 2001)

Effective leaders have vision and are supportive. They help to create, and also embody, the ethos of their organisation. In today's world they must lead change and also undertake the tasks of management. Appointed leaders, however, are not the only ones who should exercise leadership. Everyone in an organisation is in a position to exercise qualities of leadership to some extent.

From the literature about leadership and management, and from my own experience, there do seem to be a few things that stand out in relation to what makes an effective manager who is also a leader:

- a commitment to the agency, its ethos and care value base
- self-awareness and a lack of personal agendas to be achieved
- a commitment to sharing leadership with team members and to optimising everyone's development
- a willingness to get to know staff and build relationships with them

- a thorough grasp of the strategic issues to be tackled
- a willingness to share decision making with staff and service users, while at the same time establishing authority to make decisions when necessary
- relevant experience that enhances understanding of the jobs that care workers do
- an ability to stay calm under pressure and a willingness to 'persevere' even when the going is very tough
- being sufficiently present to know what is going on, to influence it, to lead when necessary and to provide opportunities for everyone to gain experience in leadership in areas of interest or expertise
- and, as Bennis says, to wear a sombrero!

The quality of leadership can usually be judged by the quality of work done when the leader is not there, as well as when they are. A good leader will have established an ethos that is evident whether they are present or not:

> *... they will have done this through creating a vision, inspiring others through effective communication of the vision, encouraging others to think creatively and question the way things are done and coaching people to be responsible for their own development and effectiveness.*
>
> (Taylor Clarke Partnership, 2003)

Good leaders value their most precious asset, the workers. They will give people the confidence to feel that what they are doing is worthwhile; they will include people in the decision-making process; they will empower people to be as autonomous as possible and trust them to take control of the work for which they are responsible; they will be open about the decisions that are made and how they were reached; and most importantly, they will value workers both as individuals and as team members.

Attention to safeguarding well-being and the protection of everyone from harm and abuse

Rayner *et al.* (2005, p.2) emphasise the catastrophic and lasting damage that can result from **unfairness, neglect, unpredictability, madness or cruelty**. Organisations providing a social, health and/or care service and all of the people involved with those organisations have a responsibility to support, protect and safeguard the well-being of individuals and to protect them from harm and abuse. In this respect organisations must have safeguarding and protection policies and procedures in place, and training and development for staff in relation to these that is robust, enables staff to know about harm and abuse, their roles and responsibilities, and to know to whom they should refer if they are aware that individuals are being insufficiently protected or if they know about harm or abuse taking place, whether within the workplace or outside of it. This is especially the case with all children and young people and with adults who fall within protection legislation.

As a care worker you need to be able to recognise signs of abuse and to report these to the named person in your organisation, usually initially your manager, or if you are not satisfied with their response to a more senior manager or designated member of staff. If you continue to be dissatisfied with the response from your organisation and feel that individuals continue to be at risk you can report directly to the Care Inspectorate.

There are five categories of abuse to look out for: physical abuse, emotional abuse, sexual abuse, financial abuse, and neglect.

- **Physical abuse** means causing physical harm and may involve hitting, shaking, poisoning, throwing, scalding, burning, suffocating or drowning. Physical abuse may also be caused when a carer feigns symptoms of or deliberately causes ill health to an individual they are looking after.
- **Emotional abuse** is persistent emotional neglect or ill treatment that has a long-term and on-going emotional impact on the individual and their emotional development. It includes conveying to the person that they are unloved, worthless or inadequate, or only valued when they are being successful or meeting the needs of another person. It may instil fear or avoidance and is a source of emotional pain. There is some degree of emotional abuse in all of the other kinds of abuse, but emotional abuse sometimes occurs without other kinds of abuse being present.
- **Sexual abuse** occurs when a person is involved unwillingly in any activity for the sexual gratification of another person, or in the case of a child or adult protected by adult protection legislation, whether they have consented or not. This abuse refers to both penetrative and non-penetrative acts, and may involve non-contact activities such as watching sexual activities or images of sexual activity, indecent images, using sexually inappropriate language or encouraging individuals to behave in sexually inappropriate ways.
- **Financial abuse** is the deliberate withholding, stealing or misusing of an individual's finances without their consent. It can involve stealing cash, stealing from a person's bank account or other account using their account details, not giving the person enough of their own money to meet their needs, forcing the individual to take out loans on behalf of another person, not paying bills when you have been requested to do so, and a whole host of other possible forms. It is often also associated with emotional abuse.

CASE STUDY

Fred

Fred had suffered from dementia for many years. Eventually he needed support to remain at home and was allocated a care worker, June, to assist with his daily needs, ensure that he got up in the morning and had meals and his medication. June was aware that Fred was becoming more forgetful about money and less aware of how much he had. She asked him to lend her some money for medical treatment for her young son, whom she said had a disability and needed urgent treatment not available on the NHS to help him to walk. This was all untrue but Fred had grown fond of June, who was very attentive to him. He lent her £5000 from his savings. June found this too easy. She had soon worked her way through all of Fred's savings and then she started to get him to take out credit cards on the strength of the value of his house so that she could 'borrow' more money from him. Fred started to get a lot of bills he didn't understand. Fortunately he told a neighbour who, with his permission, took the bills to the Citizen's Advice Bureau (CAB). A concerned CAB worker uncovered the criminal financial abuse and referred the matter to the police. June was suspended from her job pending the investigation.

- **Neglect** is the persistent failure to meet an individual's basic physical and/or psychological needs, which is likely to result in serious impairment to health and/or development. It may involve failing to provide enough food, warmth, adequate shelter, clothing or medical care. In the case of a child it may result in a diagnosis of 'non-organic failure to thrive', where the child has failed to reach the growth and development milestones appropriate to his or her age for no other explicable reason. Neglect can result in death and very young children and very old people are particularly susceptible.

The table below illustrates the signs for each of the categories of abuse, except financial abuse, which is often associated with emotional abuse and neglect. When considering the possibility of abuse it is important to remember that the signs listed below may have other causes, such as genuine accidents or physical or psychiatric illness or conditions.

Table 6.6 Alerting signs of abuse

Physical abuse	Sexual abuse	Emotional abuse	Neglect
Unexplained injury Improbable excuses Refusal to discuss Untreated injury Excessive physical punishment Fear of returning home Arms and legs covered in hot weather Avoidance of swimming, physical exercise, etc. Running away Frequent attendance at A&E departments	Lack of trust Fear of particular adults, medical examinations, bathrooms, closed doors Social isolation Sleep disturbance Running away Reluctance to participate in physical activity or change clothes for activities Low self-esteem Drug, alcohol or solvent abuse Display of sexual knowledge in a child beyond their years Inappropriate affection Recurring urinary infections, vaginal infections, sexually transmitted infections Soiling or wetting Self-mutilation or suicide attempts	Low self-esteem Self-deprecation Sudden speech disorder Significant decline in concentration Socioemotional immaturity Neurotic behaviour Self-mutilation Compulsive stealing Extremes of passivity or aggression Running away Indiscriminate friendliness	Poor hygiene Malnutrition and untreated medical concerns Inadequate supervision Hunger Significant lack of growth Weight loss Hair loss Poor skin or muscle tone Circulation disorders

To inform yourself more fully about safeguarding and protecting people from harm and abuse you should refer to your own relevant organisation or local authority policies and procedures and/or some of the recommended guidance and reports listed at the end of this chapter. These include inter-agency child protection procedures, adult protection procedures and reports on failures to safeguard and protect individuals from harm and abuse.

Supervision and mentoring

Supervision is very often overlooked because managers may make the excuse that there is not enough time for it. It is seen as an optional extra 'if there's time for it'. But time must be made for it. It is a vital element in maintaining quality and is included in the National Care Standards (2002), which specify that:

> *You can be assured that staff and volunteers are properly supervised and appraised and have access to advice and support.*

Even when the care service is understaffed and overworked, supervision is a vital component of care. Indeed, it is probably *more* important in this situation, since workers will require more support and may encounter non-routine incidents that they need to discuss. Thompson (2002) identifies the tasks of supervision as follows:

- monitoring work tasks and workload
- supporting staff through difficulties
- promoting staff development
- acting as a mediator between workers and higher management where necessary
- problem solving
- ensuring adherence to legal and organisational requirements and policies
- promoting team work and collaboration.

While supervision provides opportunities for reflection and discussion about work *within* the organisation, **mentoring** can provide opportunities for work-related reflection, discussion and development with someone *outside* the care service. This has the advantage of not being connected to any line management issues or work relationships that may be hampering progress.

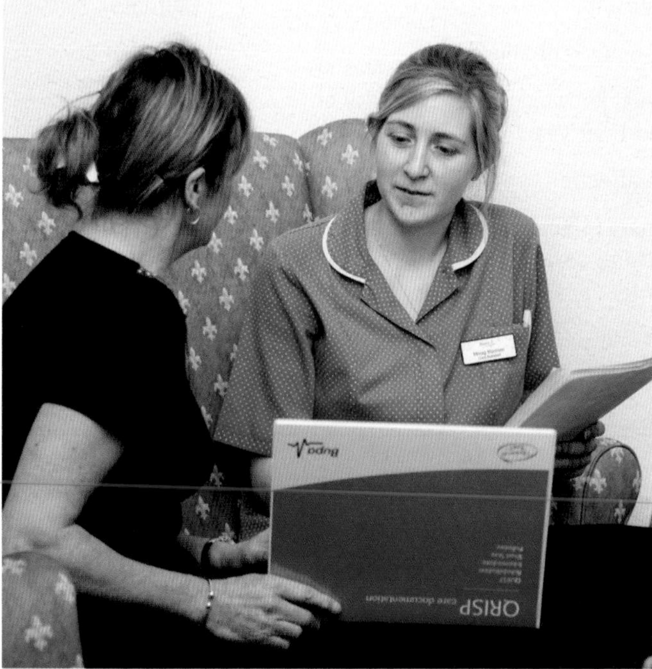

Figure 6.14 Supervision and learning
(Source: Scottish Social Services Council (SSSC))

Supporting learning and development

Organisations that support learning and development, both professional and personal, provide ways in which people can improve their practice and learn to meet changing demands. Rogers (2002) refers to learning as follows:

> *... learning is an activity in which we take part all the time in the course of everyday living. It is the process by which we face, cope with and use our experience. Throughout our lives we face situations in our work, in our domestic settings and in our wider relationships that were not conceived of when we were at school or college, and they all call for new learning.*
>
> *We need to learn to meet the changing demands of our various occupations, whether heart surgeon, historian or handicraft expert. All the tasks we engage in, whether they comprise paid employment or work in the home, call for new knowledge, new skills and new attitudes at various stages.*
>
> (Rogers, 2002, pp.46–7)

Learning takes place in many ways, for example through formal training, supervision, attendance at conferences, reading, and through becoming a reflective practitioner. Developing the habits of reflective practice enables you to think beyond the obvious and to think on your feet, often a requirement of the busy worker. Schon (1983) expressed the view that workers build up a catalogue of experiences and reactions to those experiences, like a repertoire they can draw upon: a central feature of reflective thought. Further information about the reflective process is contained in Chapter 7.

The Continuous Learning Framework (CLF) has been developed to support the learning and development of social service workers in Scotland. It sets out key capabilities that people in social services need in order to be able to do their jobs. It offers a framework for development and describes what employers need to do to support this. For example, a care and education centre has developed a learning log and supervision using the framework. The framework has four key elements: knowledge, skills and values; qualifications and training; personal capabilities; organisational capabilities. You can download the framework and view an accompanying video at: **www.iriss.org.uk**

'Promoting Excellence: A framework for all health and social services staff working with people with dementia, their families and carers' has been developed collaboratively by the SSSC and NHS Education Scotland (SSSC and NES, 2011) as a learning resource for all health and social service workers. One quotation from a person diagnosed with dementia summarises why such a framework is necessary:

> *Once the word dementia comes into a conversation, people more or less dismiss you. They think you have no views, no thoughts of your own; you can't speak for yourself, you can't do things for yourself and you have a very very difficult job persuading these people to listen to you, to take you seriously, and to get help of any manner or kind because they're very dismissive. All of a sudden you become useless. This is not the case.*
>
> (SSSC and NES, 2011, p.11)

Promoting Excellence provides a tool to help you identify your learning needs and plan appropriate learning activities. It outlines the knowledge and skills you will need at various levels to reach identified outcomes. For example at dementia-informed practice level the outcomes are:

- **People with dementia feel empowered and enabled to exercise rights and choice, maintain their identity and to be treated with dignity and equity.**
- **People with dementia have access to a timely and accurate diagnosis of dementia.**
- **People with dementia maintain their best level of physical, mental, social and emotional well-being.**
- **People with dementia feel empowered and enabled to exercise rights and choice, maintain their identity and to be treated with dignity and equity.**

NES has also helped to produce an educational resource, 'Working with People who have a Learning Disability and Complex Needs: The essentials' (NHS Education for Scotland, 2011) which aims to offer workers supporting people with learning disabilities and complex needs opportunities to develop their knowledge, skills and values in ways that maximise the involvement of service users and families and increase health and well-being.

You will find that much of the material contained in Chapter 2 in relation to the value base, anti-discriminatory practice and communication and in Chapter 6 in relation to person-centred and personalised approaches is relevant to utilising these learning tools. Resources to support them are available on the Social Services Knowledge Scotland website: **www.ssks.org.uk**

The physical environment: the building and other material factors

> *Children care about shabby, run-down buildings, lack of privacy in bedrooms, showers, toilets and bathrooms. They recognise them as indicators that they are undervalued and that their needs have been overlooked.*
>
> (Kahan, 1994)

Any care environment offers potential for both good and harm. One of the greatest dangers is that of institutionalisation, discussed in detail in Chapter 1. To recap briefly, **institutionalisation** is a state of being that is characterised by apathy and an inability to make independent choices. It results from a deprivation of choice and an over-insistence on routine and practices that ignore each person's individuality. Planners and care workers should strive to create an environment free from institutionalising forces. In any kind of care environment, even the person's own home, there is inevitably a stress between the needs of individuals for personal choice and individual expression, and the needs of the agency to be well organised, hygienic, efficient and cost effective. Care workers are responsible for maximising the former (as well as giving attention to the latter), for looking at the care environment in which they work and ensuring that it is not only predominantly keeping the needs of service users paramount but also creating and using the environment in partnership and collaboration with them. The physical environment plays a part in this.

The National Health Service and Community Care Act 1990, which is still a key influence on the way care is planned and provided, talks about providing homely settings in the community for those who are unable to live in their own homes, and maintaining people in their own homes so far as this is possible. A homely setting is somewhere that 'feels like home'. Among the things that count here are care workers who are concerned about what the place looks like and feels like, and who care about consulting the people who are spending time in this environment.

Some other things that can enhance the physical environment include:

- participation of service users in decisions about the environment
- a warm, welcoming entrance area (and warm, welcoming staff)
- attractive, well-framed pictures on the walls of corridors and rooms, chosen by service users and perhaps contributed by service users, relatives or local artists
- grounds, gardens and allotments which optimise the choices of service users
- photographs, both informal and formal, of service users and staff
- items of furniture and other belongings brought by service users
- facilities such as a tea room or shop, chosen, designed and/or run by service users for the benefit of themselves, their relatives, friends and sometimes also the general public
- pets
- a cupboard full of items that can be used in reminiscence sessions: old photographs, clothes, household items, etc.

And additionally, in a children's centre:

- murals painted by the children and staff in the main lounge/play room
- a play area free from the need to be careful with the furniture, and with enough space for some physical activity
- a cosy, private room where children can have some peace and quiet and can take family members and other visitors
- enough computers, books and play equipment for all children to be able to participate in creative activity
- sturdy, challenging play equipment in the grounds.

Food, clothing, and comforts and luxuries to enhance well-being, are also important aspects of the physical environment. Enabling service users to choose the meals they eat and to participate whenever possible in their preparation, to have such luxuries as pleasant-smelling toiletries that they have selected, and the opportunity to live in a place that not only looks good but also feels good, all contribute to a positive physical environment.

The community environment: external links

Since they are closely integrated into all the aspects of the care environment approach, the importance of family/friendship ties and links with the wider community should be emphasised. There will be service users who may need protection from some of the negative aspects of these links or a great deal of support in maintaining them, and there are links with the wider community that could be seen as intrusive and invasive. This whole issue, then, should be approached with care and thought, and it should not be assumed that the promotion of such links is always necessarily a good thing. There is, however, a great deal of evidence that suggests care environments that fail to promote links with family and community networks can become isolated, institutionalised and more likely to result in settings in which service users are neglected or abused. For example, the Waterhouse Report (2000) into the wide-scale abuse that took place in residential homes in Wales reported systematic abuse, a climate of violence and a culture of secrecy that existed for more than two decades. These abuses took place in settings that received few outside visitors and were not integrated or included in local communities.

CARE IN PRACTICE

Community links and opportunities

As a conclusion I mention emphasis on seeing care settings as part of the community and as community resources, and on universal services available to everyone, presenting service users with a wider range of opportunities to enhance their lives. One building, previously used only as an adult resource centre, now also houses a community nursery, a drop-in coffee shop, a crèche, and resource workers who can provide a wide range of support. It has developed links with the local community college, which some service users attend and which also uses the centre for some outreach courses, including an English course for people for whom English is not their first language. Service users from the resource centre often gain work placements in the nursery and a local garden centre, and boundaries among the various services have become very flexible. The development of such centres seems to be one way forward in breaking down barriers, though such provision must be carefully planned to take account of service users' needs. Personalisation, person-centred practice, an outcomes focus, the integration of services and the opportunity to use direct payments from self-directed support present opportunities to think in new ways about how to meet the needs of service users and about their optimum participation in decisions and choices.

Evaluation: monitoring and review

The final link in the care planning and helping process is to evaluate all of the work that has been done. This involves looking at both the process and the outcomes. It should be achieved on an on-going monitoring basis, and at regular, scheduled intervals, for example every six months, usually through a review meeting. The aim of evaluation is to determine whether the plan is being implemented properly, how far needs and outcomes are being met, and whether the plan is still appropriate or if it needs to be changed in light of the person's changed needs or circumstances. Evaluation can also be used to improve practice in the future, help others to improve their practice, justify the use of any resources that were used, and to identify any unexpected or unplanned outcomes.

The evaluation should not be the task of one person, since it needs to be as objective as possible and include the views of those who participated. In care practice, as with all other aspects of the helping process, evaluation should focus on the service user and be done with the service user at the centre of the process. The service user, relevant family members and friends, care staff and professionals across a multi-disciplinary spectrum are among those who can play a part in the review process. Participants should be prepared, with a review of their own work and role, in order that a comprehensive picture of all aspects of the helping process can be achieved. Keep in mind essential concepts from the value base and from human development and behaviour, from personalisation and self-directed support, and from person-centred and outcomes approaches. If the process of assessment, planning and action has been shared, the processes of monitoring and evaluation are both enhanced and streamlined.

SUMMARY

This chapter has introduced you to a model of care practice based on assessment, planning, implementation and evaluation. The importance of thorough, clear assessment has been emphasised as a way of developing outcomes to be included in the care plan. Need was considered from several perspectives, including a return to Maslow's hierarchy and SPECCS (social, physical, emotional, cognitive, cultural and spiritual) and an examination of the PROCCCESS model. Two models of care planning – the exchange model and the person-centred model – were considered. Implementation/action was discussed in relation to working with strengths and using environments in person-centred, personalised and self-directed ways, with service users having optimum choice and control while also being safeguarded from harm and abuse. The importance of monitoring and evaluation and of building these into the helping process was emphasised.

Suggested reading

Books and documents

McCormack, J. (2007) *Recovery and Strengths-based Practice.* **SRN Discussion Paper Series. Report No. 6. Glasgow: Scottish Recovery Network.**
This discussion paper clearly sets out a strengths-based approach with useful examples.

Ritchie, P., Sanderson, H., Kilbane, J. and Routledge, M. (2003) *People, Plans and Practicalities.* **Edinburgh: SHS Ltd.**
Explores the practical application of person-centred planning using lots of interesting examples.

Ward, A. (2006) *Working in Group Care.* **Birmingham: BASW/Policy Press.**
This is an excellent book that looks at work in group care, the service user's stay and the worker's shift.

Websites and media

GIRFEC www.scotland.gov.uk/gettingitright – an overview video of Getting it Right for Every Child.

Health and Safety Executive www.hse.gov.uk – provides useful guidance in relation to risk. The document 'Sensible risk assessment in care settings' is especially helpful, available from: www.hse.gov.uk/healthservices/sensible-risk-assessment-care-settings.htm

Helen Sanderson Associates www.helensandersonassociates.co.uk – one of my favourite websites, loaded with information about person-centred thinking and planning, developing outcomes and working towards them. There are comprehensive articles and some brilliant video discussions, and every care worker, student and educator should gain a great deal from accessing all the available information.

Nutshell Communications www.nutshellcomms.co.uk – Gill Phillips of Nutshell Communications has invented a board game called 'Whose shoes?®', which provides thought-provoking scenarios to enable groups of people (workers, service users, volunteers, family members; everyone) to share good practice and challenge attitudes and assumptions in a non-threatening way. Unfortunately it costs quite a bit of money, but your organisation may think it's worth it.

Social Care Institute for Excellence www.scie.org.uk – some excellent guidance in relation to many aspects of positive care practice, though you do need to be aware that any legislation and policy mentioned applies to England and Wales rather than Scotland. There is information and case studies about, for example, person-centred and strengths-based approaches and personalisation. 'Personalisation: a rough guide' is clearly written and can be accessed at: www.scie.org.uk/publications/guides/guide47/files/guide47.pdf

Providing for need: useful organisations and websites

Age Scotland – www.ageuk.org.uk/scotland

Alzheimer Scotland – www.alzscot.org

Care Information Scotland – www.careinfoscotland.co.uk/home.aspx

Care Inspectorate – www.careinspectorate.com

Citizens Advice Scotland – www.cas.org.uk

Duke of Edinburgh's Award Scotland – www.dofe.org/en/content/cms/takepart/notice-boards/scotland

Department for Work and Pensions – www.gov.uk/government/organisations/department-for-work-pensions

National Health Service Scotland – www.show.scot.nhs.uk/index.aspx

Scottish Care – www.scottishcare.org

Social Services Knowledge Scotland – www.ssks.org.uk

Who Cares Scotland – www.whocaresscotland.org

Safeguarding and protection from harm and abuse

Edinburgh, Lothians and Borders Executive Group (2012) *Inter-agency Child Protection Procedures.* **Edinburgh: ELBEG Public Protection Office**.

Glasgow City Council (2014) *Adult Protection Procedures.* **Glasgow: GCC.**

Laming, W. (2003) *The Victoria Climbié Inquiry Report.* **London: The Stationery Office.** Also online at: http://webarchive.nationalarchives.gov.uk/20130401151715/http://www.education.gov.uk/publications/eOrderingDownload/CM-5730PDF.pdf

This report points to missed opportunities to save the life of Victoria Climbié, who was 8 years old when she died.

Social Work Inspectorate (2004) *Report of the Inspection of Scottish Borders Council Social Work Services for People Affected by Learning Disabilities.* **Edinburgh: SWIS.**

Another account of missed opportunities to protect and safeguard people.

Learning and development

Scottish Social Services Council and Institute for Research and Innovation in Social Services (2008) *The Framework for Continuous Learning in Social Services.* **Dundee: SSSC.**

Known as the CLF, this framework is a valuable learning tool for all care workers and can be used to provide useful benchmarks for supervision.

Scottish Social Services Council and NHS Education for Scotland (2011) *Promoting Excellence: a framework for all health and social services staff working with people with dementia, their families and carers.* **Edinburgh: Scottish Government.**

A learning tool that supports the delivery and aspirations of Scotland's Dementia Strategy 2010.

NHS Education for Scotland (2011) *Working with People who have a Learning Disability and Complex Needs: The essentials.* **Edinburgh: NHS Education for Scotland (NES).**

This educational resource aims to offer workers supporting people with learning disabilities and complex needs opportunities to develop their knowledge, skills and values in ways that maximise the involvement of service users and families and increase health and well-being.

CHAPTER 7
Integration and course assessment

> *The best way to find yourself is to lose yourself in the service of others.*
>
> (Mahatma Gandhi, 1869–1948)

Introduction

Whenever you undertake a course that provides you with a qualification there is inevitably accompanying assessment. This may seem to detract from the enjoyment of the course but it is in fact a positive way of consolidating your learning, of investigating supporting and interesting information, and of demonstrating to yourself and others that you have reached the required standard. For Higher and National 5 Care and many other courses your assessment necessitates the preparation of a project. The skills, knowledge and understanding you use will require the integration of your learning, a reflective approach and application to practical situations. You will investigate the needs of individuals requiring care and the services that meet these needs. SQA (the Scottish Qualifications Authority) will provide you with a choice of topics, but whatever the topic you choose you will be expected to demonstrate skills, knowledge and understanding in several areas, including:

- needs
- care services
- psychological theories
- sociological theories
- positive care practice.

This chapter aims to provide you with useful information to help you to integrate and consolidate your learning and to tackle your project. It doesn't provide a prescriptive pro-forma, since your project requires your own original thinking and planning skills, but it does try to give some useful ways of approaching your project as well as some case studies, including 'A tale of two families' referred to at various points in the book, to help you to consolidate your learning, and also examples that provide opportunities for you to apply your thinking. While this chapter focuses on Higher and National 5 Care, much of the material presented is also of relevance to National 4 Care, as well as HNC Social Care, HNC Health Care and other care qualifications.

By the end of this chapter you should be able to:

- ★ integrate your thinking about the various topics covered in the book
- ★ think reflectively
- ★ prepare for and plan your project
- ★ apply your learning to practical situations
- ★ identify the main messages of the book.

Integration

Integration means combining things to make a whole. The many subjects of this book are all part of a holistic approach to positive care practice. It is possible to see integration in relation to many of the ideas, concepts and theories that are explained at different points in the book. For example, need, socialisation and discrimination have connections in different parts of the book and can be viewed from sociological, psychological and care practice perspectives. In order to illustrate integration, ideas are presented below in the style of answers to Frequently Asked Questions (FAQs) often found on websites: a quick way of distilling essential information about a topic.

How do I relate the concept of need to various parts of the course?

When you looked at needs in Chapter 6 you had already gained some knowledge of what needs are from the preceding chapters.

- All individuals have unique needs shaped by their genetic inheritance and the experiences they have had (nature and nurture in Chapter 2). If they were born, for example, with an impairment such as deafness, they may need help to optimise their communication skills, and they may need special input during the socialisation and educational process, but they can be independent in all other ways. Thus they may have particular communication needs (Chapter 2).
- The concept of attachment (Chapter 3) indicates particular needs for people where attachment is lacking, or potentially lacking, so that the negative impact that can result from a lack of attachment can be allayed. The most important aspect of attachment is the need for love and belongingness, with accompanying consequences on an individual's development and life chances if at an early stage in life these needs can't be supplied because of parental or carer inability, or abuse or neglect.
- From a psychological perspective (Chapter 4) you can look at need in relation to theories you can use to understand individual development and behaviour. For example, Erikson's lifespan theory indicates that where emotional needs are met in infancy the outcome is autonomy; where they are not met the outcome is shame and doubt. For older people, where their emotional needs have been met in one way or another during their lifetime they can reach a stage of integrity, with the alternative being despair. Maslow's hierarchy of needs (Chapter 4) provides you with a theory

about need and the ways in which some needs, for example food and shelter, have to be met before other needs can be pursued.

- It is impossible to look at need without also examining social influences (Chapter 5). Poverty and discrimination, for example, can influence whether and how particular needs are met or not met.

All of this content can be placed in the context of models of need such as Maslow's hierarchy (Chapter 4) and the PROCCCESS model (Chapter 6), which encourage you to take a wide-ranging perspective in considering physical, relationship, organisational, communication, cognitive, cultural, emotional, social and spiritual needs. You can also look at need in terms of service provision, including the personalisation and self-directed support agenda, availability of resources and the way care is delivered, as well as the kind of service and workers' values, knowledge, skills and understanding. You can begin to sort out your ideas about need by making a concept map such as the one illustrated below. Concept maps are helpful too when deciding on the structure of your project as a whole.

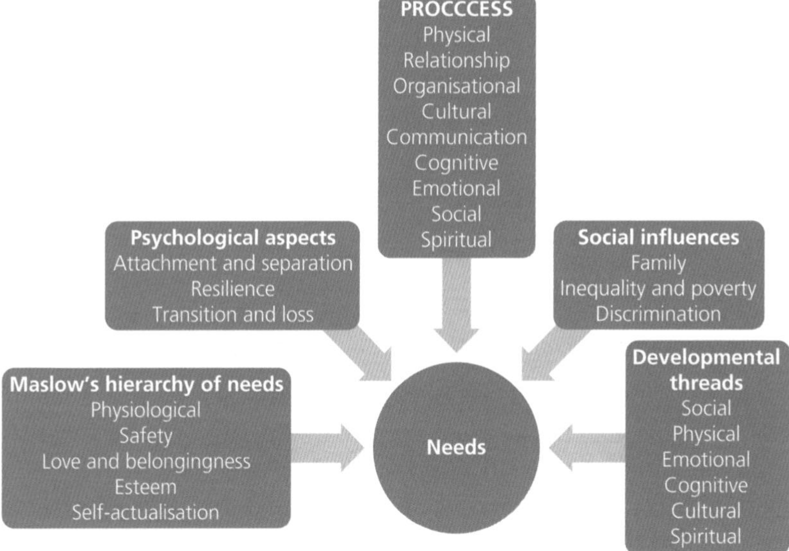

Figure 7.1 Concept map: needs (in reality this would be handwritten and very untidy, with more layers to it as thoughts come into your head)

Activity *Concept maps*

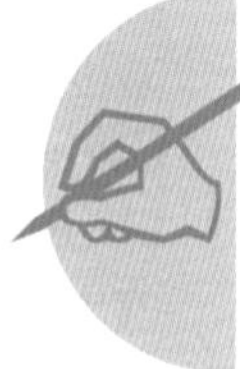

Choose another concept, such as socialisation or discrimination, and draw a concept map to illustrate how it links to different aspects of the book.

What about values and principles? How do they help me to integrate my thinking?

Values and principles are the most important aspect of this book. Without a sound value base care practice is meaningless. You can have all the psychological and sociological skills and knowledge in the world but people cannot benefit from them unless they are applied within a sound ethical framework. Values and principles permeate every aspect of practice and should be second nature to everyone practising as a care worker. There are never occasions when it is okay to show disrespect, or to deny someone their human rights. When you are undertaking assessment, developing outcomes, preparing a care plan with a service user and putting all of this into action, the value base is a vital component. The value base is integral to all of the practice models presented, to GIRFEC (Getting it Right for Every Child), to personalisation and self-directed support, to a person-centred approach and inclusion. Not only are the negatives of institutionalisation avoided through the application of a positive value base, but it paves the way for imaginative, progressive practice and for your accountability as a care worker. Accountability requires the application of all values and principles and refers to accepting your responsibility to meet relevant standards. You are accountable to service users and carers, to your employer, and to your profession, for providing the best possible service. Accountability is thus also an integrating concept and is stated in the *Code of Practice for Social Service Workers* as follows:

> *As a social service worker, you must be accountable for the quality of your work and take responsibility for maintaining and improving your knowledge and skills.*
>
> (SSSC, 2014b)

Activity *Values and principles*

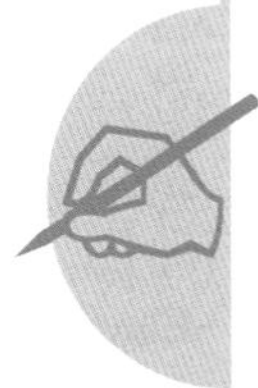

On a piece of card small enough to carry around, write out the principles from the National Care Standards on one side and the six practice codes from the *Code of Practice for Social Service Workers* on the other. Keep this with you and refer back to it when you are preparing your project.

There are separate chapters about psychology and sociology. How can I use them in an integrated way?

Psychology and sociology provide tools to help you understand people and the social groups and institutions within which they live their lives. It could be said that the starting point for psychology is a focus on the individual, and the starting point for sociology is a focus on society. Society is of course made up of individuals, though the focus in sociology is upon people in the plural, acting together in various groups and institutions. Both disciplines provide insight into how individuals cope with their lives and point to areas where they may need support. The psychological emphasis is upon understanding individuals but much of psychology, and especially areas covered in this book, relates to people in their relationships with and inter-dependencies on others. Concepts such as attachment and resilience are about people's need for emotional input in their lives through relationships with parents, carers and others. The sociological emphasis is on how people are inter-dependent as groups in the family, culture, education, and the institutions in which they participate. It looks at social influences and indicates areas where a change in social circumstance can affect individual development, behaviour and life chances. There are some aspects of theory that seem relevant to both disciplines. For example, the nature/nurture debate may be about what affects individual development and behaviour, but it requires sociological understanding of social and cultural influences.

When you look at theory, there is a distinction in sociology between macro- and micro-sociological theories. Macro theories focus very much on society as the subject and starting point, but micro theories are much more concerned with how ideas about society are an interaction between the individual and their interpretations of social concepts. Symbolic interactionism emphasises the influence individuals have on their social reality; it views individuals as constantly influencing and creating reality through the use of symbols and their meanings. This focus on both the individual and society is almost psychological in its interpretation, but is sociological in terms of maintaining a focus on social reality. Similarly, in psychology there are parts of the discipline that focus very much on the human brain and how this affects such areas as cognitive development (this is known as cognitive psychology), and parts of psychology that focus very much on individuals in their social relationships (social psychology). The theories of Erik Erikson and Carl Rogers look at people in their relationships with others and how there is a whole host of influences on behaviour and development. While the focus remains on the individual, society in the form of relationships and institutions plays an important part. Even at the extremely scientific end of the psychology spectrum, neuroscience indicates that brain structure that affects cognitive development is influenced by attachment in early life.

The point about all this is that not only is there a huge middle ground between psychology and sociology where it is quite difficult to differentiate which is which, but also that both are necessary for an understanding of human development and life chances. This understanding in turn provides a framework for the assessment of need and the areas where intervention may be effective. It also takes some of the emphasis away from the individual as the sole focus of attention, towards seeing that social influences very often play an enormous part in development and behaviour and can be part of both the problem and the solution.

Thinking reflectively

> *We reflect in order to learn or we learn as a result of reflecting.*
>
> (Moon, quoted in Crawford and Walker, 2014)

As well as encouraging you to consider your work in an integrated and holistic way, this chapter re-emphasises the importance of thinking reflectively. Reflective practice is an essential skill, providing opportunities to examine and improve your practice. It provides an approach that can enable you to examine complexity, look at your assumptions, and be more responsive and creative in your work. Reflection involves **thinking** about your practice, **learning** from what you have thought about, and then **making use** of what you have learnt. Genuinely reflective thoughts often reveal areas for further development as well as strengths. Figure 7.2 shows a useful framework for thinking reflectively, provided by SSSC (Scottish Social Services Council) on its Workforce Solutions website.

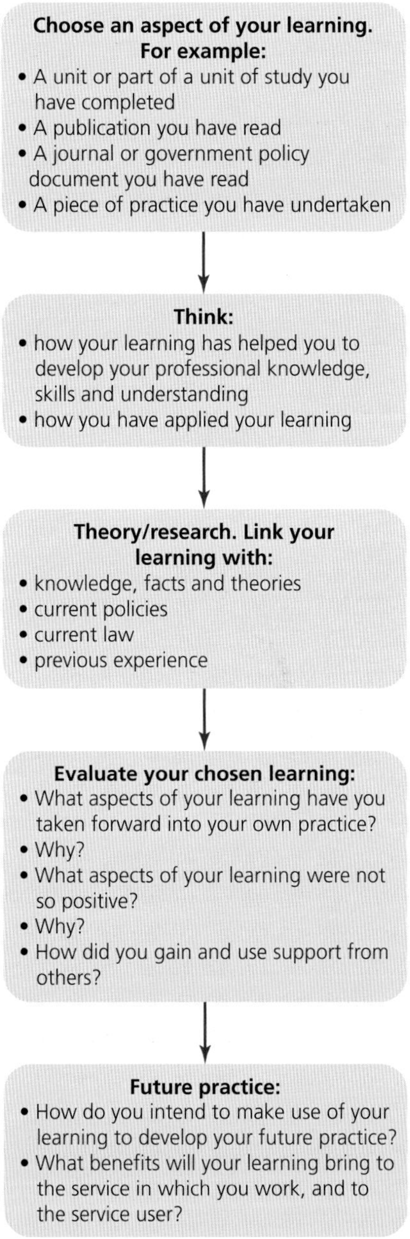

Choose an aspect of your learning. For example:
- A unit or part of a unit of study you have completed
- A publication you have read
- A journal or government policy document you have read
- A piece of practice you have undertaken

↓

Think:
- how your learning has helped you to develop your professional knowledge, skills and understanding
- how you have applied your learning

↓

Theory/research. Link your learning with:
- knowledge, facts and theories
- current policies
- current law
- previous experience

↓

Evaluate your chosen learning:
- What aspects of your learning have you taken forward into your own practice?
- Why?
- What aspects of your learning were not so positive?
- Why?
- How did you gain and use support from others?

↓

Future practice:
- How do you intend to make use of your learning to develop your future practice?
- What benefits will your learning bring to the service in which you work, and to the service user?

Figure 7.2 Thinking reflectively (Source: produced by Frances Barbour and reproduced with permission of SSSC)

Example of a reflective account

A student support worker in a residential care home for older people writes below about her work with Annie, a recently admitted resident. She assists Annie with day-to-day tasks and is concerned about her withdrawn behaviour and occasional outbursts of temper. She is determined that she will do her best to make her residence in the home as positive as it can be.

REFLECTIVE ACCOUNT

Choose a piece of learning

I have chosen to reflect on my learning during the first three weeks I worked with Annie. I wanted to try to understand why she was so unhappy and I wanted to contribute to a care plan with her, in collaboration with the staff, that would give her a positive experience in the home, emphasise her strengths and optimise her well-being.

Think

When I thought about how I could help Annie towards a positive care plan, I considered what I already knew and whether there were areas where I might need a bit more knowledge or some new skills to be able to help her. From my care course I already knew that communicating and developing a trusting relationship with Annie were important foundations for moving forward. To achieve these I set aside time every morning when I was on placement to have a chat with her and walk with her down the corridor to lunch. I also found that assisting with the practical task of dressing, which Annie was finding difficult, gave us a chance for a bit more chat. I used humour, acceptance and quite a lot of patience to go at Annie's rather slow pace, and Annie responded to this one-to-one attention. It was when she got with the other residents that she seemed to withdraw, but she did show a spark of humour in response to a good-natured approach. In college I took the opportunity to look for books and articles that might be of use in expanding my knowledge about older people. I also wanted to improve my knowledge and skills in assessment and care planning. I discussed Annie with my placement supervisor in a supervision session and this enabled me to make a plan for my own development as well as to assist with a plan for helping Annie. The main areas I needed to develop were:

- understanding the impact on Annie of admission to the home
- developing a care plan
- conditions common in older people in residential care, e.g. dementia.

Theory/research

I'll focus this discussion on care planning since this is where I needed to develop most. The theory I found most helpful was person-centred thinking and planning. My placement supervisor suggested a really good book called *People, Plans and Possibilities*, and also a website with lots of examples and video discussions (**www.helensandersonassociates.co.uk**). I also got a book, *Where Memories Go* by Sally Magnusson, after hearing about it on the radio, to enable me to understand a bit more about dementia. These made me realise how important it is to work with a person to develop *their* care plan, that it's not the worker's plan but that person's; also that a care plan isn't just about getting practical things done but can let the person dream about what things they would like in their life and what their strengths are. It also made me realise what a huge impact dementia can have on the individual's ability to participate, but that it's still really important to include them as much as possible.

Sally Magnusson's book emphasised how important music can be for people with dementia. It turned out that Annie had only the beginning stages of dementia and that there were lots of things she was interested in. There were also lots of things she was really worried about and was really missing. She loved flowers and didn't have any in her room or any plants to look after. She also missed having a dog as she'd always had one until her last one, Mandy, had died; she missed her husband even though he had died many years earlier; she missed her house and she missed having the good health she'd always had before. On the positive side she knew and cared a lot about flowers, dogs, and having a full life. So when we made a plan about what we were going to do we included outcomes about how we could best deal with the difficulties and build on the strengths. These outcomes included Annie feeling better about her life through having flowers in her room and plants to look after and animals in her life, and enabling Annie to feel more at home. I asked her about what music she liked and it turned out she enjoyed a good singalong to old songs and film tracks.

In the remaining three weeks of my placement I assisted with putting Annie's plan into action. It wasn't possible for us to achieve everything but we had a plan: we would choose some plants for her room, we would communicate with her niece to see if there were any more belongings she could bring from her house, we would make sure that Annie was around when we had a weekly visit from a large and friendly dog, and we would ensure that she had a medical assessment to determine how to deal with her health issues. A musician visited the home once a month and I made sure Annie knew which day that was on. It was only a start but just that one piece of learning about person-centred planning had provided a launch pad.

Other theory that I drew on related to my reading about dementia and illnesses of old age, and about transition and loss, which explained some of Annie's difficulties with the change in her circumstances.

Evaluate

I was able to take forward my learning about person-centred thinking and planning into my work with Annie. I felt that I was being encouraged by some staff to see care from a very practical point of view, of having tasks to perform and getting them done. Person-centred planning uses communication skills and valuing people's dignity and strengths, while also pushing your thinking beyond the everyday practical tasks of a caring job. My placement supervisor was a great help in pointing me in the direction of good reading material in books and online, as well as enabling me to make suggestions in a supportive environment.

Future practice

In my future work I will now feel more confident to work with people to develop their care plans in a person-centred way. This has huge benefits for service users as they feel more valued and listened to. Often improvements can be made in their lives that require only quite small changes, but these can have a big impact on how they feel about being in a home.

References

Magnusson, S. (2014) *Where Memories Go: Why dementia changes everything.* London: Hodder and Stoughton.

Sanderson, H., Kennedy, J., Ritchie, P. and Goodwin, G. (1997) *People, Plans and Possibilities.* Edinburgh: SHS.

www.helensandersonassociates.co.uk

Preparing for and planning your project

Higher Care and National 5 Care are assessed through the presentation of a project. SQA (Scottish Qualifications Authority) presents a brief or a choice of briefs for this project. SQA has produced documents at both Higher and National 5 levels to provide 'Care project general assessment information'. This section refers to information provided in the document produced for Higher, as well as supplementing this with additional guidance. In your project you are expected to investigate the needs of people requiring care and the services that meet these needs. You will be assessed on the skills, knowledge and understanding specified for the project, which are:

- applying detailed knowledge and understanding of needs and care services
- applying detailed knowledge and understanding of human development and behaviour and psychological theories
- using sociological theories to demonstrate knowledge and understanding of the ways in which social influences can impact on individuals
- investigating detailed features of positive care practice
- researching, investigating, analysing, evaluating and presenting information.

Getting started

Imagine that you have a brief that asks you to:

> *Speculate about what might influence decisions about the help that may be needed by either a child or an older person with a physical disability.*

How do you go about tackling this brief? When you first get your project brief, writing your project probably seems a rather daunting prospect. You may panic a bit, or a lot; you may start to write things down in a rather unstructured way as they come into your head. This isn't a bad thing and you should keep any notes you write at this stage in a log of your progress. In fact, this is the best time to start keeping a log of your whole project, recording all the work you do, any problems or difficulties you encounter, the parts that go well, all the actions you take and conversations you have. This gives useful information for all stages of the project and is helpful to refer back to when you come to write your conclusions and evaluate your work.

Very early in the process of preparing your project you need to think about the project structure. It is a good idea, first of all, to take the project brief to pieces, to identify key words and to circle or underline them.

> *Speculate about what might influence decisions about the help that may be needed by either a child or an older person with a physical disability.*

This gives you the key words and phrases:

- what might influence decisions
- the help that may be needed
- child or older person
- physical disability.

Now that you have the key words and phrases, look at the list of areas that your project has to cover:

- Explain three needs of one or more people requiring care in relation to your brief.
- Analyse two aspects of human development in relation to your brief.
- Evaluate the relevance of three psychological theories in relation to your brief.
- Analyse three social influences in relation to your brief.
- Use three sociological theories to explain points in relation to your brief.
- Evaluate features of positive care practice within three care services in relation to your brief.
- Provide a conclusion about the question posed in your brief.
- Present at least five appropriate pieces of referenced information from a variety of sources.

You don't necessarily have to tackle your project in the above order and you may integrate discussion of some aspects of it. You may find it useful to make a table so that you can see the project brief alongside the project requirement, as illustrated in Table 7.1.

Table 7.1 Project brief and project requirements

Project brief	Project requirements
Speculate about **what might influence decisions** about **the help that may be needed** by a **child** or an **older person** with a **physical disability**	Explain **three needs** Analyse **two aspects of human development** Evaluate the relevance of **three psychological theories** Analyse **three social influences** Use **three sociological theories** to explain points Evaluate features of **positive care practice** within **three care services** Provide a **conclusion** Present at least **five appropriate pieces of referenced information** from a variety of sources

Planning

Once you have sorted out in your mind the component parts of the project brief and the project requirements, you should make a plan about how you will tackle the requirements. If you are going to refer to specific individuals in your project you must ensure that you maintain confidentiality, changing names so that the person or people can't be identified, and respecting people's boundaries and dignity at all times.

The plan should include the ways in which you propose to do and present things. You need to set out the order in which you intend to present your information, the theories, aspects and influences you are likely to consider, and a plan of how you are going to get the information you need. This may include speaking to people, researching sources on the internet and in books and journals in the library, and thinking reflectively about your experiences and research. You may find it useful to make concept maps at this stage. You should be keeping notes of all this in your project log, along with notes of any discussions you have with your course assessor.

Responding to the project brief

You are now ready to carry out your investigation. This involves researching, investigating, analysing, evaluating, explaining, using, providing and presenting information. It is useful to consider carefully what these terms mean.

- **Researching** refers to actively finding out relevant information, which may include research findings.
- **Investigating** is similar to researching and refers to making a systematic search for detailed information.
- **Analysing** refers to looking at a topic critically and in depth.
- **Evaluating** means making an appraisal of ideas or theories or of what you have presented.
- **Explaining** refers to giving details about how or why something is as it is.

- **Using** indicates applying or drawing on a theory or information, often for a particular purpose.
- **Providing** means that you must make something available.
- **Presenting** information is how you put down all the information you have accumulated.

When you do this it is a good idea to use the checklist below.

Project checklist

- Have I done enough research and investigation?
- Have I met the project brief?
- Have I covered all the required aspects?
- Have I met the requirements to explain or analyse or use or evaluate in enough depth?
- Is what I have written relevant and to the point, without trying to include everything I know, whether it is relevant or not?
- Is the content accurate as far as possible?
- Does the project read well; is it logical and easy to follow?
- Have I sufficiently demonstrated relevant values, knowledge, skills and understanding?
- Have I provided relevant examples?
- Have I included conclusions and evaluation?
- Have I remembered to include sources of information and correct referencing?

Providing references

At the end of your project you are asked to present at least **five appropriate pieces of referenced information** from a variety of sources. It is important when you present your referenced information that you do this is in an acceptable way, understood throughout the academic and publishing world. One way of presenting references is the 'Harvard system', which is set out in Appendix 3. This provides accepted ways to set out book, journal, online and media references. If you can begin to do this in your current qualifications it will stand you in good stead if you go on to pursue further learning. You should at this point read Appendix 3 and write down your references in this format as you work on your project. Try not to leave this task until the end because it does take time. If you try to complete all of your references the night before hand-in day you could be up very late indeed.

The MacDonald and Ahmed families in 2015

At various points in the book Activity sections have referred you to the MacDonald and Ahmed families in Chapter 7 and Appendix 1. The relevant case studies in 2015 are below, with earlier versions from 2007 and 1999 given in Appendix 1. These are written to help you consolidate and apply your learning, and are followed by further Activity questions. It should be noted that the accounts of the families and the agencies described are entirely fictional, except for Barnardo's, The Open University, Stonewall Scotland and the Welcoming Association, though these are discussed in terms of fictional characters.

CASE STUDY

A tale of two families

The MacDonalds

Senga MacDonald, aged 52, has recently taken up a post as manager of The Birches, a privately run residential home for older adults, where she is promoting personalisation, focusing on person-centred approaches. She continues to work hard, and as depute at Queen's View (where she worked previously) she gained her SVQ4 in Social Services and Healthcare and SVQ4 in Leadership and Management for Care Services (LMCS). She has tried to set a good example to her children and her staff, both throughout her studies and through trying to lead a healthy lifestyle. She doesn't always succeed in the latter but at least she tries. She gave up smoking many years ago and isn't even tempted to start again. Her continuing efforts to lose weight have been modestly successful. She still wouldn't consider leaving Edinburgh, where she was born and brought up, and where she has a good circle of friends in the neighbourhood and through her interests in dressmaking, dancing and more recently walking. Since her divorce thirteen years ago she has remained single but has a male friend with whom she socialises occasionally. She says this is enough after her difficult marriage and a few awkward encounters with people she met online.

Joe MacDonald. It is now eighteen years since Joe, now 58, and Senga separated. Joe's subsequent relationship with his girlfriend, Vicky, didn't survive his addiction to alcohol. Alcohol and cigarettes have led to some quite severe health problems, including emphysema and the beginnings of dementia. He lives alone in rented accommodation but has a close relationship with one of the other residents of his tenement block, with whom he drinks. Sadly he rarely sees Callum, his son with Vicky, and his visits are supervised by the Social Work Department. Two of his children with Senga, Andy and Joey, keep in touch with him, but find him to be very demanding. When he sees them he always has jobs for them to do and is more often than not under the influence of alcohol. Joe has tried several times to turn over a new leaf but his lifelong addictions to drink and cigarettes, and what he calls his other 'disappointments', have meant that he was never able to sustain long-term employment or relationships. He no longer works and is dependent on benefits for his income. He has a support worker, Bob, at Riverside, the local support network for people with addiction problems. The network has an internet café at which Joe rather unreliably helps out occasionally on a voluntary basis. One of the aims of the network is to provide routes back to employment through a personalised approach to working with individuals.

Callum MacDonald, aged 10, was born one month prematurely to Vicky and Joe and got off to a rather slow start. He quickly made up for lost time. He has a lovely out-going nature and is very active. He can be quite a challenge sometimes because of the sheer amount of physical energy he has. In spite of difficulties in his family life he has made good progress at school and is popular with his classmates. His mother has done her best to give him as happy and loving a childhood as possible. She met her current partner, Doug, four years ago. Doug had been widowed and left with two daughters, Melissa and Mandy, now aged 12 and 14. They love Callum very much but also tease him and find him a nuisance sometimes when they want time to themselves. Vicky and Doug have decided not to have more children but to bring up their families together. Callum attends Glenbank Primary School and loves his current teacher, Mr Ambler, who also runs the local boys soccer club. He has also formed a close relationship with Doug, who is an easy-going and affectionate character. Doug takes Callum as he finds him and enjoys fatherhood and taking him swimming, something the whole family does every Saturday.

Andy MacDonald, 32, was a rebellious teenager but in his twenties pursued his love of music alongside a career in painting and decorating. He and an old school friend have a successful business as painters and decorators, supporting local builders and businesses, and doing occasional work for friends and family. His relationship with Emma didn't develop, especially when he admitted to himself that he wasn't that interested in girls at all. He had tried, but his preference was for his workmate, **Ed**. They say they have one of the few gay painting-and-decorating businesses in Scotland. They are renowned for the high standard of their work. They are saving to buy their own house but currently live in a rented flat on the south side of Edinburgh. Once they have saved enough they would also like to get married now that the Marriage and Civil Partnerships (Scotland) Act 2014 enables them to do so. Andy and Ed have just signed up to do an 'authentic role models' programme with Stonewall Scotland which aims to enable LGBT people to be confident enough to be role models for other LGBT people in the community.

Linda MacDonald's development continues to be greatly affected by cerebral palsy but she has retained her independent spirit. With her family's support she moved to and continues to live in supported accommodation at Newton Road run by a voluntary organisation. She is now 29 and after success in her college courses, especially in numeracy, she assists two days a week in the college canteen on the till, and also continues to attend courses that interest her, such as art and household skills. She manages her own tenancy, directing her support through option 2 of the self-directed support programme. She continues to need support from care workers, but she negotiates this according to what she needs. The flexible, personalised support plan she developed with her social worker has enabled her to maximise her independence and choice and to fulfil some of her wishes and dreams, especially taking an annual holiday to somewhere different and exciting. Her family is in close touch with her and they exchange visits frequently.

Joey MacDonald is now 21. From being interested in everything and doing well at school, he went through a really difficult patch in his teenage years, staying out as late as possible, sometimes skipping school and losing interest in his lifelong love of sport. This was made worse by the fact that his male befriender, Fred, who had been a stabilising influence since Joey was 5 years old, unfortunately became ill and no longer able to support Joey. Joey seemed to get into a spiral of doing worse and worse, and his mother, Senga, just didn't know what to do about him. She collaborated with the school to discuss what support could be provided for Joey after a period of a month's absence. At a discussion that included Joey, his teacher, his mother, a psychologist and a social worker, it was agreed that Joey would attend a group, part of a programme for young people run by the Social Work Department, which included each young person having a **keyworker** for ongoing support. The programme utilised ideas from GIRFEC and adopted a child-centred approach in line with the personalisation agenda. The group met every Thursday for activities and discussion and also went away for adventure weekends and outings. Those who were interested could take The Duke of Edinburgh's Award with the local youth partnership, which was open to all young people in the area. This was eventually the saving factor for Joey. He loved all the activities and after a year left the social work-run programme to continue with his Duke of Edinburgh's Award with the local youth partnership, eventually reaching Gold standard.

Senga's mother, Jean Davies, is now 80 and experiencing a few health problems. She retains a positive outlook on life, however, and continues with as many activities as she can. She reluctantly gave up volunteering at the local hospital tea shop at the age of 78 but continues to attend the Doward, a centre for older people, twice a week. This has a very full programme of opportunities, ranging from a dance class to an international development group. She says it is definitely not a care centre, but it provides useful support for older people and plays a big part in health promotion.

Maureen McKay, Senga's sister, now aged 64, has continued to be supported by admissions to the McTavish Unit, a small supportive unit of the local psychiatric hospital. She still experiences bouts of depression and has times when she just can't cope with life anymore. She is supported for short stays in hospital, and for attendance at the McTavish Day Unit when she is living at home. She was offered the opportunity to manage her own care budget under the provisions of the Social Care (Self-directed Support) (Scotland) Act 2013 but chose not to do so. Becoming a grandmother has given her a new interest in life but she is unable to provide a great deal of practical support.

Alistair McKay, Maureen's son, now 30, is not finding life as an adult as difficult as he found life as a child in care. Following a year working on building sites he decided he may prefer to be an engineer. He began taking night courses in engineering and now has a job with a local engineering company that is sponsoring him to take his HNC. This could open up all sorts of future opportunities, including the possibility of degree-level study. He says he'll have to carry on working, though, since he now has family responsibilities. He is determined to prove that he can be a success in spite of his difficulties earlier in life. He lives in rented accommodation with his partner, Sarah. Sarah was also in care as a child and the two of them are resolved that their son, Billy, aged 2, and any subsequent children they have will have a stable and happy home. Alistair often sees his mother, his Aunt Senga and cousins. Senga provides babysitting support whenever she can.

Billy McKay, aged 2, is a very energetic little boy with an outgoing personality. He doesn't sit still very much, always wanting to do things: run, play in the park, go to playgroup, go to soft play where there is a huge climbing frame and slides. He loves lots of attention and doesn't take kindly to being on his own. He has attended The Five Trees Nursery three days a week since he was 18 months old and is, most of the time, enjoying the experience. It took him a few weeks to feel settled and confident there and he had some quite spectacular temper tantrums when his parents first left him for the day. He now goes in happily, joins his friends and is often quite reluctant to leave in the evening. He loves the time he spends with his Aunt Senga but is lacking in support from his grandparents, who have problems of their own.

Sarah Liddel, 30, is Billy's mum and Alistair McKay's partner. She, Alistair and Billy share a rented, modern flat near the town centre, where Sarah works in a pharmacy in one of the large city centre stores. She works three days a week, choosing to be at home with Billy the rest of the time. She is enjoying being a mother, though she did find the transition to parenthood quite a difficult one. Although she has some support from Alistair's Aunt Senga and some of her friends, there is no one who can really offer her the family support she would have liked. Alistair and Sarah share parenting and household tasks but they both agree they could have benefited from parents who could have helped them out more with babysitting and just being there for them. Sarah's parents separated when she was very young. When her mother neglected her and her teachers became concerned for her welfare, she was fostered by a caring and loving couple with whom she maintains contact. They are in their seventies now and many miles away, but they do make a point of celebrating birthdays and Christmas with Sarah, Billy and Alistair whenever they can.

The Ahmeds

Aisha Bibi is now 51. The death of her husband, **Hassan Ahmed**, ten years ago was a severe blow to her and initially she needed some help to recover from a prolonged grieving process. And then six years ago her son **Nabeil**, who had experienced severe disability all his life, died at the age of 21. Aisha once again attended counselling at the Westgate Clinic. She has now completed her postgraduate social work degree with The Open University and admits this was much harder than she anticipated. It was a real struggle getting assignments in on time and taking exams after such a long break away from studying, especially after losing Nabeil. She continued with her full-time post with Barnardo's, a voluntary sector child care organisation, during her degree course, and was able to have one of her course placements with the organisation. Her other placement was with a local authority Social Work Department, where she is currently employed. She maintains good relationships with her son Tanveer and family, who were supportive of her decision to work and to take a degree.

Tanveer Ahmed, 31, went to work in the USA last year. He gained his engineering degree from Glasgow University at the age of 23, taking a year out before his third year to work with an engineering company in France. Following his degree he worked for a dynamic environmental engineering company in Stirling before gaining his current post. He is married to Nicola, a physiotherapist. They have two children, a boy, Kian, aged 4 and a girl, Amina, aged 2. Tanveer's mother is very upset about his move so far away, but has always encouraged his independence of thought and action. She says she will be travelling to the USA as often as she can to visit her family there. She was so much looking forward to being a hands-on grandmother to Tanveer's children but is philosophical enough to see their move in a positive as well as a personally negative light.

Nabeil Ahmed would have been 27 if he had lived. He had twelve operations in his short life and sadly died at the age of 21. His heart condition, which resulted in a stroke and severe physical disability, was always a concern. His family included him in family life and he was supported at 8 Newton Road, a house with four other people with disabilities, next door to and run by the same voluntary organisation that accommodates Linda MacDonald. He attended the local FE college, taking courses in art, and was halfway through his first year at art school when he experienced heart failure while out in his wheelchair and died. He was a very popular figure at the art school and had great potential as an artist, painting large-scale, semi-abstract landscapes, producing wonderful collages and demonstrating an amazing sense of colour.

Hassan's older brother, **Afzal Ahmed** (63), and his wife, **Sira Kahn** (55), continue to live in their large owner-occupied tenement flat in the same area as Aisha Bibi, their sister-in-law. They still run their successful general store in which many family members help out. Their sons **Faisal and Asif** are now married with children and have left home, though they continue to live in various parts of the city.

Nadia Ahmed, 26, is Afzal and Sira's daughter. She lives with her parents and is working at The Birches care home as a support worker, taking SVQ3 after successfully completing her Care Higher and three other Highers at college. She is also volunteering as a befriender with the local Welcoming Association, which helps migrants, refugees and people from indigenous Scottish ethnic minority communities who are new to the area.

Fariha Bashir, Afzal Ahmed's mother is now 88, has developed Alzheimer's disease and has become impossible to manage at home. She is a resident of Queen's View, where she used to go for respite care and to the day centre two days a week.

Faisal Ahmed, 31, married **Farah Riaz**, 29, seven years ago and they have a son, **Kamran**, and a daughter, **Alisha**. Faisal works as an accountant and partner with the firm established by his uncle Hassan and his uncle's friend Abshir Yusuf. Farah also trained as an accountant and hopes to return to her career when their children are both at school. Meanwhile, she helps out with the family businesses whenever she can.

Kamran Ahmed, 6, has had quite a few problems since he was born. His mother was concerned about his development very early in his life and she has become more concerned over the past two years when it has been apparent that he spends long periods of time in a world of his own, does not respond emotionally to other people and has terrible outbursts of temper. His physical development in terms of mobility has been fine but he has been somewhat behind the expected level of cognitive development for each stage so far and his speech is still very limited. He is attending a mainstream school but his teacher reports that he is not keeping up with the other children in the class, even with additional help from a classroom assistant. His doctor and health visitor suspect that he may be on the autistic spectrum and he has been referred to a specialist clinic for tests to see what may be causing his difficulties.

Alisha Ahmed, 6 months, is a lively and responsive baby. She smiles at everyone and appears to be very interested in her environment, watching mobiles go round, looking at pictures and playing with small toys, especially a noisy rattle and her toy duck. She holds her head up with confidence and is almost sitting independently. Her parents prop her up with cushions and she loves them to do rhymes and play peek-a-boo. She laughs if they recite 'This little piggy' or 'Pat-a-cake, pat-a-cake', anticipating their actions and waiting for the next line. She loves to spend time with members of her large extended family.

In the above study there are several individuals who require care, on both an informal basis by family members and a formal basis in care or support situations. These family members are: **Linda MacDonald**, who has cerebral palsy and lives at 6 Newton Road; Senga's sister **Maureen**, who has admissions to the McTavish Unit and also attends the day unit there; Afzal's mother **Fariha**, who lives at Queen's View; Senga's mother **Jean**, who attends the Doward; **Joey MacDonald**, who attends the local youth partnership after also being supported by a social work-run activities scheme.

Three family members work in Social Work Services: **Senga MacDonald** is the manager of The Birches home for older adults; **Aisha Bibi** works as a social worker for the local authority Social Work Department; **Nadia Ahmed** is a support worker at The Birches.

Each of the social services the families use or work in in 2015 is described below.

- **The Birches** is a small privately-run home for older adults owned by a businessman, Gerald Smith, who also owns a petrol station and other properties in the city. He sees The Birches very much as a business to make a profit. His wife is a friend of Senga MacDonald and when he heard that Senga had now gained her management qualifications he asked her if she was interested in applying for the post of manager at The Birches. She applied and was offered the post and is now installed as manager in the home. When Senga began working in the home she recognised that there was a legacy of low morale. She was determined to turn things around and have a happy, well-run home applying the principles of personalisation with a person-centred approach to working with the service users, and a well-qualified staff. She quickly realised that there was a real shortage of money and other resources and that getting money out of Gerald was going to be an uphill struggle. She determined on a strategy of convincing Gerald that the better the quality of personalised care he could offer, the better would be the reputation of the home and the more likely he would be to be able to fill all spaces all year round. Gerald has the advantage of being not entirely ruthless and also of respecting Senga and her views. Senga has in a short space of time established a learning and training strategy for staff, improved morale through her participatory leadership, and introduced some activities and improvements in person-centred care planning.

- **Queen's View** home and day care centre for older adults is a privately-run home owned by a large company that runs homes for older people throughout the UK. It has 40 residential beds, 10 respite beds and a day centre for 20 people, open five days a week. All residents have a single room with a bathroom. A new nursing care wing was added to the home in 2004 that expanded the total number of beds from 30 to 50 and added a beautiful new day unit. Meals both in the residential and day units are eaten communally at set times. A lot of resources are put into enabling staff to gain qualifications. Currently 60 per cent of staff members hold a relevant qualification, such as a Nursing diploma or Social Services and Healthcare SVQ; a further 20 per cent of staff are working towards qualifications. All staff take an induction course when they are first employed, which introduces them to the organisation and to the values and principles of care practice and a person-centred approach. Following recommendations from the Care Inspectorate, a choice of opportunities including activities and outings has been established using ideas contributed by service users. There is a cheerful, participatory and collaborative atmosphere in the home and people seem to enjoy being there.
- **The Five Trees Nursery** is a local authority nursery and provides places for children aged 0–5. It opens at 8 a.m. and closes at 6 p.m., enabling parents to bring their children early if they have jobs to go to. Hours are allocated on the basis of child and family need. Nursery staff work closely with parents and other service providers to ensure that nursery provision optimises the child's development in all areas: social, physical, emotional, cognitive, cultural and spiritual, in line with the child-centred principles of GIRFEC. The nursery itself is bright and modern with plenty of space and equipment to enable children to learn and play. Staff are well-trained, with all staff members either possessing or working towards relevant qualifications.
- **6 and 8 Newton Road** are two large adjoining houses in a residential area of Edinburgh. They were purchased several years ago by a large voluntary organisation to accommodate eight people with disability in their own tenancies. Each tenant has a small flat and each house has a communal lounge and communal cooking and eating facilities. Care staff support the tenants according to their individual needs. A lot of emphasis is placed on enabling tenants to have a fulfilling life and to gain the skills for leading as independent a life as possible. All of the tenants are currently taking part in their own re-assessments in line with the personalisation agenda and

self-directed support. All staff either have or are working towards the qualifications relevant for their job.

- **Buddies** is the local authority befriending service for young people. It was set up as a preventative service to help young people with issues that could potentially lead to problems in the future. For example, Joey's lack of a father figure combined with his hyperactivity led to a referral and the allocation of Fred to his family. This enabled Joey to have a male role model and to pursue his interest in football. It also provided the family with reliable and consistent support over a period of years. When Fred became too ill to support Joey he gained support initially from the Social Work Department and later through the local youth partnership.
- **Circle Youth Partnership** is run mostly by volunteers but has a paid full-time youth worker, Pat, who co-ordinates the partnership. The partnership is funded by a consortium of local third sector organisations and the local authority social care and health department, in line with the Scottish Government's integration strategy. The partnership is open to all local young people. There is a small converted shop premises where there is a drop-in internet café, and a number of available activities, including football, basketball, guitar tuition and the opportunity to take The Duke of Edinburgh's Award at various levels. Activities vary according to who the volunteers are. Young people are encouraged to volunteer as well as participate in the centre. The partnership also offers information and advice useful to young people, with visiting professionals who come in to talk about health issues, continuing education and careers.
- **The Doward** is a community centre established 25 years ago by a local businessman to meet the needs of anyone over the age of 55 living in the local area. It is a place with a positive atmosphere, run by a committee made up mainly of people who themselves use the service. It has registered charity status and is a non-profit-making third sector organisation run for the local community by the local community. There is a full programme of opportunities available five days a week, ranging from dance and exercise classes, arts, gardening and discussion groups to formal learning for certificates in computing and other subjects. The centre is staffed by a mixture of volunteers and employees, all of whom have a culture of learning to be the best that they can be. The manager of the centre promotes her belief in everyone's abilities and that the centre should not only be fun but should make a contribution to the life of the whole local community.
- **The McTavish Unit** is run as a partnership between the local authority social care and health department and the Health Board to meet the needs of people who experience mental health difficulties. There is a day centre and fifteen individual rooms with bathrooms for short-stay respite care. One main outcome is to enable people to continue to live their lives in the community while providing on-going support and a haven during periods of crisis. Staff come from a variety of backgrounds with varied skills, ranging from social work and social care to nursing and health care. The centre aims to promote a social model of care with emphasis on the dignity of the individual and on meeting needs through a focus on the helping, organisational, physical and community environments. There is a wish to create a safe place for individuals to flourish and deal with the issues that create stress for them within a flexible, person-centred plan established with each individual service

user. The work of the unit is compatible with the Scottish Government's policies on integrated care and a personalised approach.

- The **local authority social care and health department** provides a range of services, including services for older people, family support and care, help for adults, home care, fostering, adoption and looked-after children's services, and young people's services including advice, support and activities. It is currently devoting resources to promoting the Scottish Government's personalisation and integration strategies, including the implementation of the Social Care (Self-directed Support) (Scotland) Act 2013 and the Children and Young People (Scotland) Act 2014, through a programme of staff development.
- **The Duke of Edinburgh's Award** was described in some detail in Chapter 6.
- **Barnardo's** is a large, national, third sector organisation that provides a variety of services in many locations to children and young people in need of support. Until recently Aisha Bibi worked in a support service for children who have been accommodated by the local authority but who are moving on from a care situation, either back to their families, to live with other families or to live in other settings in the community. Often they are also at the stage of leaving school and making decisions about their future. This was demanding work with young people who had often experienced difficult lives and were dealing with complex issues. Barnardo's supports staff to gain the qualifications relevant to their work and works closely with local authority departments and the NHS to provide an integrated, person-centred approach to care. Aisha Bibi was supported to undertake the Open University postgraduate social work qualification by Barnardo's. She now works for the local authority Social Work Department but would like to return to Barnardo's in the future.
- **Riverside** is a third sector network with an internet café run mainly by and for people with addiction problems, though there is also a paid manager, herself a former addict, and two paid support workers, Bob and Alice, seconded from the local authority. It also rents an allotment and sells produce and plants in the café, which is open to the public. It offers supportive conversation with support workers, practical assistance with everyday tasks, support to find accommodation and a place to go to meet people, participate in activities and use the internet. It forms part of an integrated, collaborative and personalised approach to the provision of care.
- **Stonewall Scotland** promotes equality for lesbian, gay, bi-sexual and transgender people in Scotland. Its priorities include tackling hate crime, promoting equality in the workplace, education, marriage, and access to public services.
- **The Open University** is a university that operates through distance learning, with a style of teaching called 'supported open learning'. Aisha Bibi undertook her social work qualification with The Open University. This route to qualification is open only to people who are working in social service agencies and who are supported by their employer.
- The **Welcoming Association** provides a range of services to improve the well-being of migrants, refugees and indigenous Scottish ethnic minority communities. New residents are welcomed to their area and there is a befriending service to assist people to find their way about, accompany them to appointments and provide an introduction to the social life of the area. Free English classes, social and volunteering opportunities are provided.

- **Westgate Clinic** specialises in providing counselling support to people who have experienced difficulties in their lives. A person-centred approach is used, based on Egan's model of helping (see Chapter 2). People are initially encouraged to explore their current situation and difficulties as a way of moving towards new understanding. With new understanding they are supported to identify and take action to move them towards more satisfying and fulfilling lives.

Activity *The MacDonald and Ahmed families in 2015*

- Explain **three needs** of Linda MacDonald.
- Analyse **two aspects of human development** in relation to Nabeil Ahmed at the age of 20.
- Evaluate the relevance of **one psychological theory** in relation to Callum MacDonald.
- Analyse **two social influences** in relation to Tanveer Ahmed and his wife, Nicola.
- Use **one sociological theory** to explain points about the MacDonald and Ahmed families in Scottish society.
- Evaluate features of **positive care practice** within **two care services** described in the case study.
- Evaluate the extent to which the services described meet the Scottish Government's policies on integration and personalisation.
- Practise writing references for at least **two pieces of referenced information** that could help you to understand the circumstances of any member of the MacDonald or Ahmed family.

Main messages

You probably feel that there has been so much to take in after covering so much ground that it is difficult to see the wood for the trees. You may feel that you have just run a marathon through a maze with a lot of obstacles and challenges in it. Or perhaps you feel that you have climbed a mountain and now at last you can see the view from the top, and that view identifies clearly the most important landmarks, just as this section attempts to identify the main landmarks of this book. Before reading on, though, it is a good idea that you try to identify the main messages of this book for yourself in the Activity below.

Activity *Main messages*

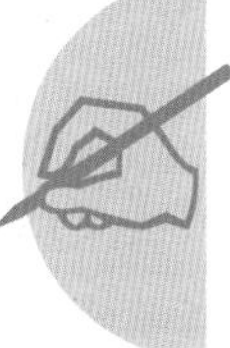

What for you have been the five most important messages of this book?

You may have suggested some of the following, or you may have thought of completely different points.

The main messages of the book are:

- People who use services know more about their needs than you do and should be at the heart of decision making about their own lives.
- Values and principles should underpin all of your practice.
- A focus on outcomes is essential to good assessment, care planning and intervention.
- It is important to implement personalisation and be person-centred in your work, working in partnership with service users, carers and all other relevant people.
- Theories and practice methods are useful tools when working with people.
- Learning is a lifelong process of continually improving your knowledge, skills and understanding.
- Be creative and imaginative; think outside the box and round corners.

And at the end of the book, here is one more story. It is the story of Adrian, who was one of my colleagues and has contributed his experience of illness, recovery and the care he received along the way. I leave you to relate his story to as many aspects of this book as you can.

CASE STUDY

Adrian's story

In the summer of 2010 I collapsed while at home and was rushed to Ninewells Hospital in Dundee, where I had a CT scan that showed I had a brain abscess. A CT scan, also known as a CAT scan, is a specialised X-ray test. It can give quite clear pictures of the inside of the body. In particular, it can give good pictures of soft tissues of the body that do not show on ordinary X-rays.

I required surgery to drain the abscess, and was also treated with antibiotics and steroids. From the white cell cultures taken it was found that there was a streptococcal infection, which had been transferred to my brain via the bloodstream. Prior to the collapse, I had had the symptoms of a summer cold and headaches, and had had a GP appointment, at which I was prescribed antibiotics.

I can't remember anything of the days preceding my collapse, and I have hazy memories of my time in Ninewells Hospital. I was unconscious for about 5 months but family and friends who visited have told me that at times I was communicative and alert, but at other times very sleepy. (Apparently one of the first questions I asked on regaining consciousness was 'Have I missed lunch?'!)

I had problems with raised pressure within my brain following the abscess, but a brain shunt was inserted in December 2010 to relieve the pressure, after which my condition improved. (A brain shunt is a narrow piece of tubing that is inserted into the brain. The shunt tubing relieves pressure on the brain, a condition known as hydrocephalus, by draining the extra fluid in the brain ventricle(s) to a different area of the body where it can be absorbed more quickly.)

I was in the intensive care unit, then the high dependency unit, before being transferred to a surgical ward.

I had many complications at Ninewells, including pneumonia and general organ failure, but once stable I was transferred in February 2011 to Cameron Hospital in Fife for in-patient rehabilitation. In total I spent 6 months in Ninewells and 4 months in Cameron Hospital.

While at Cameron an initial assessment showed I had problems with memory, attention and speed of processing, and also difficulty with planning, organising and carrying out tasks. I had programmes of physiotherapy, psychological support, speech therapy and occupational therapy.

I lost 3 stone (19 kg) in weight while in hospital and also lost a lot of muscle strength. The physiotherapy helped me with walking and balance, as the time in a hospital bed meant that the loss of muscle strength and co-ordination seriously impaired my mobility. The physiotherapy continued for a short time in St Andrews Community Hospital after discharge.

The psychological support addressed how I was feeling about my illness and my readiness to return home. The occupational therapy focused mainly on cooking and other household tasks. The speech therapy was needed because the brain illness had affected my speech.

I was assigned a social worker for a short time from just before discharge, who arranged for carers to come into my home every morning to check I was all right and to do any tasks needed (I live alone). I had the carers for a few weeks until it was felt I did not need them as I was coping with routine jobs in the house. This decision was taken jointly between me, the carers and social worker.

I still have some slight difficulty with speech, balance, processing information and short-term memory. I also have feelings of anxiety, which is not uncommon in cases like this. I also have not regained the levels of physical fitness and stamina I had before my illness.

Before my illness I was fit, active and independent. Going from independence to a state of (at times) complete dependence on others was a shock. When I was in Ninewells, and to some extent Cameron, I relied on nursing and care staff for all of my personal care (feeding, washing, toileting). Moving from independence to dependence then back to independence was a gradual journey that required adjustment on my part to my changed circumstances (and an acceptance that some aspects of my life would never be the same, for example I had to stop working because of the difficulties mentioned above).

Throughout my time in hospital and afterwards, my recollections of the people who cared for me was that they were unfailingly kind and cheerful (even when busy and doing unpleasant tasks such as toileting). When I was able to take decisions about my care and treatment, I was included and my views and needs were taken into account. Often it was an 'information exchange'; the professional and personal opinions were shared to take decisions that were in my best interests. Similarly, the interactions with all staff, from the ward cleaners to the consultants, made me feel that I was valued as an individual.

On a practical level, because there was the possibility that I had had an epileptic seizure, I was not allowed to drive for a year. I live in a rural area with limited public transport, and therefore for that year relied to some extent on friends (and the Royal Voluntary Service) for transport. The support of family and friends was also important; knowing that I had a good network of friends meant a great deal to me.

CONCLUSION

And some kind of help
Is the kind of help
That helping's all about.

And some kind of help
Is the kind of help
We all can do without.

(Shel Silverstein, 1974)

By now it should be possible to distinguish between good, empowering help and poor, patronising 'help'. The above discussion has also attempted to enable you to discover links among many of the threads of this book and the several subjects you have studied. You have had the opportunity to look at what it means to be reflective, to develop your thinking about your project, and to consolidate your learning through reflecting on 'A tale of two families' and on Adrian's story. Your development as a care worker can be carried further through gaining experience of care practice and through additional learning and training. Qualifications such as SVQs, the HNC in Social Care or Health Care, degrees in Social Work or Nursing are all ways to enhance your development. The foundations have been laid. It is now up to you to apply your knowledge, skills, understanding and value base to improve the quality of life of those with whom you work, now and in the future.

Suggested reading

At the end of a course you usually feel like taking a holiday. The suggested reading below should enable you to take your thinking further, while at the same time providing something enjoyable, interesting and reasonably undemanding to read on the beach!

Axline, V.M. (1990) *Dibs in Search of Self.* **London: Penguin.**
The story of one little boy and his journey through childhood up to his mid-teens. Also an insight into psychotherapy.

Beresford, P. (2010) *A Straight Talking Introduction to Being a Mental Health Service User.* **Ross-on-Wye: PCCS Books.**

This book, written by a service user who is also a social worker and professor, takes a closer look at the realities – not all negative – for people with mental health difficulties.

Campbell, K. (2013) *This Is Where I am.* **London: Bloomsbury Circus.**

A witty and engaging book about an asylum seeker and his befriender in Glasgow.

Galbraith, R. (2013) *The Cuckoo's Calling.* **London: Sphere.**

Lots of family dynamics as well as crime and detection. Brilliant.

Magnusson, S. (2014) *Where Memories Go: Why dementia changes everything.* **London: Hodder and Stoughton.**

This is Sally Magnusson's inspiring story about her mother, describing the changes and experiences her mother's dementia brought to the family.

Rowling, J.K. (2012) *The Casual Vacancy.* **London: Sphere.**

There's a social worker and a whole array of interesting characters in this book, including a family situation that leaves a lasting impression.

Small, E. (2013) *Mary Lily Walker: Forgotten visionary of Dundee.* **Dundee: Dundee University Press.**

Written with enthusiasm and meticulous research, a life story of one of Scotland's first social workers.

Yousafzai, M. with Lamb, C. (2014) *I Am Malala: The girl who stood up for education and was shot by the Taliban.* **London: Phoenix.**

Malala Yousafzai was shot by the Taliban, recovered in the UK and was co-recipient of the Nobel Peace Prize in 2014, aged 17. Her story is courageous and amazing.

Appendix 1

Case study: A tale of two families

CASE STUDY

The MacDonald and Ahmed families in 2007

The MacDonalds and the Ahmeds presented here are eight years older than in the original 1999 accounts (see the next section, page 335).

The MacDonald family in 2007

Senga MacDonald and her children live in the same five-apartment semi-detached house in Edinburgh in which they lived in 1999. The house is no longer rented, however, since Senga took the opportunity to purchase the property from the council. She now pays quite a hefty mortgage but feels that it's worth making some long-awaited changes. The area has maintained its air of reasonable respectability in spite of one rather noisy pub, which attracts a mixture of young-loud and older-loud people, and a fair number of young people who hang around in the evening. The adjoining tenement area has acquired an even more diverse population with many new residents from Eastern Europe.

Senga MacDonald, aged 44, works full-time as the depute manager of Queen's View, a privately-run home for older adults. She works hard and in the past five years has acquired the first qualifications of her life, her SVQ3 in Care and a Management certificate. She has tried to set a good example to her children, both throughout her studies and through giving up smoking last year. She hasn't yet lost the weight she hoped to lose. She would never consider leaving Edinburgh, where she was born and brought up, and has a good circle of friends in the neighbourhood and through her interests in dressmaking and dancing. Since her divorce five years ago she has remained single. This isn't altogether to her liking since she does not feel emotionally fulfilled, but she prefers this to living in a difficult relationship.

It is now ten years since **Joe MacDonald**, now 50, and Senga separated. Joe lives in rented accommodation with his 32-year-old girlfriend, Vicky (not the same girlfriend he had in 1999), and their two-year-old son, Callum. Joe has tried several times to turn over a new leaf but his lifelong addiction to drink and cigarettes, combined with what he calls his frequent 'disappointments' in the world of employment, have meant that his good intentions haven't amounted to much. As in 1999, he occasionally has work as a driver for various home-delivery Chinese and Indian restaurants.

Callum MacDonald, aged 2, was born one month prematurely and got off to a rather slow start. He has made up for lost time since then and now walks and runs competently and has a vocabulary of a hundred or so words, making himself understood and learning to imitate animal sounds: moo, neigh, meow. He attends The Five Trees, a local authority nursery, five mornings a week and enjoys the company of other children.

Andy MacDonald, 24, was a rebellious teenager. He left school after gaining, to his surprise, two more Standard Grades to add to the four he had already, in addition to modules in art and music. His ambition to be rich and famous hasn't materialised yet but he is working on his guitar-playing with a group at the FE college he now attends. He's taking courses in painting and decorating with a view to going into business with one of his old school friends. He continues to smoke about ten cigarettes a day. After leaving school he took several jobs, mostly in the building and painting and decorating trades, before deciding to go to college at the age of 23 to qualify in his chosen profession. He has a girlfriend, Emma, but has no thoughts of settling down just yet. He continues to live at home with his mum.

Linda MacDonald's development has been greatly affected by cerebral palsy but she has an independent spirit and with her family's support has moved to supported accommodation at 6 Newton Road, run by a voluntary organisation. She is now 21 and attends courses in basic skills (numeracy, literacy, crafts and household skills) at the local college and has surprised everyone with how well she is managing her tenancy. She is supported by care workers on a shift basis and her social worker has worked with her to develop a person-centred plan, taking account of her needs, wishes and dreams. Her family are in close touch with her and they exchange visits frequently.

Joey MacDonald is now a very lively 13-year-old, interested in everything and doing well at school, especially in sport. He has been encouraged in this by his male befriender, Fred, who has been a stabilising influence since he was 5 years old and has become a good friend of the family. Fred is employed by Buddies, the local authority befriending scheme.

Senga's mother, **Jean**, is now 72 and in good health. She has a very active retirement, seeing friends, volunteering at the local hospital tea shop and attending the Doward, a centre for older people, twice a week. The Doward has a very full programme of activities ranging from an exercise class to craft afternoons. She says it is definitely not a care centre, but it provides useful support for older people and plays a big part in health promotion. Jean's mother Annie died three years ago just after her ninetieth birthday. She had spent many years in a local authority residential home, which unfortunately closed when Annie was 89. She was transferred to a privately-run home and never really settled there, becoming ill shortly after her move.

Senga's sister, **Maureen McKay**, has had several admissions to the McTavish Unit, a small supportive unit of the local psychiatric hospital. She has experienced several bouts of depression and has times when she just can't cope with life anymore. Her family and GP now recognise her symptoms and she is supported for short stays in hospital, and attendance at the McTavish Day Unit when she is living at home.

After a rocky start Maureen's son, **Alistair McKay**, now 22, is not finding life as an adult as difficult as he found life as a child in care. He has recently gained employment and started a Modern Apprenticeship in the building trade. He likes to go drinking with his pals on a Friday night but is adamant about not taking drugs. He often stays with his Aunt Senga and cousins.

The Ahmed family in 2007

The Ahmed family have stayed in their large, comfortable, owner-occupied second-floor tenement.

Hassan Ahmed would have been 53 this year but sadly died of a heart attack two years ago. The accountancy firm that he helped set up continues to flourish. His nephew **Faisal** qualified as an accountant last year and is now working in the business.

Aisha Bibi, Hassan's wife, is now 43. The death of her husband was a severe blow to her and initially she needed some help to recover from a prolonged grieving process. She attended counselling at the Westgate Clinic and was helped to recover from a very difficult time. When she later announced that she had taken a full-time post with Barnardo's, a voluntary sector child care organisation, and intended to take a postgraduate social work degree with The Open University, her family were supportive of her decision.

Tanveer Ahmed, 23, achieved his ambition to take an engineering degree in spite of his visits to McDonald's instead of the library. He left home for Glasgow University at the age of 18 and hopes eventually to go to the USA to work. His mother is very upset about this but at the same time encourages his independence of thought and action.

Nabeil Ahmed, aged 19, has already had twelve operations in his short life. His heart condition, which resulted in a stroke and severe disability, continues to cause concern. His family has always included him in family life. Like many people of 19, he wants his independence. He is supported at 8 Newton Road, a house with four other people with disabilities, next door to and run by the same voluntary organisation that accommodates Linda MacDonald. He attends the local FE college where he is taking courses in art. He would like to go to art school and is working on preparing a portfolio of large collages, which are his speciality.

Hassan's older brother **Afzal** and his wife, **Sira Kahn**, and their children **Faisal**, 23, **Asif**, 20, and **Nadia**, 18, continue to live in their owner-occupied tenement flat in the same area as Aisha, their sister-in-law. They still run their successful general store in which many family members help out. Afzal's mother, **Fariha**, now 80, continues to be a domineering presence and misses her visits from her grandson Tanveer, who is now home only occasionally. She has mild dementia and severe arthritis, which limits her mobility. Twice a year she goes, reluctantly, for a period of respite at Queen's View. She also attends Queen's View day centre two days a week.

In the above study there are several members who require care both on an informal basis by family members and a formal basis in care or support situations. These family members are: **Linda MacDonald**, who has cerebral palsy and lives at 6 Newton Road, next door to **Nabeil Ahmed**; Senga's sister, **Maureen**, who has admissions to the McTavish Unit and also attends the day unit there; Afzal's mother, **Fariha**, who goes to Queen's View for respite care twice a year; Senga's mother, **Jean**, who attends the Doward; **Callum MacDonald**, who attends The Five Trees nursery; **Joey MacDonald**, who has Fred, a befriender from Buddies, the local authority befriending service.

Two family members work in Social Work Services: **Senga MacDonald** is the depute manager of Queen's View home for older adults; **Aisha Bibi** is working for Barnardo's, a large voluntary sector child care organisation, and is training to be a social worker.

Each of the social services that the families work in or use in 2007 is described below.

- **Queen's View** home and day care centre for older adults is a privately-run home with 40 residential beds, 10 respite beds and a day centre for 20 people. It is open five days a week. All residents have a single room with bathroom. A new nursing care wing was added to the home three years ago, expanding the total number of beds from 30 to 50 and adding the beautiful new day unit. Meals in both the residential and day units are eaten communally at set times. In the past five years a lot of resources have been put into enabling staff to gain qualifications. Currently 30 per cent of staff members hold a relevant qualification, such as a Nursing diploma or Health and Social Care SVQ; a further 20 per cent of staff are working towards qualifications. All staff take an induction course when they are first employed, which introduces them to the organisation and to the values and principles of care practice. Following recommendations from the Care Commission, a programme of activities and outings has been established that enhances the quality of life for both residents and day care attendees. There is a cheerful atmosphere in the home and people seem to enjoy living there.
- **The Five Trees Nursery** is a local authority nursery and provides places for children aged 0–5. It opens at 8 a.m. and closes at 6 p.m., enabling parents to bring their children early if they have jobs to go to. Hours are allocated on the basis of child and family need. Nursery staff work closely with parents and other service providers to ensure that nursery provision optimises the child's development in all areas: social, physical, emotional, cognitive, cultural and spiritual. The nursery itself is bright and modern, with plenty of space and equipment to enable children to learn and play. Staff are well trained, with all staff either possessing relevant qualifications or working towards them.
- **6 and 8 Newton Road** are two large adjoining houses in a residential area of Edinburgh. They were purchased several years ago by a large voluntary organisation to accommodate eight people with disability in their own tenancies. Each resident has a small flat and each house has a communal lounge and communal cooking and eating facilities. Care staff work on a rota basis to support the tenants according to their individual needs. A lot of emphasis is placed on enabling tenants to have a fulfilling life and to gain the skills for leading as independent a life as possible. All staff either have or are working towards the qualifications relevant for their job.
- **Buddies** is the local authority befriending service for young people. It was set up as a preventative service to help young people with issues that could potentially lead to problems in the future. For example, Joey's lack of a father figure combined with his hyperactivity led to a referral and the allocation of Fred to his family. This has enabled Joey to have a male role model and to pursue his interest in football. It has also provided the family with reliable and consistent support over a period of years.

- **The Doward** is a community centre established seventeen years ago by a local businessman to meet the needs of anyone over the age of 55 living in the local area. It is a place with a real buzz about it, run by a committee made up mainly of people who use the service themselves. It has registered charity status and is a non-profit-making voluntary organisation run for the local community by the local community. There is a full programme of activities available five days a week, ranging from exercise classes and arts and crafts to formal learning for certificates in computing and other subjects. The centre is staffed by a mixture of volunteers and employees, all of whom have a culture of learning to be the best that they can be. The manager of the centre promotes her belief in everyone's abilities and that the centre should not only be fun but should make a contribution to the life of the whole local community.
- **The McTavish Unit** is run as a partnership between the local authority Social Work Department and the Health Board to meet the needs of people who experience mental health difficulties. There is a day centre and fifteen individual rooms with bathrooms for short-stay residents. The aim is to enable people to continue to live their lives in the community while providing on-going support and a haven during periods of crisis. Staff come from a variety of backgrounds with varied skills, ranging from social work and social care to nursing and health care. The centre aims to promote a social model of care with emphasis on the dignity of the individual and meeting needs through a focus on the environment. There is a wish to create a safe place for individuals to flourish and deal with the issues that create stress for them.
- **Barnardo's** is a large, national voluntary organisation that provides a variety of services in many locations to children and young people in need of support. Aisha Bibi is working in a support service for children who have been accommodated by the local authority but who are moving on from a care situation, either back to their families, to live with other families or to live in other settings in the community. Often they are also at the stage of leaving school and making decisions about their future. This is demanding work with young people who have often experienced difficult lives and may be dealing with complex issues. Barnardo's supports staff to gain the qualifications relevant to the work. Aisha Bibi is receiving support to undertake an Open University postgraduate social work qualification.
- **The Open University** is a university that operates through distance learning, with a style of teaching called 'supported open learning'. Aisha Bibi is working towards her social work qualification with The Open University. This route is open only to people who are working in social service agencies and who are supported by their employer.
- **Westgate Clinic** specialises in providing counselling support to people who have experienced difficulties in their lives. A person-centred approach is used, based on Egan's three-stage model. People are initially encouraged to explore their current situation and difficulties as a way of moving towards new understanding. With new understanding they are supported to identify and take action that will move them towards more satisfying and fulfilling lives.

The MacDonald and Ahmed families in 1999

The following account of the MacDonald and Ahmed families appeared in the first edition of this book. It is reproduced here for comparative purposes.

The MacDonald family in 1999

Senga MacDonald and her children live in a rented five-apartment council house a few miles from the centre of Edinburgh. The area in which they live is one of a large 1950s housing scheme that has gained an air of reasonable respectability, with a mixture of houses and flats that are rented from the local authority, and properties that have been purchased and are now owner-occupied. The scheme borders on tenement land, which stands between it and the city centre. The tenements are a mixture of properties that are privately owned, rented from the council or privately rented, and the population is culturally diverse, with a mixture of religious and ethnic groups. It is here that the Ahmed family lives in a large, owner-occupied second floor tenement. Joe MacDonald, Senga's former husband, also lives in this area. The children of the MacDonald family and the Ahmed family attend the same schools, the families shop at the same shops and their teenage children sometimes hang about on the same streets.

Senga MacDonald, aged 36, works part-time as a care assistant in a home for older adults. She has to work very hard and regrets that she didn't stay on at school or gain any qualifications. She tries to encourage her children with their school work. She has recently been trying to cut down on her smoking (about ten cigarettes a day at the moment) and to lose weight. She was born and brought up in Edinburgh in the area in which her ex-husband, Joe, now lives. She and Joe had three children together: Andy, Linda and Joey.

Joe MacDonald, aged 42, left the family home two years ago and lives in a tenement with his girlfriend, aged 29. He is unemployed but has occasional work as a driver for various home-delivery Chinese and Indian restaurants. He says that he can't see the point of getting qualifications. He enjoys a drink and smokes about twenty cigarettes a day. Joe seems to have lost interest in his children since he and his girlfriend got a flat together, though his son Andy goes to visit him sometimes, especially if he needs money.

Andy MacDonald, aged 16, lives at home with his mum, sister and brother. He is still at school taking some modules after gaining four Standard Grades at general level last year. He would rather have left school but couldn't see much chance of getting a job. He plans to go to the local FE college next year. He'd like to be rich and famous but is having such a struggle with his modules that he thinks there must be an easier way. Although he's very fond of his mum and definitely doesn't want to end up like his dad, he also wants to establish his independence from both of them. His friends at school encourage him to go drinking and clubbing at weekends and sometimes evenings in the week. His mum despairs about this but Andy doesn't seem to take any notice of anything she says. He smokes about ten cigarettes a day, depending on how much money he has.

Linda MacDonald, 13, has cerebral palsy. She has difficulty with speech, has a mild learning disability and is unable to walk. She attends a special school and goes there on the school bus each morning. She is still very dependent on her mum, who has to attend to all of her needs when she is at home. Linda and her family have a social worker who attends her reviews, supports the family when necessary and has arranged respite care for Linda on a rolling basis every six weeks. This provides her mum with a much needed break.

Joey MacDonald is 5, a little clown with a great sense of humour and huge quantities of energy. He loves his toy building games and a toy garage. He is in P1 and loves it. He never seems to stop and Senga finds him quite exhausting, especially if she has had a hard day at work. He has just been allocated a male befriender by the Social Work Department and Senga hopes that this will provide him with a stabilising influence and give her a break sometimes.

Senga's mother, **Jean**, aged 64, lives locally and offers Senga support with the children on an occasional basis, but she works in a shop and doesn't have a lot of spare time or energy. Her second husband (not Senga's father) died two years ago and her 86-year-old mother, Annie, is in a local authority residential home not far away. Jean visits Annie a couple of times a week after work and at least once at the weekend. Annie has severe arthritis, which limits her mobility, and mild dementia.

Senga's sister, **Maureen McKay**, lives in a housing scheme a few miles from the city centre. She has three children and has had a very chequered life, with a partner involved in both drink and drugs. Maureen has spent periods in a homeless unit and has now left her partner for good. Her oldest child, **Alistair**, is looked after by the local authority in a children's unit at 16 Fir Street after committing a series of offences.

The Ahmed family in 1999

Hassan Ahmed, aged 45, is an accountant who qualified when he was in his early thirties. He set up his own practice in partnership with a fellow student. He works very long hours, spending less and less time with his family, but is improving the business – he and his partner have almost doubled the number of clients in the past five years. He has some worrying health complaints and thinks he may have an ulcer, but hasn't got time to go to the doctor. He has gained quite a lot of weight recently. He is very determined that his children get a good start in life and stresses the importance of a sound education.

Aisha Bibi, Hassan's wife, is ten years younger than her husband, a very cheerful person most of the time, but recently she has become very concerned about her husband's health. She works part-time for a voluntary organisation, supervising a sheltered housing complex, and loves her work. She tries to encourage other Asian women to assert their independence but is viewed with some suspicion by many of their husbands and families. She also encourages her children to do well at school and helps them with their homework. Her own family viewed education as the key to success and Aisha attended Edinburgh University where she gained a degree in languages (French and Spanish).

Tanveer Ahmed, aged 15, attends the local secondary school. He is doing well there and is expected to achieve several credits in his Standard Grades and to continue at school to achieve Advanced Highers. He wants to be an engineer but for the time being works one or two evenings a week in his uncle's shop. He is expected also to help with his younger brother at the weekend. Tanveer has a great wish to be accepted by the boys in his class at school, who often tease him about his colour and his younger brother who has a disability. Whenever he gets the chance he lingers after school with a group of boys and goes to McDonald's with them for a laugh, a coffee and a cigarette. He tells his mum he goes to the library.

Nabeil Ahmed, aged 11, was born with a severe heart condition that has necessitated several operations. After one major operation he had a stroke that affects his left side. He has delayed development, has great difficulty with speech and is unable to walk. His doctors think that he may eventually catch up intellectually and may gain some power of speech, though it is unlikely that he will ever walk. He faces the prospect of more heart operations in the future. He attends the same school as Linda MacDonald, though is in a different class. He is well loved and supported by his family, though they took a long time to accept his illness and disability. His mother is especially concerned to ensure he has all the opportunities possible to develop in the same ways as other children. Although the family has been reluctant to request outside help they have approached the Social Work Department to assist with day care for Nabeil during the summer so that Aisha can continue to work.

Hassan's older brother, **Afzal**, Afzal's wife, **Sira**, and their three children, **Faisal**, **Asif** and **Nadia**, live in another apartment in the same area. Hassan and Afzal originally set up in business together to run a shop but Afzal now owns the shop, while Hassan runs his accountancy business. The brothers help one another out and attend the mosque together. Their mother, who speaks very little English, lives with Afzal and his wife. She is very helpful with housework and cooking but is a very domineering woman with rather traditional views. Sira resents her constant presence and her attempts to influence her children's behaviour. Tanveer gets on well with his grandmother, whom he visits most days. She is always giving him little treats and telling him how she expects great things of him. Although this sometimes makes him uncomfortable, they have a good rapport without the stresses that his parents and aunt and uncle experience in her presence.

In the above study there are several members who require care both on an informal basis by family members and on a formal basis in care situations. These family members are: **Linda MacDonald**, who goes for respite care at Ivy Unit; **Alistair McKay**, who is looked after by the local authority children's unit at 16 Fir Street; **Nabeil Ahmed**, who will attend Heron Day Centre during the summer; **Hassan and Afzal's elderly mother**, who is due to go for a week of respite care at Queen's View, a home for older people.

Two family members work as care workers: **Senga MacDonald** works as a care assistant in a home for older adults, and **Aishi Bibi** works for a voluntary organisation, supervising a sheltered housing complex.

Each of the units that the families use or will use is described below.

- **Ivy Unit** is a 12-bed, purpose-built voluntary organisation respite care unit for children with disabilities. Each of the 50 children who attends comes for respite every six weeks (three nights, Friday to Monday, alternating with four nights, Monday to Friday) and also for a one-week summer holiday. There is a good staff ratio and a committed and trained staff team. Staff work well together, have regular meetings to discuss their work and aim to meet the needs of the children who attend through a combination of care and activities.
- **16 Fir Street** is a small children's unit at present accommodating seven children in the age range 12 to 16, who are looked after by the local authority. Most of the children attend local schools, but two of the children, including Alistair McKay, attend a care and education centre as day pupils. Here they are taught in small classes and their usual disruptive behaviour can be 'managed' by a trained and dedicated care and teaching team. There is a high rate of sickness among staff at Fir Street, so this means that often there either aren't enough staff on duty or unfamiliar sessional staff cover for absence. Although the staff want to do a good job, only four out of eight have any kind of qualification at present. The local authority is hoping that all of the others will receive some training in the next couple of years.
- **Heron Day Centre** is run by a voluntary organisation and accommodates ten children with moderate to severe disabilities during the summer months. A mixture of trained staff and untrained temporary staff is employed to work with the children, whose ages range from 3 to 12. They assess the needs of each individual child through meetings with them, their families and other workers, and devise a programme to meet these needs.
- **Queen's View** home for older adults is a private home with 25 residential beds and five respite beds. Everyone has a single room with a bathroom. Meals are eaten communally at set times. Very few of the staff have a formal qualification in care but the unit manager ensures that all staff have induction training in the values and principles of care practice. There is a cheerful atmosphere in the home and people seem to enjoy living there. Some of the more active residents, however, regret the fact that there are not more opportunities for outings and activities.

Appendix 2

Code of Practice for Social Service Workers

This section is reproduced with permission of the Scottish Social Services Council.

Introduction

This document contains agreed codes of practice for social service workers and for employers of social service workers. It describes the standards of conduct and practice within which they should work. This document, which is also reproduced in the Code of Practice for Social Service Workers, is intended to help you understand what the codes are for and what they will mean to you as a social service worker, employer, service user or member of the public.

The Scottish Social Services Council began its work on 1 October 2001, at the same time as the General Social Care Council, the Northern Ireland Social Care Council, and the Care Council for Wales. The Councils have a duty to develop codes of practice and have worked together in developing these codes as part of their contribution to raising standards in social services.

The two codes for workers and employers are presented together in this document because they are complementary and mirror the joint responsibilities of employers and workers in ensuring high standards.

What are the codes?

The Code of Practice for Employers of Social Service Workers sets down the responsibilities of employers in the regulation of social service workers. Again, this is the first time that such standards have been set out at national level.

The code requires that employers adhere to the standards set out in their code, that they support social service workers in meeting their code and take appropriate action when workers do not meet expected standards of conduct.

The Code of Practice for Social Service Workers is a list of statements that describes the standards of professional conduct and practice required of social service workers as they go about their daily work. This is the first time that standards have been set out in this way at national level, although many employers have similar standards in place at local level. The intention is to confirm the standards required in social services and to ensure that workers know what standards of conduct employers, colleagues, service users, carers and the public expect of them.

The codes are intended to reflect existing good practice and it is anticipated that workers and employers will recognise in the codes the shared standards to which they already aspire. The Councils will promote these standards through making the codes widely available.

How will the codes be used?

The codes are a key step in the introduction of a system of regulation for social services in the four countries of the UK. The Councils are responsible for the registration of those working in social services. The register will be a public record that those registered have met the requirements for entry onto the register and have agreed to abide by the standards set out in the Code of Practice for Social Service Workers.

The Councils will take account of the standards set in the Code of Practice for Social Service Workers in considering issues of misconduct and decisions as to whether a registered worker should remain on the register.

What will the codes mean for you?

As a social service **worker** you will have criteria to guide your practice and be clear about what standards of conduct you are expected to meet. You are encouraged to use the codes to examine your own practice and to look for areas in which you can improve.

As a social service **employer** you will know what part you are expected to play in the regulation of the workforce and the support of high quality social services. You are encouraged to review your own standards of practice and policies in the light of the standards set in the code.

As a **user of services or member of the public** the codes will help you understand how a social service worker should behave towards you and how employers should support social service workers to do their jobs well.

Social service workers must:

- protect the rights and promote the interests of service users and carers
- strive to establish and maintain the trust and confidence of service users and carers
- promote the independence of service users, while protecting them as far as possible from danger or harm
- respect the rights of service users while seeking to ensure that their behaviour does not harm themselves or other people
- uphold public trust and confidence in social services
- be accountable for the quality of their work and take responsibility for maintaining and improving their knowledge and skills.

These are each discussed below:

1 As a social service worker, you must protect the rights and promote the interests of service users and carers.

This includes:

1.1 treating each person as an individual.

1.2 respecting and, where appropriate, promoting the individual views and wishes of both service users and carers.

1.3 supporting service users' rights to control their lives and make informed choices about the services they receive.
1.4 respecting and maintaining the dignity and privacy of service users.
1.5 promoting equal opportunities for service users and carers.
1.6 respecting diversity and different cultures and values.

2 As a social service worker, you must strive to establish and maintain the trust and confidence of service users and carers.

This includes:

2.1 being honest and trustworthy.
2.2 communicating in an appropriate, open, accurate and straightforward way.
2.3 respecting confidential information and clearly explaining agency policies about confidentiality to service users and carers.
2.4 being reliable and dependable.
2.5 honouring work commitments, agreements and arrangements and, when it is not possible to do so, explaining why to service users and carers.
2.6 declaring issues that might create conflicts of interest and making sure they do not influence your judgement or practice.
2.7 adhering to policies and procedures about accepting gifts and money from service users and carers.

3 As a social service worker, you must promote the independence of service users, while protecting them as far as possible from danger or harm.

This includes:

3.1 promoting the independence of service users and assisting them to understand and exercise their rights.
3.2 using established processes and procedures to challenge and report dangerous, abusive, discriminatory or exploitative behaviour and practice.
3.3 following practice and procedures designed to keep you and other people safe from violent and abusive behaviour at work.
3.4 bringing to the attention of your employer, or the appropriate authority, resource or operational difficulties that might get in the way of the delivery of safe care.
3.5 informing your employer, or an appropriate authority, where the practice of colleagues may be unsafe or adversely affecting standards of care.
3.6 complying with employers' health and safety policies, including those relating to substance abuse.
3.7 helping service users and carers to make complaints, taking complaints seriously and responding to them or passing them to the appropriate person.
3.8 recognising and using responsibly the power that comes from your work with service users and carers.

4 As a social service worker, you must respect the rights of service users while seeking to ensure that their behaviour does not harm themselves or other people.

This includes:

4.1 recognising that service users have the right to take risks and helping them to identify and manage potential and actual risks to themselves and others.

4.2 following risk assessment policies and procedures to assess whether the behaviour of service users presents a risk of harm to themselves or others.

4.3 taking necessary steps to minimise the risks of service users doing actual or potential harm to themselves or other people.

4.4 ensuring that relevant colleagues and agencies are informed about the outcomes and implications of risk assessments.

5 As a social service worker, you must uphold public trust and confidence in social services.

In particular, you must **not**:

5.1 abuse, neglect or harm service users, carers or colleagues.

5.2 exploit service users, carers or colleagues in any way.

5.3 abuse the trust of service users and carers or the access you have to personal information about them or to their property, home or workplace.

5.4 form inappropriate personal relationships with service users.

5.5 discriminate unlawfully or unjustifiably against service users, carers or colleagues.

5.6 condone any unlawful or unjustifiable discrimination by service users, carers or colleagues.

5.7 put yourself or other people at unnecessary risk.

5.8 behave in a way, either at work or outside of work, that would call into question your suitability to work in social services.

6 As a social service worker, you must be accountable for the quality of your work and take responsibility for maintaining and improving your knowledge and skills.

This includes:

6.1 meeting relevant standards of practice and working in a lawful, safe and effective way.

6.2 maintaining clear and accurate records as required by procedures established for your work.

6.3 informing your employer, or the appropriate authority, about any personal difficulties that might affect your ability to do your job competently and safely.

6.4 seeking assistance from your employer, or the appropriate authority, if you do not feel able or adequately prepared to carry out any aspect of your work, or if you are not sure how to proceed in a work matter.

6.5 working openly and co-operatively with colleagues and treating them with respect.

6.6 recognising that you remain responsible for the work that you have delegated to other workers.

6.7 recognising and respecting the roles and expertise of workers from other agencies and working in partnership with them.

6.8 undertaking relevant training to maintain and improve your knowledge and skills, and contributing to the learning and development of others.

Scottish Social Services Council

Compass House
Discovery Quay
11 Riverside Drive
Dundee DD1 4NY

Telephone: 01382 207101
Fax: 01382 207215
Email: **enquiries@sssc.uk.com**
www.sssc.uk.com

In the same document there is also a Code of Practice for Employers. This is available at: **www.sssc.uk.com**

Note that the Codes of Practice for Social Service Workers and Employers are being reviewed. For the most recent version you should go to the SSSC website referred to above.

Appendix 3

Guide to referencing

This section is adapted from the SSSC Harvard Guide to Citing References, by Frances Barbour.

Introduction

The guidance in this appendix, based on the Harvard system of referencing, provides practical advice and examples to help you create references to support your project and other written work. It is essential when you reference within the text of your work and when you include the reference list at the end of your work, that you adopt a Harvard style. There are many variations on the Harvard referencing system. The one presented in this guide is the most simple. If you are familiar with another form of Harvard referencing, you are welcome to use it.

Adopting accurate referencing procedures and conventions is important for several reasons:

- Using references demonstrates the range of reading you have undertaken.
- Referencing provides evidence and support for the statements/arguments you bring forward.
- Correct referencing enables the reader of your work to locate the publications with which you have engaged.
- To add someone's work to yours without acknowledgement is plagiarism.

Presentation of references

At the end of your project, or any piece of written work, there should be two single headings:

- **References**: under which all references used within the text of your project should be listed in alphabetical order.
- **Bibliography**: under which all reading materials used to inform your written work should be listed in alphabetical order.

Alternatively, it is sometimes acceptable to combine both references and bibliography into one 'Bibliography', as in this book. You should check with your course tutor whether this is acceptable.

Reference list

References in the reference list or bibliography give, in alphabetical order by author surname, full details of all the sources you have used in the text. For example:

Beresford, P. (2010) *Being a Mental Health Service User*. Ross-on-Wye: PCCS Books.

Berry, J., Poortinga, Y., Breugelmans, S., Chasiotis, A., Sam, D. (2011) *Cross-cultural Psychology: Research and applications*, 3rd edition. Cambridge: Cambridge University Press.

Jenkinson, S. (2001) *The Genius of Play: Celebrating the spirit of childhood*. Gloucestershire: Hawthorn Press.

Matthews, R. and Young, J. (1992) *Issues in Realist Criminology*. London: Sage.

Seligman, M. and Csikszentmihalyi, M. (2000) Positive psychology: An introduction. *American Psychologist*, 55, 5–14.

UNICEF United Kingdom (2012) A better life for everyone: A summary of the UN Convention on the Rights of the Child. Available from: **www.unicef.org.uk/Documents/Publication-pdfs/betterlifeleaflet2012_press.pdf** (accessed 24 February 2015).

Citing a reference used in your project

Books

In the Harvard system, references in the text (in-text citations) are referred to by the author's name and year of publication. For example:

It is stated that … (Beresford, 2010)

Or:

Beresford (2010) states …

In the reference list you would provide details for the source in which you read the information. For example:

Beresford, P. (2010) *Being a Mental Health Service User*. Ross-on-Wye: PCCS Books.

References in the text for two authors are referred to by both authors' names and year of publication. Example in-text citations:

The evidence suggests that … (Matthews and Young, 1992)

Or:

Matthews and Young (1992) suggest …

In the reference list you would provide details of the source in which you read the information. For example:

Matthews, R. and Young, J. (1992) *Issues in Realist Criminology*. London: Sage.

For more than two authors, give the surname of the first author followed by *et al.* (*et al.* means 'and others'). Example in-text citations:

It was demonstrated that … (Berry *et al.*, 2011)

Or:

Berry *et al.* (2011) demonstrated that…

In the reference list you would provide details of the source in which you read the information. For example:

Berry, J., Poortinga, Y., Breugelmans, S., Chasiotis, A., Sam, D. (2011) *Cross-cultural Psychology: Research and applications*, 3rd edition. Cambridge: Cambridge University Press.

Quotes

If you are directly quoting material (i.e. using the exact form of words used in the original text), you will need to include the **author's name**, **year of publication** and **page number**. Clearly indicate where the quotation begins and ends by using quotation marks or italics. Example in-text citation:

According to Beresford (2010, p.19), 'the mental health or psychiatric system is not only a large one, it is also a complex one, located in different service systems and departments.'

Larger quotes should be displayed in a separate paragraph. For example:

Seligman and Csikszentmihalyi (2000, p.1) speak about their vision:

At this juncture, the social and behavioural sciences can play an enormously important role. They can articulate a vision of the good life that is empirically sound while being understandable and attractive. They can show what actions lead to well-being, to positive individuals, and to thriving communities.

If you do not name the source in the lead-in to the quote, then it must be given after it. For example:

In considering the social and behavioural sciences it is possible to have a very broad vision, as in the following quote:

At this juncture, the social and behavioural sciences can play an enormously important role. They can articulate a vision of the good life that is empirically sound while being understandable and attractive. They can show what actions lead to well-being, to positive individuals, and to thriving communities.

(Seligman and Csikszentmihalyi, 2000, p.1)

In the reference list you would provide details for the source in which you read the information. For example:

Seligman, M. and Csikszentmihalyi, M. (2000) Positive psychology: An introduction. *American Psychologist*, 55, 5–14.

Secondary referencing

You may want to use a quotation or an idea from a source referenced in a work you have read. You haven't read the original piece of work, but have discovered it through a secondary source. This is known as secondary referencing. Recognition is given within the text to both the original author and to the current author. Example in-text citation:

> Cohen (cited in Jenkinson, 2001) refers to the benefits of imaginative play.

In the reference list you would provide details of the source in which you read the information. For example:

> Jenkinson, S. (2001) *The Genius of Play: Celebrating the spirit of childhood.* Gloucestershire: Hawthorn Press.

Reports

Example in-text citation:

> Accurate information about the workforce is vital to workforce planning (SSSC, 2014).

In the reference list you would provide details of the source in which you read the information. For example:

> Scottish Social Services Council (SSSC) (2014) *Scottish Social Services Sector: Report on 2013 Workforce Data*. Dundee: SSSC.

Journals and newspaper articles

Example in-text citation for printed journal articles:

> Discussion by Brown and Morrison (2009) of the work undertaken by play specialists in a theatre setting highlights the diversity of the role of the Hospital Play Specialist.

In the reference list you would provide details of the source in which you read the information. For example:

> Brown, B. and Morrison, C. (2009) Theatre made fun. *Journal of the National Association of Hospital Play Staff,* 46, Autumn, 13–15.

Ejournal articles

Example in-text citation for ejournal articles:

> Walker (2014) suggests that poor planning has failed our children.

In the reference list you would provide details of the source in which you read the information. For example:

> Walker, C. (2014) Poor planning has failed children. *Nursing Children and Young People*, 26(1), 5 [Online], available at **www.nursingchildrenandyoungpeople.com** (accessed 12 February 2014).

Websites

The most obvious differences for websites from other referencing conventions are:

- the use of the term 'available from'
- the crucial importance of getting every detail (letters, symbols and no spaces) of a website address correct.

Example in-text citation:

> When considering aspects of discrimination that many people face, the Equalities and Human Rights Commission website includes a section on the Equality Act 2010 (available from EHRC, 2010).

In the reference list you would provide details of the source in which you read the information. For example:

> EHRC (2010) *Guide to the Equality Act 2010*. Available from: **www.equalityhumanrights.com/legal-and-policy/legislation/equality-act-2010/equality-act-codes-practice-and-technical-guidance** (accessed 24 February 2015).

Referencing to legislation

There is no standard way in which to reference legislation. However, guidance is provided by OSCOLA (2012) Oxford Standard for the Citation of Legal Authorities, and all UK legislation can be accessed at: **www.legislation.gov.uk**. Below is some general guidance.

In-text citation should include the name of the Act, the year in which it was passed and any relevant sections or sub-sections, for example:

> Adults with Incapacity (Scotland) Act 2000, s42 (2).

It is not absolutely necessary to include legislation in your reference list or bibliography. However, it is helpful to list legislation as the Act and the year in which it was passed, for example:

> Adults with Incapacity (Scotland) Act 2000.

CD-Roms

Example in-text citation:

> Shaw (2006) discusses ...

In the reference list you would provide details of the source from which you gained the information. For example:

> Shaw, P. (2006) *Cancer/Leukaemia Interactive CD*. Edinburgh: The Sick Kids Friends Foundation. CD-Rom.

Glossary

Abuse Ill-treatment through the infliction of harm or through neglect. Abuse can be physical, emotional, sexual, or neglect.

Acceptance Taking people as they are without judging them; an absence of rejection.

Accountability Accepting your responsibility to others to meet relevant standards and legal requirements. Care workers are accountable to service users and carers, their employer, and their profession.

Adolescence The stage of development between childhood and adulthood, usually seen to begin with puberty and to end with responsibility and independence.

Advising Telling others how they might act, feel or think, rather than letting them decide for themselves.

Advocacy Actively promoting and representing the cause of another; speaking on behalf of someone as if speaking as that person.

Ageism Discrimination applied to or experienced by people because of their age. This term is applicable both to older and younger people.

Agency An establishment or organisation providing a service to service users.

Agents of socialisation The groups from whom we pick up our culture: family, friends, media, religion, etc.

Aids Acquired immune deficiency syndrome, caused by the human immunodeficiency virus (HIV).

Anti-discriminatory practice Practice that acknowledges, understands and challenges the many negative effects of discrimination.

Assessment An exploration of service user needs as part of the process of care or health promotion in order to enable the service user to reach an optimum quality of life; the basis for planning.

Asylum seeker A person who has applied for asylum and is waiting for a decision as to whether or not they are a refugee.

Attachment An emotional link between two or more people that begins in infancy and continues through life. Early attachment with one or more carers is vital to the emotional health of a child.

Attitude The way something is viewed in an evaluative manner; a habitual mode of regarding anything. Attitudes affect the way people behave.

Behaviour How people conduct themselves. The way they do things and how they act in their relationships with others.

Belief An opinion or conviction that is held to be true, often without any sort of proof.

Body language Non-verbal communication expressed through the position, attitude and expression of the body, or parts of the body, e.g. the way you sit, the degree of eye contact.

Care/formal care Caring for people in society, other than self or family, in an agency whose codes of practice are dictated to and guided by legislation, policy and professional ethics.

Care plan An agreement arising from an assessment about what needs are to be met, how this will be achieved and how problems are to be dealt with.

Choice Promoting choice means giving different and realistic options from which the service user can select as independently as possible.

Client The recipient or user of a service. Although 'service user' is the term used in this book, 'client' is still an accepted term in care practice and counselling.

Communication Communication occurs whenever people receive and/or give messages that they regard as significant. It can be verbal, non-verbal or symbolic.

Community A network of people who are linked, usually by sharing a geographical locality; may also refer to those linked by occupation, ethnic background and/or other factors.

Community care Providing the services and support that people need to be able to live as independently as possible in their own homes or in 'homely' settings rather than institutions.

Confidentiality Maintaining the right to privacy of information; not divulging personal information without consent.

Congruence Being genuine; ensuring that your verbal and non-verbal behaviour give the same messages.

Counselling A process that, through communication, aims to help people help themselves to make better choices and become better decision makers.

Culture The way people live, lifestyles, values; can also be seen as consisting of all the messages received from society about what is good, bad, desirable, undesirable, etc.

Demography The study of the structure and changes in the population through the analysis of statistical and qualitative information.

Development Gradual unfolding; increase in complexity involving change and movement. Human development can be social, physical, emotional, cognitive, cultural and spiritual.

Discrimination The process whereby some groups or individuals in society, as a result of prejudice and stereotypes, treat others less favourably.

Empathy Putting yourself in someone else's shoes and attempting to imagine how they feel.

Empowerment Enabling people to take control of their lives; gaining the power to make decisions and choices.

Equality of opportunity The belief that everyone should get an equal chance to access opportunities in society.

Ethnic group A group with a long shared history and cultural tradition of its own. Other important characteristics may be common geographic origin, language, literature and religion.

Feminism Sets out to explain the position of women in society; to focus attention upon how women have been subordinated and oppressed and how this can be changed.

Gender The term used to describe socially constructed differences between men and women. Sex refers to biological differences.

Genetic The influence of genes, which are inherited from parents and determine bodily aspects such as eye colour and some illnesses, e.g. haemophilia.

GIRFEC Getting it Right for Every Child. Scottish Government policy presenting a consistent way of working with all children and young people.

Implementation Putting plans into effect; carrying out what has been agreed upon in the planning process.

Inclusion See 'Social inclusion'.

Independence Having as much control as possible over your life and decision making.

Institution A part of society that has regular and routine practices, regulated by social norms.

Institutional discrimination The routine, day-to-day, ingrained discrimination that exists in any of the different institutions in society.

Institutionalisation Becoming dependent upon the routines and narrow confines of an institution, resulting in such characteristics as apathy, lack of initiative and inability to make personal plans.

Keyworker A worker who is allocated to work more closely with a service user than other workers and who has a co-ordinating role with that service user within the agency.

Labelling Attaching a (usually negative) name to acts or conditions that then becomes a 'master status', e.g. labelling people as deviant, neurotic or difficult.

Legislation The law; Acts of Parliament.

Migration The movement of people between countries, usually for the purpose of settlement.

Modelling Demonstrating behaviour, feelings or thoughts to others that may, if adopted, improve the quality of life for the service user.

Monitoring On-going evaluation; keeping a check on what you are doing to ensure that it meets objectives.

Nature/nurture debate Refers to the discussion about the extent to which nature (inherited characteristics) or nurture (the environment, socioeconomic factors and socialisation) influence behaviour and development.

Norms The shared, unwritten rules in a society that define acceptable behaviour.

Oppression Abuse of power by a group or individual over a less powerful group or individual, with the effect that those less powerful are denied their rights.

Outcome Statement about what success would look like in terms that matter to the individual.

Patriarchy The systematic dominance of men over women in society.

Personalisation Enabling the individual alone, or in groups, to find the right solutions for them and to participate in the delivery of a service. From being a recipient of services, citizens can become actively involved in selecting and shaping the services they receive. Personalisation means that people become more involved in how services are designed and they receive support that is most suited to them.

Prejudice A strongly held negative attitude or set of attitudes based upon irrational beliefs, lack of understanding and/or stereotypes, rather than fact or reason.

Primary socialisation The first influence on how your culture is acquired, usually through family.

Principles The practical manifestation of values.

Private sector Part of the independent sector of service provision made up of organisations providing services that are run on a for-profit basis by individuals or companies.

Protection This usually refers to keeping people safe from danger, harm or abuse.

Psychology The study of mind and behaviour. There are many different definitions.

Racism Discrimination applied to, or experienced by, people on the basis of their race, nationality or ethnic origin.

Record A written account of significant information, including decisions, incidents, feelings, actions and monitoring of the implementation of assessments/plans.

Refugee A person who 'owing to a well-founded fear of being persecuted for reasons of race, religion, nationality, membership of a particular social group, or political opinion, is outside the country of his nationality, and is unable to or, owing to such fear, is unwilling to avail himself of the protection of that country', Article 1, *1951 Convention Relating to the Status of Refugees*. A refugee is entitled to the same social and economic rights as any UK citizen. Refugees have full access to medical treatment, education, housing and employment.

Relationship Being connected in some way with another; a helping relationship is characterised by empathy, genuineness and unconditional positive regard.

Resilience Favourable development in unfavourable circumstances.

Respite care A temporary period usually spent in a supported, residential environment in order to give carers a break and/or to provide help and a change for those in need of care. It can also be used as an opportunity for assessment or re-assessment.

Safeguarding Keeping people safe from danger, harm or abuse.

Scapegoats Individuals or groups of people who have been inaccurately and unjustly targeted as being responsible for a problem.

Secondary socialisation Groups apart from the family who influence how we pick up our culture, e.g. friends, school, the media, work.

Self-concept The view you hold about yourself.

Self-directed support Options from which individuals can choose about how their care is delivered. Under the Social Care (Self-directed Support) Scotland Act 2013 the options are direct payment or the person directs the available support or the local authority arranges the support, or a mix of these.

Self-esteem A sense of your own worth. This can be a positive or negative evaluation of yourself.

Service user One who avails themselves of help or assistance towards fulfilling needs and/or improving their quality of life; sometimes also called a client or resident.

Sexism Discrimination applied to, or experienced by, people on the basis of their gender.

Siblings Brothers and sisters.

Social class People in the same or similar socioeconomic circumstances. Socioeconomic differences result in disparities of wealth, power and life chances. New definitions take into account social, cultural and economic capital.

Social constructionism A sociological theory that proposes the 'truth' about society is socially constructed and changes over time.

Social exclusion The prevention of some people/groups from taking a full and valued part in society, e.g. those who are marginalised because of poverty or disability.

Social grades Socioeconomic groupings drawn up by the Office of National Statistics.

Social inclusion Taking positive steps to assist and include people who have traditionally been excluded from society; includes treating everyone as a valued member of society and facilitating their participation in that society.

Socialisation The process or way in which people learn the culture of their society.

Society Usually, but not always, the country or nation-state, defined in terms of language, laws, education and religion.

Sociology The study of societies and the analysis of the structure of social relationships as constituted by social interaction. No single definition is satisfactory because of the diversity of sociological perspectives.

Status Position in society or social institution; what a person is; can also mean the prestige associated with that position.

Statutory sector All the organisations that are obliged by legislation to provide or commission services. This includes all local authorities and health boards.

Stereotype A fixed, general, over-simplified and usually negative image of what a particular individual or group is like because of the possession of certain characteristics, e.g. the false 'stereotypes' that all gay men are promiscuous or all people from Aberdeen are mean.

Stigma A distinguishing mark or characteristic that is both noticeable and regarded as objectionable by some individuals or groups. Stigmas have the power to affect a person's social and personal identity.

Summarising Making statements that briefly give the main points of what you or another person has been saying; may include feedback from you.

Support Giving whatever is needed to another, including encouragement, help, understanding and warmth.

SVQ Scottish Vocational Qualification; awarded at different levels upon successful completion of a detailed assessment of practice by an approved workplace assessor.

Symbolic communication Messages, behaviour and actions that represent something else, e.g. an unwelcoming physical environment says 'We don't care about you'.

Symbolic interactionism Sociological theory focusing on the meanings individuals give to social actions using symbols.

Team A group of people who work together to achieve the philosophy and goals of their agency.

Third sector Part of the independent sector of service provision consisting of voluntary organisations, charities, community groups, social enterprises, co-operatives and individual volunteers.

Transitions Changes from one life state to another, which people undergo during their lives, e.g. marriage, loss of a partner, retirement.

Transvestite A person who dresses in the clothes of the opposite gender.

Value That which is desirable and worthy for its own sake.

Voluntary organisation A not-for-profit, non-statutory organisation; often a charity.

Bibliography

Abbot, P. and Wallace, C. (1997) *An Introduction to Sociology: Feminist perspectives*, 2nd edition. London: Routledge.

Abercrombie, N., Hill, S. and Turner, B. (2006) *The Penguin Dictionary of Sociology*, 5th edition. London: Penguin.

Aberdeen City Council (2011) Social Care and Wellbeing: Policy on spirituality in social care. 13 January 2011. Available from: **http://committees.aberdeencity.gov.uk/documents/s11478/Spirituality%20Policy.pdf**

Adams, G., Guillotta, T. and Montemayor, R. (1992) *Adolescent Identity Formation*. Newbury Park: Sage.

Adams, J.D., Hayes, J. and Hopson, B. (1977) *Transition: Understanding and managing personal change*. London: Martin Robertson.

Ainsworth, M.D.S., Blehar, M.C., Waters, E. and Wall, S. (1978) *Patterns of Attachment: A psychological study of the strange situation*. London: Lawrence Erlbaum Associates.

Aldridge, H., Fenway, P., McInnes, T. (2013) Monitoring Poverty and Social Exclusion in Scotland 2013. Available from: **www.jrf.org.uk**

Allan, G. (1985) *Family Life: Domestic Roles and Social Organization*. London: Blackwell.

Allan, J. (1935) Farmer's boy. Reprinted in Maclaren, A. (1976) *Social Class in Scotland*. Edinburgh: John Donald.

Amato, P.R. (1993) Children's adjustment to divorce: theories, hypotheses and empirical support. *Journal of Marriage and the Family*, 55, 23–38.

Anderson, C. and Wilkie, P. (1992) *Reflective Helping in HIV and AIDS*. Milton Keynes: Open University Press.

ASH (Action on Smoking and Health), BMA (British Medical Association) and HEA (Health Education Authority) (1988) Two Good Reasons for a Tobacco Pricing Policy. London: ASH/BMA/HEA.

Axline, V.M. (1990) *Dibs in Search of Self*. London: Penguin.

Bamford, C. (1995) *Equal Treatment and the Law: A guide to European Community law in Scotland*. Edinburgh: European Representation in Scotland.

Bandura, A. (1965) Influence of model's reinforcement contingencies on the acquisition of imitative responses. *Journal of Personality and Social Psychology*, 1, 589–95.

Bandura, A. (1977) *Social Learning Theory*. Englewood Cliffs: Prentice Hall.

Bandura, A., Ross, D. and Ross, S. (1963) Imitation of film-mediated aggressive models. *Journal of Abnormal and Social Psychology*, 66, 3–11.

Barber-Fleming, P. (2007) Seven days society. *Sunday Herald*, 18 February.

Barnard, A. and Burgess, T. (1996) *Sociology Explained*. Cambridge: Cambridge University Press.

Bartholomew, J. (2006) *The Welfare State We're In*. London: Politico Publishing.

BBC (2005) Meet Tanni Grey Thompson. BBC Sport/Disability Sport. Available from: **http://news.bbc.co.uk/sport1/hi/other_sports/disability_sport/4354422.stm**

Becker, H. (1963) *Outsiders: Studies in the Sociology of Deviance*. New York: The Free Press.

Becket, C. and Taylor, H. (2010) *Human Growth and Development*, 2nd edition. London: Sage.

Bee, H.L. and Mitchell, S.K. (1984) *The Developing Person*. New York: Harper and Row.

Bell, N. and Vogel, E. (1959) *A Modern Introduction to the Family*. London: Collier-Macmillan.

Bennis, W. in van Maurik, J. (2001) *Writers on Leadership*. London: Penguin.

Beresford, P. (2007) Service user wishlist goes back to basics. *Community Care*, 11–16 January.

Beresford, P. (2010) *A Straight Talking Introduction to Being a Mental Health Service User*. Ross-on-Wye: PCCS Books.

Beresford, P. (2012) *Social Care, Service Users and User Involvement*. London: Jessica Kingsley.

Beresford, P. (2013) *Personalisation*. Bristol: Policy Press.

Beresford, P. and Branfield, F. (2004) Shape up and listen. *Community Care*, 4–10 November.

Berger, P. and Luckmann, T. (1991) *The Social Construction of Reality*. London: Penguin.

Berry, J., Poortinga, Y., Breugelmans, S., Chasiotis, A., Sam, D. (2011) *Cross-cultural Psychology: Research and applications*, 3rd edition. Cambridge: Cambridge University Press.

Biggart, A. and Furlong, A. (1996) Educating 'discouraged workers': Cultural diversity in the upper secondary school. *British Journal of Sociology of Education*, 17(3), 253–66.

Bingham, M. and Stryker, S. (1995) *Things Will be Different for My Daughter: A practical guide to building her self-esteem and self-reliance*. New York: Penguin.

Bion, W. (1968) *Experiences in Groups*. London: Tavistock.

Birren, J.E. and Fisher, L.M. (1990) Aging and slowing of behaviour. *Current Theory and Research in Motivation*, 39, 1–37.

Black, N., Boswell, D., Gray, A. and Murphy, S. (eds) (1984) *Health and Disease: A reader*. Milton Keynes: Open University Press.

Blair, J. (2013) How Scottish personalisation legislation will affect social work, *Community Care*, May 15 2013. Available from: **www.communitycare.co.uk/2013/05/15/how-scottish-personalisation-legislation-will-affect-social-work-practice/**

Blakemore, K. and Drake, R. (1996) *Understanding Equal Opportunities Policies*. London: Prentice Hall/Harvester Wheatsheaf.

Blane, D., Brunner, E. and Wilkinson, R. (eds) (1996) *Health and Social Organisations: Towards a health policy for the 21st century*. London: Routledge.

Bottomore, T. and Ruben, M. (eds) (1963) *Karl Marx: Selected writings in sociology and social philosophy.* Harmondsworth: Penguin.

Bowlby, J. (1951) *Maternal Care and Mental Health.* Geneva: World Health Organization.

Bowlby, J. (1953) *Child Care and the Growth of Love.* Harmondsworth: Penguin.

Bowlby, J. (1969) *Attachment and Loss, Vol. 1: Attachment.* New York: Basic Books/ Hogarth Press.

Bowlby, J. (1973) *Attachment and Loss, Vol. 2: Separation: Anxiety and anger.* New York: Basic Books.

Bowlby, J. (1980) *Attachment and Loss, Vol. 3: Loss: Sadness and depression.* New York: Basic Books.

Bowlby, J. (1988) *A Secure Base: Clinical applications of attachment theory.* London: Routledge.

Bowles, S. and Gintis, H. (1976) *Schooling in Capitalist America.* London: Routledge & Kegan Paul.

Bradford Social Services Department, Community Health NHS Trust and Bradford Interfaith Centre (2002) *Spiritual Wellbeing: Policy and practice.* Leeds: NIMHE.

Bradshaw, J. (1972) The concept of social need. *New Society*, 30 March.

Branfield, F. and Beresford, P. (2006) *Making Service User Involvement Work: Supporting service user networking and knowledge.* York: Joseph Rowntree Foundation.

Breitenbach, E. (1995) *Quality through Equality: Good practice in equal opportunities in Scottish local authorities.* Glasgow: Equal Opportunities Commission.

British Sociological Association (2015) 'Discover sociology'. Available from: **www.britsoc.co.uk/what-is-sociology/discover-sociology.aspx**

Bronfenbrenner, U. (1974) The origins of alienation. *Scientific American*, 231, 53–61.

Brown, C.H. (1979) *Understanding Society.* London: John Murray.

Brown, G.M. (1995a) *Beside the Ocean of Time.* London: Flamingo.

Brown, G.M. (1995b) *Winter Tales.* London: Flamingo.

Brunner, E. (1996) The social and biological basis of cardiovascular disease in office workers. In D. Blane *et al.* (eds) *Health and Social Organisations*. London: Routledge.

Bryman, A. (1988) *Quality and Quantity in Social Research.* London: Unwin Hyman.

Burnard, P. (1989) *Teaching Interpersonal Skills.* London: Chapman and Hall.

Campbell, K. (2013) *This Is Where I Am.* London: Bloomsbury Circus.

Cardwell, M., Clark, L. and Meldrum, C. (2004) *Psychology for A2 Level*, 3rd edition. London: Collins.

Cardwell, M., Clark, L. and Meldrum, C. (2008) *Psychology*, 4th edition. London: Collins.

Carers UK (2014) Facts about caring. Policy Briefing May 2014. Available from: **www.carersuk.org/for-professionals/policy/policy-library/facts-about-carers-2014**

Carlen, P. (1988) *Women, Crime and Poverty.* Milton Keynes: Open University Press.

Carstairs, V. and Morris, R. (1991) *Deprivation and Health in Scotland.* Aberdeen: Aberdeen University Press.

CCPS (2010) *An outcomes approach in social care and support: an overview of current frameworks and tools*. Edinburgh: CCPS.

Centre for Research on Families and Relationships (2002) Research Briefing Number 6: Divorce. Available from: **www.crfr.ac.uk/publications/research-briefings**

Chambliss, W.J. and Mankoff, M. (1976) *Whose Law? What Order?* New York: John Wiley.

Cheetham, J. (1992) *Evaluating Social Work Effectiveness.* Buckingham: Open University Press.

Chiesa, A. (2007) National champion for children in care. *The Herald*, 16 January.

Clough, R. (1987) *Scandals in Residential Centres. An unpublished report for the Wagner Committee.* Bristol: University of Bristol.

Commission for Racial Equality (1995) *Annual Report.* London: Commission for Racial Equality.

Commission for Racial Equality (1997) *Annual Report.* London: Commission for Racial Equality.

Community Care magazine (1998a) Study paints picture of isolation. *Community Care*, 28 May–3 June, p.3.

Community Care magazine (1998b) Scots unclear about Children Act Legislation. *Community Care*, 9–15 July, p.4.

Community Care magazine (1998c) Deaf people from ethnic minorities feel isolated. *Community Care*, 13–19 August, p.5.

Community Care magazine (1998d) *Community Care*, 1–7 October.

Comptroller and Auditor General (2004) *Improving Patient Care by Reducing the Risk of Hospital Acquired Infection: A progress report.* London: The Stationery Office.

Comte, A. (1986) *The Positive Philosophy.* London: Bell and Sons.

Conway, C. (2012) *Uncertain Legacies: Resilience and institutional child abuse – A literature review.* Edinburgh: Scottish Government Social Research. Available from: **www.gov.scot/Publications/2012/06/7287**

Cooley, C.H. (1902) *Human Nature and Social Order.* New York. Shocken.

Cooper, N., Purcell, S., Jackson, R. (2014) *Below the Breadline: The relentless rise of food poverty in Britain.* Church Action on Poverty, Oxfam, the Trussell Trust. Available from: **www.trusselltrust.org**

Coser, L. and Rosenberg, B. (eds) (1976) *Sociological Theory: A book of readings.* New York: Macmillan.

COSLA and Scottish Government (2010) *Caring Together: The carers strategy for Scotland 2010–2015.* Edinburgh: COSLA and Scottish Government. Available from: **www.gov.scot/Resource/Doc/319441/0102104.pdf**

COSLA, Scottish Government and NHS Scotland (2010) *Reshaping Care for Older People: A programme for change 2011–2021.*

Coulshed, V. and Orme, J. (2012) *Social Work Practice*, 5th edition. Basingstoke: Palgrave Macmillan.

Craib, I. (1984) *Modern Social Theory.* Brighton: Wheatsheaf Books.

Crawford, K. and Walker, J. (2014) *Social Work and Human Development*, 4th edition. London: Sage.

Cromer, F. and Maclean, S. (2011) *The Social Work Pocket Guide to Personalisation.* Lichfield: Kirwin Maclean Associates Ltd.

Crompton, M. and Jackson, R. (2004) *Spiritual Well-being of Adults with Down Syndrome.* Portsmouth: Down Syndrome Educational Trust.

Cunningham, J. and Cunningham, S. (2014) *Sociology and Social Work.* London: Sage.

Currie, E. (1989) *Life Lines: Politics and health 1986–88.* London: Sidgwick and Jackson.

Dahrendorf, R. (1964) Out of utopia. Reprinted in L. Coser and B. Rosenberg (eds) (1976) *Sociological Theory: A book of readings.* New York. Macmillan.

Dalrymple, J. and Burke, B. (1995) *Anti-Oppressive Practice: Social care and the law.* Buckingham: Open University Press.

Daniel, B. (2008) The concept of resilience, messages for residential child care. In A. Kendrick (ed.) *Residential Child Care: Prospects and challenges.* London: Jessica Kingsley.

Davies, M. (ed.) (2013) *The Blackwell Companion to Social Work*, 4th edition. Oxford: Blackwell.

De Beauvoir, S. (1972) *The Second Sex.* Harmondsworth: Penguin.

Dobash, R. and Dobash, R. (1980) *Violence Against Wives.* New York: The Free Press.

Dominelli, L. (1997) *Sociology for Social Work.* London: Macmillan.

Dominelli, L. (2002) *Feminist Social Work Theory and Practice.* Basingstoke: Palgrave.

Donnelly, R. (2008) *Living and Dying Well.* Edinburgh: Scottish Government.

Donohue, E. (1985) *Echoes in the Hills.* Surbiton. SCA Publications.

Douglas, J.W.B. (1964) *The Home and the School*. London: MacGibbon & Kee.

Douglas, J.W.B. (1975) Early hospital admissions and later disturbances of behaviour and learning. *Developmental Medical Child Neurology*, 17, 456–80.

Douglas, T. (1978) *Basic Groupwork.* London: Routledge.

Dryden, W. (2006) Rational emotive behaviour therapy. In C. Feltham and I. Horton (eds) *The SAGE Handbook of Counselling and Psychotherapy*, 2nd edition. London: Sage.

Dryden, W., Neenan, M., Yankura, J. and Ellis, A. (1999) *Counselling Individuals: A rational emotive behavioural handbook*, 3rd edition. London: Whurr.

DTI (2006) Work and families: Choice and flexibility. Department of Trade and Industry. Available from: **http://webarchive.nationalarchives.gov.uk/20070603164510/http://www.dti.gov.uk/files/file23932.pdf**

Durkheim, E. (1938) *The Rules of Sociological Method.* New York: The Free Press.

Eagleton, T. (2000) *The Idea of Culture.* Oxford: Blackwell.

Earle, M. (2003) *Obesity.* Edinburgh: Scottish Parliament.

Eastbank Health Promotion Centre (1997) *First Annual Report.* Glasgow: Greater Glasgow Health Board.

Eaude, T. (2006) *Children's Spiritual, Moral, Social and Cultural Development.* Exeter: Learning Matters.

Edgell, S. (1980) *Middle Class Couples.* London: Allen and Unwin.

Edinburgh, Lothians and Borders Executive Group (2012) *Inter-agency Child Protection Procedures.* Edinburgh: ELBEG Public Protection Office.

Egan, G. (2014) *The Skilled Helper*, 10th edition. Pacific Grove, CA: Brooks Cole.

Eldridge, J.E.T. (1970) *Max Weber: The interpretation of social reality.* London: Joseph.

Engels, F. (1972) *The Origin of the Family, Private Property and the State.* London: Lawrence and Wishart.

Equal Opportunities Commission (1997) *Making Equality Work: The challenge for Government. EOC Annual Report (Scottish Extract).* Manchester: EOC.

Equal Opportunities Commission (2006) Twenty years on from landmark case, sexual harassment remains all too common. Available from: **www.hrmguide.co.uk/diversity/sexual_harassment.htm**

Erikson, E.H. (1968) *Identity: Youth and crisis.* New York: Norton.

ESRC (2003) Young offenders and victims of crime are often the same people. ESRC Press release 10 August 2003. Economic and Social Research Council. Available from: **www.eurekalert.org/pub_releases/2003-08/esr-yoa080503.php**

Eysenck (2000) *Psychology: A student's handbook*. Hove: Psychology Press.

Fenton, S. (1987) *Ageing Minorities: Black people as they grow old in Britain.* London: Commission for Racial Equality.

Ferguson, A. (2007) Passing of Bill belies problem. *The Scotsman*, 23 February. Available from: **http://news.scotsman.com/opinion.cfm?id=291122007**

Field, D. and James, N. (1993) Where and how people die. In D. Clark (ed.) *The Future of Palliative Care.* Buckingham. Open University Press.

Fitzgerald, R. and McKay, A. (2006) *Gender Equality and Work in Scotland: A review of the evidence base and the salient issues*. Glasgow: Equal Opportunities Commission.

Flanagan, C. (1996) *Applying Psychology to Early Child Development.* London: Hodder and Stoughton.

Fletcher, R. (1988) *The Family and Marriage Under Attack.* London: Routledge.

Ford, J. and Sinclair, R. (1987) *Sixty Years On: Women talk about old age.* London: Women's Press.

Foucault, M. (2002) *The Archaeology of Knowledge.* London: Routledge.

Frude, N. (1997) *Understanding Family Problems.* London: Wiley.

Furlong, A. and Cartmel, F. (1995) Aspirations and opportunity structures: 13-year-olds in areas with restricted opportunities. *British Journal of Guidance and Counselling*, 23(3), 361–75.

Furnival, J. (2011) *Attachment-informed Practice with Looked After Children and Young People.* Glasgow: IRISS. Available from: **www.iriss.org.uk**

Galbraith, R. (2013) *The Cuckoo's Calling.* London: Sphere.

Galpin, D. (2012) How research on age discrimination in health and social care should inform social work practice. *Community Care*, 23–29 October.

General Register Office for Scotland (2014a) *Population Estimates for Scotland's Centenarians*. Edinburgh: GROS.

General Register Office for Scotland (2014b) *Scotland's Population 2013*. Edinburgh: GROS.

Giddens, A. and Sutton, P. (2013) *Sociology*. Cambridge: Polity Press.

Gill, A. (1999) Do you recognise this family? *Scotland on Sunday*, 31 January.

Gilligan, R. (2008) Promoting resilience in young people in long-term care – the relevance of roles and relationships in the domains of recreation and work. *Journal of Social Work Practice*, 22(1), 37–50.

Glasgow City Council (1997) *Language Matters: A guide to good practice*. Glasgow: GCC.

Glasgow City Council (2014) *Adult Protection Procedures*. Glasgow: GCC.

Glasgow University Media Group (1980) *Bad News*. London: Routledge & Kegan Paul.

Goffman, E. (1968) *Asylums*. Harmondsworth: Penguin.

Gough, E. (1959) Is the family universal? The Nayor case. In N. Bell and E. Vogel (eds) *A Modern Introduction to the Family*. London: Collier-Macmillan.

Gould, R.L. (1978) *Transformations: Growth and change in adult life*. New York: Simon and Schuster.

Gray, L. (2006) Outcry at new laws allowing gay adoption. *The Scotsman*, 8 December. Available from: **http://news.scotsman.com/politics.cfm?id=1822862006**

Greer, G. (1970) *The Female Eunuch*. London: MacGibbon & Kee.

Gross, R. (1996) *Psychology: The science of mind and behaviour*, 3rd edition. London: Hodder and Stoughton.

Guardian (1998) Girl kept in attic. *Guardian*, 2 July.

Guardian (2007) The 100 club wants you. *Guardian*, 12 January.

Haralambos, M. and Holborn, M. (2013) *Sociology: Themes and perspectives*, 8th edition. London: Collins.

Harrell, E. and Howie, M. (2006) Violent crime by women up 50 per cent in past 4 years. *The Scotsman*, 1 September. Available from: **http://thescotsman.scotsman.com/index.cfm?id=1290372006**

Harris, J. and White, V. (2013) *Oxford Dictionary of Social Work and Social Care*. Oxford: Oxford University Press.

Hayes, N. (1994) *Foundations of Psychology: An introductory text*. New York: Routledge.

Health and Safety Executive (2014) *Sensible Risk Taking in Care Settings*. London: Health and Safety Executive. Available from: **www.hse.gov.uk/healthservices/sensible-risk-assessment-care-settings.htm**

Health Education Board for Scotland (1997a) *Scotland's Health at Work*. Edinburgh: HEBS.

Health Education Board for Scotland (1997b) *Strategic Plan 1997 to 2000*. Edinburgh: HEBS.

Heidensohn, F. (1985) *Women and Crime*. London: Macmillan.

Heim, A. (1990) *Where Did I Put My Spectacles?* Cambridge: Allborough Press.

Herald Scotland (2014) The gender gap… Sturgeon's rise doesn't mask absence of women in Scots public life. *Herald Scotland*, 18 October.

Heraud, B.J. (1970) *Sociology and Social Work (Perspectives and Problems)*. Oxford: Pergamon Press.

Herbert, M. (1986) *Psychology for Social Workers*. Leicester: British Psychological Society.

Herbert, M. (2002) The human life cycle: Adolescence. In M. Davies (ed.) *The Blackwell Companion to Social Work*, 2nd edition. Oxford: Blackwell.

HMSO (1987) *British Crime Survey.* London: HMSO.

HMSO (1992) *Scotland's Health: A Challenge to Us All.* London: HMSO.

HMSO (1998a) *Scottish Statistical Survey.* London: HMSO.

HMSO (1998b) *Social Trends.* London: HMSO.

Holmes, T.H. and Rahe, H. (1967) The social re-adjustment rating scale. *Journal of Psycho-Somatic Research*, 11, 213–18.

Houston, S. (2010) Building resilience in a children's home: results from an action research project. *Child and Family Social Work*, 15(3), 357–68.

IRISS (Institute for Research in Social Services) Imagining the future of support and social services in 2025. Available from: **www.iriss.org.uk**

Ishii-Kuntz, M. (1990) Social interaction and psychological well-being: Comparison across stages of adulthood. *International Journal of Ageing and Human Development*, 30(1), 15–36.

James, P.D. (2000) *A Time to Be in Earnest: A fragment of autobiography.* London: Faber and Faber.

Jones, A. (1990) *Charles Rennie Mackintosh.* London: Studio Editions.

Joseph Rowntree Foundation (2002) Poverty levels remain high in Scotland despite falling unemployment. Available from: **www.jrf.org.uk/pressroom/releases/051202.asp**

Kahan, B. (1994) *Growing Up in Groups.* London: HMSO.

Katz, J. and Siddell, M. (1994) *Easeful Death: Caring for dying and bereaved people.* London: Hodder and Stoughton.

Kidd-Hewitt, D. and Osborne, R. (1995) *Crime and the Media: The post-modern spectacle.* London: Pluto Press.

Kinsey, R. (1993) *Policing in the City: Public, police and social work.* Edinburgh: Scottish Office, Central Research Unit.

Klein, M. (1940) Mourning and its relationship to manic-depressive states. *International Journal of Psychoanalysis*, 21, 125–53.

Labov, W. (1973) The logic of non-standard English. In T. Young (ed.) *Tinker, Taylor... The myth of cultural deprivation.* Harmondsworth: Penguin.

Laing, R. and Esterson, A. (1970) *Sanity, Madness and the Family.* Harmondsworth: Penguin.

Laming, W. (2003) *The Victoria Climbié Inquiry Report.* London: The Stationery Office. Available from: **http://webarchive.nationalarchives.gov.uk/20130401151715/http://www.education.gov.uk/publications/eOrderingDownload/CM-5730PDF.pdf**

Lawson, T. (1991) *GCSE Sociology: A conceptual approach.* Chester: Checkmate Publications.

Leach, E. (1971) *A Runaway World?* London: BBC Publications.

Lemos, G. (2006) More than a place to stay. *Community Care*, 29 June–5 July.

Levin, E. (2004) *Involving Service Users and Carers in Social Work Education.* London: Social Care Institute for Excellence (SCIE).

Lewis, I. and Munn, P. (1987) *So You Want to Do Research!* Edinburgh: The Scottish Council for Research and Education.

Lishman, J. (2005) *The Case for Change.* Leading to Deliver Module 2 paper. Aberdeen. The Robert Gordon University.

Long, P. (1996) *Anne Redpath 1895–1965.* Edinburgh: National Galleries of Scotland.

Macaskill, M. (2014) Blame society, not Buckfast. *The Sunday Times*, 16 February.

McCall Smith, A. (1998) *The No. 1 Ladies Detective Agency.* London: Abacus.

McCormack, J. (2007) *Recovery and Strengths-based Practice.* SRN Discussion Paper Series. Report No. 6. Glasgow: Scottish Recovery Network.

McCurry, P. (1999) Wired for work. *Community Care*, 14–20 January.

McLaren, A. (1976) *Social Class in Scotland.* Edinburgh: John Donald.

Maclean, S. (2015) *Social Care and the Law in Scotland*, 9th edition. Lichfield: Kirwin Maclean Associates.

McLellan, D. (1980) *Karl Marx 1818–1883: Selections in English.* London: Macmillan.

Macleod, N. (2007) Registration of the social care workforce: A UK agenda. *Care Appointments*, Issue 21, March.

Macoby, E.E. (1980) *Social Development, Psychological Growth and the Parent Relationship.* New York: Harcourt Brace Jovanovich.

Magnusson, S. (2014) *Where Memories Go: Why dementia changes everything.* London: Hodder and Stoughton.

Mallinson, I. (1995) *Keyworking in Social Care.* London: Whiting and Birch.

Mannheim, H. (1960) *Comparative Criminology.* London: Routledge & Kegan Paul.

Martin, V. (2003) *Leading Change in Health and Social Care.* London: Routledge.

Marx, K. and Engels, F. (1915) *Manifesto of the Communist Party: Authorised English translation.* Chicago: C.H. Kerr.

Matthews, R. and Young, J. (1992) *Issues in Realist Criminology*. London: Sage.

Matthews, Z. (1998) The outsiders. *Nursing Times*, 94(37), 16 September.

Maylor, E.A. (1994) Ageing and the retrieval of specialized and general knowledge: Performance of masterminds. *British Journal of Psychology*, 85(1), 105–14.

Mead, G.H. (1934) *Mind, Self and Society*. Chicago: University of Chicago Press.

Meggitt, C. (2012) *Child Development: An illustrated guide*, 3rd edition. Harlow: Pearson Education Ltd.

Meighan, R. (1981) *A Sociology of Education.* London: Holt Rinehart.

Merton, R.K. (1968) *Social Theory and Social Structure*, enlarged edition. New York: The Free Press.

Messer, D. and Jones, F. (eds) (1999) *Psychology and Social Care.* London: Jessica Kingsley.

Miller, J. (1996) *Social Care Practice.* London: Hodder and Stoughton.

Miller, J. (ed.) (2005) *Care Practice for S/NVQ 3.* London: Hodder Arnold.

Mills, C.W. (1959) *The Sociological Imagination*. New York: Oxford University Press.

Montemayor, R. (1983) Identity formation during early adolescence. In G. Adams *et al.* (1992) *Adolescent Identity Formation*. Newbury Park: Sage.

Moonie, N. (1994) *Health and Social Care.* Oxford: Heinemann.

Morison, M. (1986) *Methods in Sociology*. London: Longman.

Multiple Sclerosis Society (2014) Your care, your choice (Scotland) campaign. Available from: **www.mssociety.org.uk/get-involved/campaigns/scotland/self-directed-support**

Murdock, G.P. (1949) *Social Structure.* New York: Macmillan.

Murray Parkes, C. and Prigerson, H. (2010) *Bereavement: Studies of grief in adult life*, 4th edition. London: Penguin.

National Council for Voluntary Organisations (NCVO) (2015) *Volunteering*. National Council for Voluntary Organisations. Available from: **www.ncvo.org.uk/policy-and-research/volunteering-policy**

National Records of Scotland (2011) *Projected Population of Scotland – 2010 based.* Edinburgh: National Records of Scotland.

National Records of Scotland (2015) *Mid-2014 Population Estimates Scotland.* Edinburgh: National Statistics.

Naysmith, S. (1994) Out in the cold. *The Big Issue (in Scotland)*, 6(94), 22–3.

NDCS (2011) *Social Care for Deaf Children and Young People*. National Deaf Children's Society. **www.ndcs.org.uk**.

Nelson-Jones, R. (1988) *Practical Counselling and Helping Skills*, 3rd edition. London: Cassell.

NHS Education for Scotland (2012) *Positive Behaviour Support – A learning resource.* Edinburgh: NES. Available from: **www.nes.scot.nhs.uk/media/570730/pbs_interactive_final_nov_12.pdf**

NHS Scotland (2005) Scottish health statistics. Edinburgh: ISD (NHS Information Services Division).

Nicolson, P. (2014) *A Critical Approach to Human Growth and Development.* Basingstoke: Palgrave Macmillan.

Nobbs, J., Fielding, R., Hine, B. and Flemming, M. (1989) *Sociology*, 3rd edition. London: Macmillan Education.

Oakley, A. (1974) *Sociology of Housework.* Oxford: Martin Robertson.

Oakley, A. (1982) Conventional families. In R. Rapoport (ed.) *Families in Britain.* London: Routledge & Kegan Paul.

Oakley, A. (1985) *Sex, Gender and Society.* London: Gower/Maurice Temple Smith.

Oakley, A. (1993) *Essays on Women, Medicine and Health.* Edinburgh: Edinburgh University Press.

Oakley, A. (1997) *Man and Wife: Richard and Kay Titmuss – My parents' early years.* London: HarperCollins.

Oates, S. (1982) *Let the Trumpet Sound.* London: Search Press.

O'Brien, E. (2011) *Psychology for Social Care: An Irish perspective.* Dublin: Gill and Macmillan.

O'Brien, J. and Lovett, H. (1992) *Finding a Way Toward Everyday Lives: The contribution of person-centred planning.* Harrisburg: Pennsylvania Office of Mental Retardation.

O'Donnell, M. (1993) *New Introductory Reader in Sociology.* Walton-on-Thames: Nelson.

O'Donnell, M. (1997) *Introduction to Sociology*, 4th edition. Walton-on-Thames: Nelson.

Office for National Statistics (2004) *Family Resources Survey.* London: Office for National Statistics.

Office for National Statistics (2009) *Social Trends, 39th Edition*. London: Palgrave Macmillan.

Oldman, C. and Beresford, B. (1998) A space of our own. *Community Care*, 1–7 October.

Open University U205 Course Team (1985) *Birth to Old Age.* Milton Keynes: Open University Press.

OSCOLA (2012) *Oxford Standard for the Citation of Legal Authorities*, 4th edition. Oxford: Faculty of Law, University of Oxford.

Papalia, D., Wendkos Olds, S. and Feldman, R.D. (2009) *Human Development*, 11th edition. New York: McGraw Hill.

Park, A., Bryson, C., Clery. E., Curtice, J., Philips, M. (2013) *British Social Attitudes 30.* London: NatCen.

Parsons, T. (1937) *The Structure of Social Action.* New York: McGraw Hill.

Partridge, C. and Barnitt, R. (1987) *Research Guidelines: A handbook for therapists.* London: Heinemann.

Patrick, J. (1973) *A Glasgow Gang Observed.* London: Eyre Methuen.

Payne, G. and Abbott, P. (eds) (1990) *The Social Mobility of Women: Beyond male mobility models.* London: Falmer Press.

Payne, M. (2014) *Modern Social Work Theory*, 4th edition. Basingstoke: Palgrave Macmillan.

Peter, L. (1982) *Quotations for Our Time*. London: Methuen.

Pilsbury, B. (1984) Doing the month. In N. Black *et al.* (eds) *Health and Disease: A reader.* Milton Keynes: Open University Press.

Pollack, N. (2007) Like father, like son? *Guardian*, 3 February.

Powell, T. (1997) *Free Yourself from Harmful Stress.* London: DK Publishing.

Puttick, H, (2013) Revealed: Deaths during childbirth are on the rise. *Herald Scotland*, 4 January.

Radcliffe-Brown, A. (1935) Structure and function in primitive society. *American Anthropologist*, 37, 394–402.

Rapoport, R.N., Fogarty, M.P. and Rapoport, R. (eds) (1982) *Families in Britain.* London: Routledge & Kegan Paul.

Rayner, E. with Joyce, A., Ross, J., Twyman, M. and Clulow, C. (2005) *Human Development: An introduction to the psychodynamics of growth, maturity and ageing.* Hove: Routledge.

Redl, F. (1966) *When We Deal with Children.* New York: Free Press.

Richardson, A. (1995) *Preparation to Care.* London: Bailliere Tindall.

Ritchie, P., Sanderson, H., Kilbane, J. and Routledge, M. (2003) *People, Plans and Practicalities.* Edinburgh: SHS Ltd.

Robinson, L. (2002) The human life cycle: Nigrescence. In M. Davies (ed.) *The Blackwell Companion to Social Work*, 2nd edition. Oxford: Blackwell.

Rogers, A. (2002) *Teaching Adults.* Berkshire: Open University Press.

Rogers, C. (1991) *Client-centred Therapy.* London: Constable.

Rogers, J. (1990) *Caring for People: Help at the frontline.* Milton Keynes: Open University Press.

Rogoff, B. (2003) *The Cultural Nature of Human Development.* Oxford: Oxford University Press.

Ross, D. (2013) *Scotland: History of a nation*, new edition. Edinburgh: Lomond Books Ltd.

Rosser, R. and Harris, C. (1965) *The Family and Social Change*. London: Routledge & Kegan Paul.

Rowlands, O. (1998) *Informal Carers: An independent study.* Office for National Statistics, Social Survey Division. London: The Stationery Office.

Rowling, J.K. (2012) *The Casual Vacancy*. London: Sphere.

Rutter, M. (1979a) Maternal deprivation (1972–78): New findings, new concepts, new approaches. *Child Development*, 50, 283–305.

Rutter, M. (1979b) *Maternal Deprivation Re-assessed*, 2nd edition. Harmondsworth: Penguin.

Sanderson, H., Kennedy, J., Ritchie, P. and Goodwin, G. (1997) *People, Plans and Possibilities.* Edinburgh: SHS Ltd.

Schaefer, N. (1978) *Does She Know She's There?* London: Harper and Row.

Schaffer, H.R. and Emerson, P.E. (1964) The development of social attachments in infancy. *Monographs of the Society for Research in Child Development*, 29(3), serial number 94.

Schaie, K.W. (ed.) (1988) *Methodological Issues in Aging Research.* New York: Springer.

Schaie, K.W. (1994) The course of adult intellectual development. *Developmental Psychology*, 19, 531–543.

Schaie, K.W. and Labouvie-Vief, G. (1974) Generational versus ontogenetic components of change in adult cognitive behaviour: A fourteen-year cross-sequential study. *Developmental Psychology*, 10, 305–20.

Schon, D. (1983) *The Reflective Practitioner: How professionals think in action.* London: Temple Smith.

Scotland on Sunday (2014) No room for intolerance. *Scotland on Sunday*. 2 June.

The Scotsman (1998) Parents' hands tied by Euro judgement. *The Scotsman*, 24 September.

Scottish Executive (2000) *The Same as You?* Edinburgh: The Stationery Office.

Scottish Executive (2001a) *Joint Future Agenda in Community Care and Health Bill 2001.* Edinburgh: Scottish Executive.

Scottish Executive (2001b) *Single Shared Assessment Guidance*. Edinburgh: Scottish Executive.

Scottish Executive (2002) *National Care Standards: Care Homes for Children and Young People.* Edinburgh: Scottish Executive.

Scottish Executive (2003a) Inequalities in Health: Report of the Measuring Inequalities in Health Working Group. Edinburgh: Scottish Executive. Available from: **www.gov.scot/Resource/Doc/47171/0013513.pdf**

Scottish Executive (2003b) Social justice: A Scotland where everyone matters. Indicators of progress. Available from: **www.gov.scot/Publications/2003/12/18693/31074**

Scottish Executive (2006a) *Changing Lives: Report of the 21st century social work review.* Edinburgh: Scottish Executive.

Scottish Executive (2006b) HM Chief Inspector of Prisons for Scotland: Annual Report 2005–06. Available from: **www.gov.scot/Publications/2006/10/26121221/3**

Scottish Executive (2006c) *Getting it Right for Every Child.* Edinburgh: Scottish Executive.

Scottish Executive Health Department (2002) *Adding Life to Years: Report of the expert group on healthcare of older people*. Chapter 5 Ageism in NHS Scotland. Available from: **www.sehd.scot.nhs.uk/publications/alty/alty-05.htm**

Scottish Government (2008) *Personalisation: A shared understanding.* Edinburgh: Scottish Government.

Scottish Government (2010) *Self-directed Support: A national strategy for Scotland.* Edinburgh: Scottish Government.

Scottish Government (2011) Time to be heard: A pilot forum. Available from: **www.gov.scot/Publications/2011/03/07122331/0**

Scottish Government (2012a) *A Guide to Getting it Right for Every Child*. Edinburgh: Scottish Government.

Scottish Government (2012b) *Mental Health Strategy for Scotland 2012–2015.* Edinburgh: Scottish Government.

Scottish Government (2013a) *New Scots: Integrating refugees in Scotland's communities 2014–2017*. Edinburgh: Scottish Government.

Scottish Government (2013b) *Play Strategy for Scotland: Our vision*. Edinburgh: Scottish Government.

Scottish Government (2013c) *Scotland's Dementia Strategy 2013–2015*. Edinburgh: Scottish Government.

Scottish Government (2013d) *Statistical Bulletin: Domestic abuse recorded by the police in Scotland.* Edinburgh: Scottish Government.

Scottish Government (2013e) *The Keys to Life: Improving quality of life for people with learning disabilities*. Edinburgh: Scottish Government.

Scottish Government (2014a) *Health of Scotland's Population.* Available from: **www.scotland.gov.uk**

Scottish Government (2014b) *National Practice Guidance on Early Learning and Childcare*. Edinburgh: Scottish Government.

Scottish Government (2014c) *Scotland's People. Scottish Household Survey Annual Report: Results from 2013.* Edinburgh: Scottish Government.

Scottish Government (2014d) See Hear: A strategic framework for meeting the needs of people with a sensory impairment in Scotland. Available from: **www.gov.scot/Publications/2014/04/7863**

Scottish Government and COSLA (2008) *The Early Years Framework*. Edinburgh: Scottish Government.

Scottish Human Rights Commission (2013) *Scotland's National Action Plan for Human Rights*. Edinburgh: SHRC.

Scottish Office (1991) *The Patient's Charter.* London: HMSO.

Scottish Office (1997) *Scotland's Parliament.* London: HMSO.

Scottish Office (1998a) *Working Together for a Healthier Scotland: A consultation paper.* London: HMSO.

Scottish Office (1998b) Social Work Research Findings No. 11. The range and availability of domiciliary care services in Scotland. Available from: **www.gov.scot/Publications/1998/12/d87a32a4-171d-45df-8615-4ac030c7b8e7**

Scottish Parliament (2006) Justice 2 Report, Volume 2 Evidence. Available from: **http://archive.scottish.parliament.uk/business/committees/justice2/reports-06/j2r06-16-vol02-00.htm**

Scottish Parliament (2011) *SPICe Briefing: Healthcare-associated infections.* Edinburgh: The Scottish Parliament.

Scottish Parliament (2012) *Stage 1 Report on the Social Care (Self-directed Support) (Scotland) Bill.* Edinburgh: The Scottish Parliament.

Scottish Parliament (2015) *Carers (Scotland) Bill 2015*. Edinburgh: The Scottish Parliament.

SCRA (2004) Annual Report 2003–04. Scottish Children's Reporter Administration. Available from: **www.scra.gov.uk**

Scottish Social Services Council (SSSC) (2002) *Codes of Practice for Social Service Workers and Employers.* Dundee: SSSC.

Scottish Social Services Council (SSSC) (2005) New body boosts sector skills. SSSC News No. 14, Autumn. Dundee: SSSC.

Scottish Social Services Council (SSSC) (2014a) *Code of Practice for Social Service Workers and Employers*. Dundee: SSSC.

Scottish Social Services Council (SSSC) (2014b) *Scottish Social Services Sector: Report on 2013 Workforce Data.* Dundee: SSSC.

Scottish Social Services Council and NHS Education (2011) *Promoting Excellence: A framework for all health and social services staff working with people with dementia, their families and carers.* Edinburgh: Scottish Government.

Scottish Women's Aid (2010) Information Briefing No. 4. Children and young people's exposure to domestic abuse. Available from: **www.scottishwomensaid.org.uk**

Seabrook, J. (1990) Law and disorder. *New Statesman and Society*, 5 October, 18.

Seligman, M. and Csikszentmihalyi, M. (2000) Positive psychology: An introduction. *American Psychologist*, 55, 5–14.

Sharp, D. (ed.) (2006) *Annual Abstract of Statistics 2006.* London: Office for National Statistics.

Sharrock, D. (1993) Anthony Quinn's lust for life results in 11th child at age 78. *Guardian*, 20 August.

Sheridan, M. (1997) *From Birth to Five Years.* London: Routledge.

Silverman, P.R., Nickman, S., and Worden, J.W. (1992) Detachment revisited: The child's reconstruction of a dead parent. *Americal Journal of Orthopsychiatry,* 62, 494–503.

Simpson, C.L. (2010) Resilience in women sexually abused as children. *Families in Society,* 91(3), 214–47.

Skidmore, W. (1975) *Theoretical Thinking in Sociology*. Cambridge: Cambridge University Press.

Slater, R. (1995) *The Psychology of Growing Old.* Buckingham: Open University Press.

Smale, G., Tuson, G., Biehal, N. and Marsh, P. (1993) *Empowerment, Assessment, Care Management and the Skilled Worker.* London: HMSO.

Small, E. (2013) *Mary Lily Walker: Forgotten Visionary of Dundee.* Dundee: Dundee University Press.

Social Work Services Inspectorate (SWSI) (2004) *Report of Scottish Borders Council Social Work Services for People Affected by Learning Disabilities.* Edinburgh: SWSI.

Spender, D. (1983) *Invisible Women: Schooling scandal*. London: Women's Press.

Spitz, R.A. (1965) *The First Year of Life*. New York: International University Press.

Spitz, R.A. and Wolf, K.M. (1946) Anaclitic depression. *Psychoanalytic Study of the Child*, 2, 313–42.

SRC (1993) *Training Package in Residential Care.* Glasgow: SRC.

Stapleton, K. (1998) Signs of improvement. *Community Care*, 30 April–6 May, 26–7.

Steel, L. (2012) *The Family (Skills-based Sociology).* Basingstoke: Palgrave Macmillan.

Stephens, P., Leach, A., Taggart, L. and Jones, H. (1998) *Think Sociology.* Cheltenham: Stanley Thornes.

Stevenson, A. and Waite, M. (eds) (2011) *Concise Oxford English Dictionary*, 12th edition. Oxford: Oxford University Press.

Stevenson, H. (2014) Stand up for what we believe. *Professional Social Work*, July/August, 9.

Strathclyde Regional Council (1991) *Strathclyde Social Trends, 1988–1995.* Glasgow: Business Information Centre.

Suchet, J. (2010) *My Bonnie.* London: HarperCollins.

Sudbery, J. (2010) *Human Growth and Development.* Abingdon: Routledge.

Taylor, A. (1993) *Women Drug Users.* Oxford: Clarendon Press.

Taylor Clarke Partnership (2003, 2005) Leading to deliver. Course Pack for Module 1, Changing to Lead.

Taylor, S. and Field, D. (eds) (1993) *Sociology of Health and Healthcare*. Oxford: Blackwell.

The Telegraph (2015) Ex-Cabinet Minister David Mellor 'regrets' tirade against 'sweaty, stupid' taxi driver. *The Telegraph*, 2 February.

Thompson, K. and Tunstall, J. (1971) *Sociological Perspectives.* Middlesex: Penguin, in association with Open University Press.

Thompson, N. (2009) *People Skills*, 3rd edition. London: Palgrave Macmillan.

Thompson, N. (2012) *Anti-discriminatory Practice*, 5th edition. Basingstoke: Palgrave Macmillan with BASW.

Thomson, H., Holden, C., Hutt, G. and Meggit, C. (1995) *Health and Social Care for Advanced GNVQ*, 2nd edition. London: Hodder and Stoughton.

Thomson, H. and Manuel, J. (1997) *Further Studies for Health.* London: Hodder and Stoughton.

Thorne, B. (1992) *Carl Rogers.* Thousand Oaks, CA: Sage.

Thorpe, N. (1998) Scottish women: Second class citizens. *The Scotsman*, 20 November.

Timms, L. (2014) Law on our side in promoting welfare. *Professional Social Work*, October, 10.

Tizard, B. and Hodges, J. (1978) The effect of early institutional rearing on the development of eight-year-old children. *Journal of Child Psychology and Psychiatry*, 19, 99–118.

Tossell, D. and Webb, R. (1994) *Inside the Caring Services*, 2nd edition. London: Edward Arnold.

Townsend, P., Davidson, N. and Whitehead, M. (eds) (1992) *Inequalities in Health: The Black Report and the health divide.* Harmondsworth: Penguin.

Volkan, V. (1985) Complicated mourning. *Annual of Psychoanalysis,* 12, 323–348.

Wagner, G. (1988) *Residential Care: A positive choice.* London: HMSO.

Walker, J. (2013) Partnership and parenting. In M. Davies (ed.) *The Blackwell Companion to Social Work.* Chichester: Wiley-Blackwell.

Ward, A. (2006) *Working in Group Care.* Birmingham: BASW/Policy Press.

Ward, B. and Houghton, J. (1967) *Good Grief: Exploring feelings of loss and death with over-11s and adults.* London: Cruse.

Waterhouse, R. (2000) *Lost in Care.* London: Department of Health.

Wheal, A. in collaboration with Buchanan, A. (1994) *Answers: A handbook for residential and foster carers of young people aged 11–18 years.* Brighton: Pavilion.

Whitaker, A. (2014) Lack of qualified nurses puts old people at risk in hospital. *The Scotsman,* 20th March.

Wilkinson, R. (2005) *The Impact of Inequality.* London: Routledge.

Wilkinson, R. and Pickett, K. (2014) The Spirit Level authors: why society is more unequal than ever. *The Observer*, 9 March.

Williams, L. (1994) *Finding Out About Society.* London: Bell and Hyman.

Willis, P. (1977) *Learning to Labour.* Farnborough: Saxon House.

Wilson, G. (2003) Stay-at-home fathers hit a record high. *The Scotsman*, 26 October.

Worden, W. (2010) *Grief Counselling and Grief Therapy: A handbook for the mental health practitioner*, 4th edition. East Sussex: Brunner-Routledge.

Young, T. (ed.) (1973) *Tinker, Taylor ... The myth of cultural deprivation.* Harmondsworth: Penguin.

Young, M. and Wilmott, P. (1957) *Family and Kinship in East London.* London: Routledge & Kegan Paul.

Younghusband, E. (1964) *Social Work and Social Change.* London: Allen and Unwin.

Yousafzai, M. with Lamb, C. (2014) *I Am Malala: The girl who stood up for education and was shot by the Taliban.* London: Phoenix.

Websites

Age Scotland: **www.ageuk.org.uk/scotland**

Alzheimer Scotland: **www.alzscot.org**

British Sociological Association: **www.britsoc.co.uk**

Cambridge Dictionary Online: **http://dictionary.cambridge.org/dictionary**

Care Information Scotland: **www.careinfoscotland.co.uk/home.aspx**

Care Inspectorate: **www.careinspectorate.com**

Carers Trust Scotland: **www.carers.org/scotland**

Citizens Advice Scotland: **www.cas.org.uk**

Coalition of Care and Support Providers in Scotland: **www.ccpscotland.org**

Convention of Scottish Local Authorities (COSLA): **www.cosla.gov.uk**

Department for Work and Pensions: **www.gov.uk/government/organisations/department-for-work-pensions**

Duke of Edinburgh's Award Scheme in Scotland: **www.dofe.org/en/content/cms/takepart/notice-boards/scotland**

Equality and Human Rights Commission (EHRC): **www.equalityhumanrights.com**

General Register Office for Scotland (GRO): **www.gro-scotland.gov.uk**

Health and Safety Executive: **www.hse.gov.uk**

Helen Sanderson Associates: **www.helensandersonassociates.co.uk**

Limping Chicken: **www.limpingchicken.com**

Legislation: **www.legislation.gov.uk**

National Health Service Scotland: **www.show.scot.nhs.uk/index.aspx**

National Records of Scotland: **www.nrscotland.gov.uk**

Scotland's Commissioner for Children and Young People: **www.sccyp.org.uk**

Scottish Care: **www.scottishcare.org**

Scottish Council for Voluntary Organisations (SCVO): **www.scvo.org.uk**

Scottish Government: **www.gov.scot**

Scottish Refugee Council: **www.scottishrefugeecouncil.org**

Scottish Social Services Council: **www.sssc.uk.com**

Self-directed Support Scotland: **www.sdsscotland.org.uk**

Social Care Institute for Excellence: **www.scie.org.uk**

Social Services Knowledge Scotland: **www.ssks.org.uk**

Stonewall Scotland: **www.stonewallscotland.org.uk**

Volunteer Scotland: **www.volunteerscotland.net**

Welcoming Association: **www.thewelcoming.org**

Who Cares Scotland: **www.whocaresscotland.org**

Index

D

E

F

P

Q

R

S

T

U

V

W